D1446229

IRELAND

Suggested by an Ancient Irish Manuscript

THE FIRE

"for the great gaels of ireland
are the men that god made mad.
for all their wars are merry
and all their songs are sad..."
G. k. chesterton

LAND
READER

Compiled by

Helen O'Clery

decorated by ann o'clery

franklin watts, inc. new york 22

watts
international

Author's Appreciation

The compiler and the decorator wish to give special thanks, for help and advice, to:—

Dr. A. T. Lucas, M.A., D.Litt., of the National Museum
Mr. F. J. E. Hurst, M.A., A.L.A., of Trinity College Library
Mrs. M. Looby of Trinity College Library
Mr. M. Gill of M. H. Gill & Son
Mr. R. Lyon of The Talbot Press Ltd.
Mr. A. Hanna of Fred Hanna Ltd.
Mr. J. Addis of Browne & Nolan Ltd.

Also to the staffs of the National Museum and of Rathmines, Terenure and Pearse Street Public Libraries.

To
Una Coonan

About this Book:

THE IRELAND READER began by the fireside of my house in Dublin some years ago, when my publisher's wife, Helen Hoke Watts, was here on a visit from America. I played some records for her; amongst these was the poem EASTER 1916, by W. B. Yeats, and ANNALIVIA by James Joyce—read by himself in that Irish voice of his which he never lost in all his long years of self-appointed exile. Then we got talking about EASTER WEEK and all that is conjured up for an Irishman by those two words.

We talked about the G.P.O., The Troubles, The Land League, The Rebellion of '98, Cromwell, The Flight of the Earls, The Red Branch Knights, Saint Patrick, Finn McCool, Cuchulain, The Dagda, The Fairy People, and the Archaeological remains which suggest that many an Ancient Irish Legend might well have been founded on fact.

We talked about Joyce who deliberately lived out of Ireland "to forge the conscience of his race," as he said himself. He wrote of Dublin and nothing but Dublin. Every stick and stone of his native city was far more familiar to Joyce after thirty years abroad than it is to any Dubliner who lives in the midst of it. Every traveler from Ireland who went to visit him on the continent was bombarded by questions about Dublin. What was the latest gossip? What changes had been made? How was so and so? Who won such and such a prize, such and such a medal, such and such a game? Pockets had to be turned out and bus tickets, press clippings, old receipts—anything at all was asked for, so long as it came from Dublin. And yet, Joyce would not go home.

He began by writing as true a description of his student days in Dublin as he could possibly write. It was as if his Jesuit upbringing had left him with a strong compulsion to examine his conscience; as if stripped naked before God, concerning the truth—the truth as he saw it—the truth about Dublin, to him.

Joyce could dip back into the past and bring up a vivid description of anything he had seen, heard or learned in his childhood or young manhood; but nothing out of the present day, because he was not there, and because he was not concerned with the present day. In the end, his writings became so distilled that they seemed to become a special sort of short-hand version of his own thoughts about Dublin.

Helen and I talked about other writers who had written about Dublin in recent times and in the past. We paused to consider how many had written their best from afar: George Bernard Shaw lived in England for almost all his adult life; and so did Wilde. Yeats spent many years abroad—and we began counting the many Irish writers who emigrated to America, until we ran out of fingers.

We discussed the reasons for this, then inevitably came to the censorship of books and the hold the clergy tend to have over the Irish people. This quite naturally brought us back to the Penal Code. From there we wandered happily to and fro through the pages of "not always so happy" Irish history . . . till an idea began to take shape: the idea was this—to take the skeleton of Irish history, and dress it in the writings of famous Irish men, and other writers who had written about Ireland.

The idea has now been turned into print and here it is— IRELAND, A Nation Once Again.

Helen O'Clery

Dublin, Ireland, July 1963

A Word About Spelling:

If suddenly as you read of the ancient Irish hero Cuchulain, you should become aware that on another page his name is written *Cuchulainn*, and elsewhere it appears *Cuchullin*, the reason is not that your eyes are playing you tricks nor that the proofreader has been napping. It is rather that in all the writing from the British Isles, the original spelling has been kept, and since Cuchulain, like Shakespeare (known also as Shakspere, Shakspir, and Shaxper), was variously spelled, the various forms are here. In all the other writing, including that of Helen O'Clery, the spelling is American.

Contents

About this Book: vii
B.C.   Pagan Ireland   1
432 A.D.   St. Patrick and the Coming of Christianity   53
1014   Brian Boru and the Overthrow of the
                   Vikings   77
1167   Strongbow   87
1607   The Flight of the Earls   103
1644   The Curse of Cromwell   117
1798   The Dread Days of the 1798 Rebellion   141
1829   The Fight for Catholic Emancipation   177
1846   The Fearful Days of the Famine   191
1879   The Fight Against the Landlords   273
1916   Easter Week and the Troubles   295
Dublin: Yesterday, Today—and Tomorrow?   331
Acknowledgments   381
Index of Titles   387
Index of Authors   391
Index of Subjects   393
Index of First Lines of Poems   395
Index of First Lines of Prose   397

A Nation Once Again

By THOMAS DAVIS
(1814–1845)

When boyhood's fire was in my blood
   I read of ancient freemen
For Greece and Rome who bravely stood—
   Three hundred men and three men.
And then I prayed I yet might see
   Our fetters rent in twain,
And Ireland, long a province, be
   A Nation once again.

And from that time, through wildest woe,
   That hope has shone, a far light,
Nor could love's brightest summer glow
   Outshine that solemn starlight:
It seemed to watch above my head
   In forum, field and fane;
Its angel voice sang round my bed
   "A Nation once again."

It whispered, too, that Freedom's ark
   And service high and holy,
Would be profaned by feelings dark
   And passions vain and lowly:
For Freedom comes from God's right hand,
   And needs a godly train;
And righteous men must make our land
   A Nation once again.

And as I grew from boy to man
   I bent me to that bidding—
My spirit of each selfish plan
   And cruel passion ridding;
For thus I hoped some day to aid—
   Oh, *can* such hope be vain?—
When my dear country shall be made
   A Nation once again.

B. C.

PAGAN IRELAND

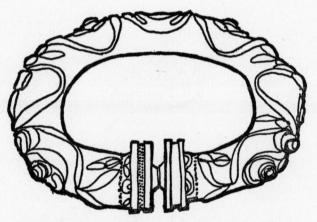

Repoussé gold collar, found at Broighter near Limavady, Co. Derry, 1st Century B.C.

This is part of an ancient Irish saga which was old before history began to be recorded:

The Son of the Young Ones

By JAMES STEPHENS
(1882–1950)

In the days that are past and gone, Angus mac an Og, the son of the Dagda Mor, was resting at the Brugh.

He had the gift of perpetual youth, and was therefore called the mac an Og—The Son of the Young Ones. He had the gift of perpetual beauty, and was so called the Wonder; and he had the gift of magic, and was known by it as the Envious.

When he went abroad there accompanied him a cloud of birds that wheeled and sang about his head, so that when we see a cloud of wheeling and singing birds, all frantic with energy and exaltation, we know that the son of the Dagda is passing, and we make obeisance to Youth and Beauty and Magic.

It happened that Angus was staying at his father's palace, the Brugh of the Boyne, in the Shi of Ulster, for he had not yet cozened his father out of this palace. There had been a feast, and the time had passed in music and singing, and in the recitation of their verse by poets.

After the banquet, Angus went to bed, but he could not sleep. He lay looking on the darkness of his chamber, wondering why he was wakeful, and finding no reason for it. For he was in good health and spirits, and nothing had occurred to disturb his mind.

"Someone," he thought, "is practicing a magical art against me, and but that I do not wish to get out of bed I would weave magic also and destroy that influence, or I should find out where it comes from.

"And indeed," he thought also, "if I cannot go to sleep it is no great calamity, for I have slept many times and shall sleep many a time again."

3

While he was thus considering, the room lightened, and he saw a figure standing at a little distance from the bed. The young god raised himself on his elbow and looked intently on the figure.

He knew it was not real, because real things do not happen in this way; he knew it was not a dream, because he was awake; and he knew, therefore, that this must be a vision, or the wraith of a person come to visit him.

But the figure did not speak, nor did Angus.

They but looked at, and recognized each in the other the extreme and goal of all that was lovely in the world.

Angus sunk himself in that gaze, as a fish is immersed in water. He forgot all but the delicious face on which he was gazing. He forgot that this was but a vision; and he could only remember to look and look again, and to so concentrate his sight that he could see not only with his eyes, but with every member of his being, and with all the faculties of his mind. He was lost in that look and drowned in it, so that when the vision faded he could not withdraw his eyes from that rigid forwardness and contemplation.

But the darkness did at last cloud his mind and enable him to withdraw his faculties and to become master of himself.

He sank back on the bed, full of joy, full of wonder and surmise, with his heart hurried by such happiness that it nigh broke from his bosom; and for a long time he lay in the stillness and darkness reconstructing a beauty such as even he had never contemplated before.

The hours of the long night passed for him in an ecstasy of wonder, in a recollection that was all happiness. But when the pale wraith of day began to move through the room, so that all things looked uncertain and discolored, his mood changed with the change that came to his eyes, and he began to remember that he did not know where that lovely being might be, nor could he tell if she who had appeared would ever appear to him again.

For he knew that things which begin in one place can have their sequel in another, and may end far from either; and that the whole story may be unknown to any person except that lonely soul which is fulfilling itself in its own experiences.

Therefore, when he left the bed he left it wearily, and his bearing was so depressed that all the people of the Shi noticed it, and at last his mother noticed it also.

4

His mother was Boann, the wife of the Great Good God.

She questioned him, but as his replies were evasive or distraught, she gave up a fruitless inquiry and sought elsewhere for a solution of her son's trouble.

It was trouble indeed. He fell sick of it, and would not talk to nor look at anyone, nor would he reply to any person who addressed him.

He might glance for a moment on the questioner as though wondering why an inquisitive person should be in the room with him, and then he would turn his eyes aside and stare, far away in space, at something seen only by himself.

The physicians of the Shi were brought, but against his obstinate silence they could do nothing, for they did not seem to exist for him, and he himself did not seem to exist in the world where they were real.

Among these there was a physician whose name was Fergne.

He was a clever doctor. Not only did he understand the afflictions which the body may endure, he was versed also in those ills which come to the body from the mind; and when he had been with Angus for a little time he knew that, however bad his health might seem, the reason was not physical.

He spoke to Angus, and by dint of much speaking he insisted in time on being listened to.

"You know, Angus, dear heart, no one should lie in bed whose body is as healthy as yours is, and what I think is, that there must be a trouble in your mind which is drawing the energy from your limbs, and which will drain all virtue out of you unless you make a stand against it." He went then and told Angus' mother.

"The boy is in love. That is all that's wrong with him."

"But he always is in love," cried Boann; "love is his normal condition."

"It is his normal condition to have love given to him," replied Fergne; "but this time someone is withholding love from him, and he is sick from desire and dissatisfaction."

Boann and Fergne then returned to where Angus was.

"Brightness of my heart," said Boann severely, "we know what is wrong with you."

He smiled a scornful disbelief at that.

5

"You are not sick at all," said his mother; "you are in love."

And then, for those in love are convinced that all other people are foolish, Angus did not smile any longer. He looked admiringly at his mother and admitted that she had told the truth.

Then, for one discovered in love can no longer be silent about it, he told her of the vision which had come to him on the night of the banquet, and how, such was his trance of amazement and delight, he had let it go; and he told that he would die unless he saw the girl again; and he so told and retold these things that his mother had to stop him from any more tellings.

"Darling," she said, "I know all the women of Ireland, but I do not know one who resembles in any way the person you describe."

But Fergne declared that the mac an Og had given a full description of every woman in the world, and he developed this theme to Angus.

"If your fawn had a hump on her back, or a lame leg; if she were one-eyed or covered with warts; if she were even a lunatic, or out-and-out mad, we should have something to look for.

"But," he continued, to Boann, "it is an endless chase that we are asked to go on; and, as an endless chase is a chase without an end, it is useless to begin it."

They heard then that the Dagda had returned from his visit to the Provincial Shis of Ireland, so Boann and Fergne went to him, and described the condition of his son, and how no one could tell what should be done.

The Dagda Mor considered the extraordinary position.

"Angus does not know who the girl is?" he inquired.

"He does not."

"If he knew," the Dagda continued, "we could pick his brain and take the information from it; but, as nobody knows, why, there is no brain to pick, and I do not see what can be done. The boy has managed to get sick by himself, he must manage to get well by himself."

"There is nothing wiser than that to be said," Fergne agreed.

But Boann was not satisfied.

"We must do something," she insisted.

"Make a suggestion," said the Dadga.

Boann then suggested that the Dadga should send visions to

6

Angus of all the beautiful women of the Shis of Ireland; and, if that failed, of all the beautiful women of Ireland itself.

"It is a lengthy and cumbersome arrangement," quoth the Dadga.

"Can you suggest a better one?" she asked.

But he could not do so; and it was arranged that the experiment should be tried.

"I must be in the room passing the visions before him," said the Dagda, "so that when he recognizes his beloved we shall know which of them it is, for the boy has become featherbrained, and might forget which woman of the sequence was the one he sought, and it would all have to be done again."

"And I," said Boann, "will be present also, for I should like to know which woman of the women of Ireland could make anybody sick for lack of her."

"I," Fergne cried gleefully, "will attend those visions with you, for there is nothing I like better than looking at pretty women, and this time I may see my fill of them."

The Dagda was considering:

"In what order and precedence should these ladies be presented?" he inquired.

"Queens first," replied Boann, "and then Princesses who are rulers of territories, and next Princesses of birth, and then Princesses of beauty, and after them—"

"I do not like that way. We should arouse the rage and jealousy of all the women of the Shi, for not one of them would be satisfied with the precedence allotted to her, except the very first one of all. Make another suggestion."

"Let them go in order of age," she advised.

"They are all twenty years of age," the Dagda mused, "and whoever denied that of any one of them would make a mortal enemy of that one. Make another suggestion."

"I can't," sighed Boann.

"Have you a suggestion?" he demanded of Fergne.

"I have indeed."

"Then let us hear it," cried the Dagda.

"This is my suggestion," said Fergne. "Let the women be marshalled in the visions according to fatness and thinness; the fat beauties pacing before Angus according to their varying fatnesses, and the slender heroines moving before him in a diminishing

7

scale."

"And when we come to the ones that are too thin to be seen?" the Dagda queried.

"These doves need not be shown at all," Fergne replied.

"There will yet be a question," the Dagda continued, "as to whether this one is as fat as this one, or whether this one is as slim as that?"

"Then let those dainty ones be marshalled according to colour; the golden-haired, winsome enchantresses marching before Angus according as their hair is the colour of old gold or new; the proud dark-haired fawns moving in the like descending gradations; the brown-haired doves following in graded beautiful battalions; and the ardent red-haired sorceresses keeping their own brisk companies."

"It is good advice," said the Dagda, "and that is the way I shall do it."

This scheme was explained to Angus, and he agreed that it should be tried. But he was so anxious to see the girl again that he would have tested any scheme which promised to revive that loveliness.

He was ashamed, too, that he, the Master of Magic, could have been taken unawares, and should have been so stupefied by any occurrence that he could neglect the very primaries and school texts of his art; and he knew that the lady who was concerned would not easily forgive that carelessness.

He settled himself, therefore, to observe the visions.

His mother sat at one side of the couch; Fergne sat at the other, and at the head of the couch, between it and the wall, his father sat.

"When you see the lovely one you want, cry Hola," said the Dadga.

Angus Og nodded comprehension.

"I," said Fergne, "shall look very particularly at that one."

By the power of the Dagda the sunlight which was pouring into the room faded and disappeared, and for a moment they sat in darkness.

Then the darkness glowed to a light that was like molten gold, with, seen far through it, a haze of purple, and while they stared through the golden radiance and at the purple haze, a figure moved

8

out of the haze and stood in the golden light, and it seemed indeed as if the light flowed from her, so beautiful and proud was she, and it seemed also that if she retired the world would go black for lack of her.

"That is Fand, daughter of Bove, the King of the Shi of the Men of Femen," said Boann.

"Whether this be the right one or the wrong one," said Fergne, "what I counsel is, that Angus should take this one quickly, for, by my hand, there can be nothing more beautiful than she is under the eye of day."

But Angus made no remark and the vision faded.

"This one," Boann commented, "is Ailne of the White Shoulder, a Princess from the Shi of Leinster."

"She is lovely as a rose," said Fergne, "she is healthy as a trout, and sweet flavoured as an autumn nut. If Angus is not satisfied with this fawn it is because nothing will satisfy him."

"And this one," said Boann, "is ruler over the Shi of Meath."

"She is a joy forever," Fergne cried. "She cannot be beaten, and she is the very girl that Angus craves for."

"Do you let this dove pass?" he cried reproachfully as the next vision came. "Will you blink at the Pearl of the World?"

But Angus let her go.

"Now," Fergne said, "you will cry Hola: now you will surely say, this is the Queen."

And after that, in despair, Fergne ceased to importune him.

"I perceive," said the physician, "that you have begun with the plump women, and I perceive also that of created beings a well-rounded woman overtops all others, for she can set the heart at ease and fill the mind with fancy."

"There is," he said later, "much to be said of slender women; they have grace of movement that is infinitely satisfying; they curve and flow."

"How agile the thin maidens are!" he murmured thoughtfully. "How deep is the appeal of their willowy youth!"

"But," he said again, "golden-haired is the one colour for women: only with gold are they adequately crowned."

"And yet," he murmured, "how winsome brown hair can be! What a shy sparkle lies in the braided tress, and how tenderly it finds the heart!"

9

"Noble," he asserted, "noble is the darkness piled above the dawn: majestic are the black-haired heroines; full of frolic and loveliness are they of the fragrant locks."

"To the red-haired queens I give the palm," he cried; "they warm the world; they are the true Honey of Delight."

The visions came and went, and Angus stared in a fever of hope and despair on each.

Ladies of all ages were there, from the wild young fawn of fifteen to the massive and magnificent dame of forty.

There were ladies of royal fatness who moved vehemently upon the vision as a great ship, with all sail spread, bears mightily down the sea.

There were others, plump as corn-fed pigeons, active as hares, raising the wind as they passed and lifting the soul to journey with them.

And others again, vehement and bewitching, moving like fierce swans upon the water.

Eyes looked upon Angus that were proud and radiant. Eyes that were meek as doves or soft as the glance of a doe. Sparkling and forward-looking eyes stared from the vision as an eagle stares hardily on the sun. Eyes that were languishing and appealing. Side-sliding eyes. Eyes that tantalized. Eyes that shone with mischief, or stared with stubborn pride. Eyes that promised and appealed and dared and cajoled; and eyes that were contented or indifferent or curious.

They came and went, and as each came, Boann named her name and Fergne murmured a benediction.

"Here," he would say, "is a dove to satisfy even the mac an Og."

Or:

"This is the Cluster of Nuts. This is the True Blossom of the Branches."

Or:

"To this one I give the palm, for she is surely the Berry of the Mountain."

Or again he would say:

"Now cry Hola, for here is the Star of the Bright Dawn; here is the Loveliness that Broods above the Day."

But Angus took no heed of these admonishments, except that at times he gave a groan, and, at times again, he sighed as though

10

his heart had come and gone upon a bubble of air.

For a year and a day the visions continued, and at the end of that time the women of all the Shis of Ireland had been shown to Angus, and all the women of Ireland had been discovered to him as well.

The wives and daughters of Princes, the winsome consorts of ruling Chieftains, and the dear companions of Champions and Dragons of the Gael were brought before him; but among them he did not discover her for whom he sought; so that when the visions were ended he closed his eyes and lay back upon the bed, and he was delivered to a silence and despair twice as great as that in which he had been beforetime plunged.

"I can do no more," said the Dagda.

"Nor could anyone," Fergne interposed.

"There is not a woman in the two worlds of Ireland whom I have not brought before our son, and if among them all he cannot content himself, it is because he cannot be contented."

"Now," said Fergne, "we are listening to the truth."

"Still," Boann insisted, "the child is sick."

"Make a suggestion," said the Dagda.

But she could not make a suggestion.

Also at that time she became ill at ease, and was agitated by movements and jerks, and half-sittings up and half-sittings down, so that even the Dadga noticed it.

"Dove of Time and Heart of the Heart of the World," said the Dagda, "tell me what it is that moves you and agitates you, so that you can neither sit nor stand nor stay easy."

"I have seen too many women," Boann replied, "and I must go to some place where I can get the sight out of my eyes."

"Surely—" Fergne began in a tone of astonishment and expostulation.

"I wish," said Boann, "to go among my men-servants, and to watch them as they move with agility and circumspection about their work. I wish to look at our soldiers as they perform martial evolutions and leap and run. I wish to see short hair on heads and long hair on chins. I wish to see bald people—

"I wish to look into the eyes of oxen that do not squint or languish or peep. I wish to see legs," said she; "so I shall look steadily on horses and hens, on goats and sheep and warriors."

11

"In the matter of legs," said Fergne eagerly, "I can assure you—"

"I wish to look," she continued, "on hard and angular and uncomfortable things, for my mind is clouded and there is a bad taste in my mouth from the sight of those endless females."

"There is nothing," cried Fergne, "there is nothing more tonic to the soul or more lifting to the imagination—"

"I can quite understand," said Boann, "why Angus would not lay a finger or an eye on any one of them, for women are hideous and hairy and ridiculous."

"This is not wisdom," said Fergne; "this is not sound common sense."

"And," she continued, "when they are not long and bony and unpleasant they are short and stumpy and squashy, and I must go away now until I can forget that there are any of them living, and until I can discover if there are truly men moving in the world, for I have come to doubt all good things."

Boann left them then, in a condition of agitation and wrath, but Fergne thought that he would shortly have two patients under his hand, and that of the two it was the mother who was the most rankly ill.

"Now," said the Dagda, "I don't know what to do, for I have shown Angus all the women of the worlds, and, unless it was a dream my son had instead of a vision, there is a woman somewhere whom we have not seen."

"That," Fergne commented, "is a ripe statement of the case. There must be someone who has hidden a notable pearl, or there is a dove that is modestly concealing itself among the branches."

"Have you a suggestion to make?" said the Dagda.

"I have."

"Then make it."

"Not hard to do," said Fergne, "and here it is. One of your vassal kings is famous for his knowledge of visions and apparitions and sorceries."

"Which of them is that?"

"It is Bove the Red, King over the Shi of the Men of Femen, and if you set him on the work he will discover the charmer that we lack."

"Let the message be sent to that Shi," the Dadga commanded, "to say that we will ourselves follow the messenger and that we shall expect a reply to our question."

"It may be," Fergne continued, "that Bove will have to call up those visions again, so I will go to him myself, for I should not like to miss the sight."

He set out then, and, when a reasonable time had elapsed, the Dagda followed with Angus, and they came to the Shi that Bove reigned over in Munster.

They were brought with all observance to the palace, and were given a feast which lasted for three days, and after the feast a banquet was given in their honour.

* * *

On the day following the banquet the Dadga asked an account from Bove of the work he had ordered him to do.

"That girl," said he, "who has been destroying my son Angus; what have you discovered about her?"

"I have found the girl," said Bove.

"Was I a good counsellor?" Fergne cried joyfully.

"Who is she?" the Dadga inquired.

"She is Caer, the daughter of Ethal Anbual, King of the Shi of Uaman in the kingdom of Connacht; and she is in her father's Shi at the Lake of the Dragon's Mouth, hard by the place known as the Harp of Cliach."

"Now," said Fergne, "Angus can go to that place and take his treasure."

"I have no power," cried the mac an Og peevishly. "I am consumed by a desire, and cannot control my will."

"But let us be certain," the physician continued, "that you have found the right girl, for if we make a mistake now we might give the matter up in despair. Call her up in a vision," he suggested eagerly.

So that was done.

The Dagda made first a darkness, and then a golden radiance, and then they looked through the purple haze which was beyond the radiance.

They saw a sandy strip, and sunshine, and a rolling sea; and upon the strand a band of girls were romping. Among them there was one taller than the rest, and, although the others were beauti-

13

ful, this one was so lovely that she could scarcely be looked at. She dazzled the eye as the sun does, and she filled the mind with delight and wonder, so that the person who looked at her forgot to think, and could remember nothing beyond that beauty.

"Do you cry Hola to that?" gasped Fergne. "If you do not say Hola to her I shall say it myself."

"She is my love beyond the loves of the worlds," said Angus, "she is the crown of the soul and the fulfilment of desire."

"She is," cried Fergne. "I swear by my hand that she is all that has been said, and all that has not been said, and it is to her I give my palm."

The vision then faded, and Angus sat with Bove and Fergne on his either hand, and they were all stupefied with wonder.

"Why has Ethal Anbual concealed his daughter from me?" the Dagda asked.

"He conceives that you have no right to demand her," Bove replied.

"And it is true that I have no such right," said the Dadga, "and, therefore, there is no more to be said on this matter, and we may all go home."

"But the boy!" said Fergne, "the boy will fade away."

"Have you a suggestion to make?" said the Dagda.

"I have one," Bove interposed.

"Make it," said the Dagda.

"It would be very wrong of us to do a thing that was wrong," said Bove, "and, therefore, we shall not do it."

"We certainly shall not," Fergne agreed.

"But there are other people, and it is right for those people to do what is wrong."

"How so?" said Fergne, scandalised.

"Wrongdoing is their base of existence," said Bove.

"What people are those?" the Dagda inquired.

"Mortals," Bove replied.

"Indeed," cried Fergne, "I do not often hear truth and wisdom spoken, but this time I hear it with my two ears."

"Give power for a day to mortals," Bove counselled. "They will get the girl for us, and there will be an end to all this anxiety."

"Who is the mortal King of Connacht?" the Dagda asked.

"There is not really a King," Bove replied; "there is a Queen

14

and her consort."

"And this Queen?"

"She is Maeve, daughter of the High King of Ireland: she is the noblest of the queens of the world, and she is the most beautiful woman under the sun."

"I shall certainly look closely on that Queen," said Fergne.

"We shall visit Maeve of Connacht about the Feast of Samhain," said the Dagda, "for at that time the doors are opened between this world and that one, and whoever dares . . . Will this Queen dare to enter Faery?"

Bove replied with conviction: "There is nothing that Maeve of Connacht would not dare, for she is not alone beautiful, she is greatly courageous."

"I shall seek her assistance," the Dagda announced.

"Now, Angus, my heart," cried Fergne jovially, "you may begin to get well, for although that fawn is not yet in your arms, she is condemned to them and cannot escape."

"I do feel better," said Angus; "I begin indeed to feel well."

"But," Fergne concluded, "the person I wish to see, and the person whom I must see, is this courageous and lovely Queen, for I feel assured that she is the Silk of the Flock and the Early Fragrance of the Hawthorn. How does this fawn look?" he asked. "Is she dark and slender and of a middle stature?"

"She is tall and well rounded," Bove replied. "She is long faced and pale, and her hair shines like gold."

"It is thus she should be," Fergne agreed, "and it is in that fashion I shall think of her."

The Feast of Samhain was at hand, and when it wanted but three days to the Feast, the Dagda, with Angus and Bove and Fergne, set out for Connacht, and a company of sixty chariots went with them. They reached Connacht at noon of the day before the feast, and a messenger was sent from them to the palace demanding an interview with Ethal Anbual.

But the King of the Shi of Connacht refused to grant it.

"I know what the Dagda wants," he said; "I will not consent to give my daughter to Angus Og."

When the messenger returned evening was advanced, and the hour was almost at hand when the doors are down between the two realms, so that the Dagda and his company mounted their chariots and drove in the direction of the door in the hillside. When they reached it the door was open, and they passed through it and rode into the world of men.

From the hillside to the palace at Cruachan Ai was but a short journey, and in five minutes the guards at Cruachan reported that a company was advancing on the palace. In another minute preparations had been made to receive them, and in one minute more they were at the fortifications.

They were ushered into the palace with ceremony and respect, for neither the guards, the chamberlains, nor the servants had ever before seen a host so beautifully apparelled, or with such comely dignity of bearing, for they were plumed and crested with fire, and they were radiant as the sun itself.

Maeve was seated on her throne in the great reception hall, but when the Dagda appeared so great was his majesty and so noble his regard that she rose to receive him, and seated him on a throne on her right hand, Ailill, her husband, on her left, and the other people of the Shi were given honourable places.

"Will you tell your name and qualities yourself," asked Maeve, "or shall we send for your heralds to recite them?"

"I am the Dagda Mor," said her guest. "I am the High King of the people of Dana, and Lord Supreme of the Kingdoms of the Dead."

"And I am Maeve of Cruachan, daughter of the High King of Ireland, and Ruler of the Realm of Connacht."

The people of the Dagda and Maeve's people were introduced to each other in seemly order, and then, for Maeve was a famous housekeeper, a feast was brought in, and for the space of three hours it was enjoyed by all who were present and was praised.

"I think," said Fergne, who had been looking at Maeve as one in a trance, "I certainly think that this Queen is more worthy to be called Hola to than even the daughter of Ethal Anbual is."

"This Queen is married," Bove remarked.

"Would you limit the joy of life?" cried Fergne reproachfully. "Would you put a stay to happiness?"

He stroked the beard that flowed down to his middle like a river of silver silk, and became lost in contemplation.

The Dagda then set before Maeve the whole of the story that has been told, and, after she had spoken with her counsellors, and

16

been advised by them that she should have nothing to do with the matter, Maeve decided that she would give the assistance required.

"For," said she, "I have never yet paid a visit to Faery, and as I am the ruler of Connacht I should like to see the ruler of the Shi of my own country."

One of her counsellors interposed:

"There has always been peace between the Shi and Cruachan; but after this there may be ill-feeling and bicker, and who knows if the High King of the Shi will protect us from the vengeance of the Tribes of Dana."

"I will answer for that," replied the Dagda. "No harm shall come to Connacht from the people of the Shi, although much may happen in Connacht in consequence, for no action can cease until it has worked out all its possibilities."

"If you guarantee me against the Shi," said Maeve, "I will be my own guarantor for all that may happen in Connacht or in Ireland."

That was settled, and, as the evening was advanced and the darkness great, it was decided that they should set out at once while the doors of Faery were open, and in half an hour Maeve, at the head of a thousand chariots, was dashing to the hill of Cruachan.

She sacked the Shi of Uaman, and took away booty and treasure, and she took Ethal Anbual and all his chief people prisoner, and she brought away from the Shi two young bulls, one of which was known as The Whitehorn and the other was called The Brown Bull.

"These bulls," said Ethal Anbual, as he stared fiercely on Maeve, "will avenge me."

"They will do what they can," Maeve replied, "and in order that you may have fair chance of being revenged, I shall keep the bulls."

"That is sound sense and queenliness," said Fergne.

"And," said Bove, "our famous Swineherds are off on their travels again."

"Are those the two you told me of?" the Dagda inquired.

"They are the identical two," Bove answered. "There go Friuc and Rucht."

"There is many a man of Ireland and of Connacht will come

17

to my realm because of these bulls," Ethal Anbual repeated.

"Is that true?" Maeve inquired.

"It is not a lie indeed," the Dagda replied.

"We must all come sometime to the Country of the Dead," said Maeve, "and whether we come on account of these bulls or on some other account does not greatly matter, and, therefore, I shall take the bulls."

"And now about your daughter!" said the Dagda.

"My daughter is no concern of yours," replied Ethal Anbual. "It is true that I am your vassal, and in all proper ways I render obedience and service, but my daughter does not come within your rights."

"That is verity," the Dagda agreed. "I do not properly see what we can do."

"I do not wish to see my daughter married to the mac an Og," Ethal Anbual continued, "for there is a feud between Angus and myself, and therefore I shall not give her up to him."

"There is nothing left us but to go home," said the Dagda.

"But we cannot go home until we have performed what we set out to do," Bove insisted.

"Have you a suggestion to make?" cried the Dagda.

"I have indeed."

"Then make it," said the Dagda.

"It is," said Bove, "that if this thing is to be done by mortals, we should let mortals do it."

"Now . . ." cried Fergne.

But Maeve broke in tempestuously:

"I came to get this girl, and I shall not go away until I have got her.

"I think also," she continued, turning fiercely on Ethal Anbual, "that it is an impertinence for any chit to refuse the embraces of a proper man like Angus."

"The girl does not wish for these embraces," he replied stubbornly.

"Let her wish or not wish, she must be given to me, for by my hand, I shall not leave without her, and the booty I have already seized is nothing to the plunder I shall presently take unless that girl is given to me."

"That is the way to talk," cried Fergne. "It is thus deeds are

18

done, even by a dove."

"The girl does not desire to go," said Ethal Anbual. "I cannot force her. She is a Mistress of Arts."

"How do you know that she does not wish to go with Angus?" asked the Dagda.

"She told me that herself," he replied triumphantly.

"That settles it," said the Dagda mounfully. "If she does not wish to go she cannot be forced."

"Of course she wishes to go," cried Maeve.

"But she told her father . . ."

"What a girl tells her father is seldom of any importance and is never true."

"She is cold-headed as a spring morning," cried Fergne. "She is warm-blooded as a summer noon. Now we are listening to wisdom indeed."

Maeve leaned to Ailill.

"That companion of the Dagda pleases me very much, and although he is old, he is robust."

She turned again to Ethal Anbual.

"If you wished to conceal your daughter, why did you send her wraith and vision to Angus the mac an Og?"

"By my word," cried Ethal Anbual, "I did not send that vision, and, by my hand, I would not let the son of the Dagda see anything I possess, for he is envious, and a thief."

"If you did not send the vision," said Bove, "who sent it?"

"I know nothing of that."

"The girl sent it herself," said Maeve, "and she sent it because she wanted Angus to see her, and to desire her, and to come after her."

"Yes?" said Bove.

"And the reason she wanted the mac an Og to desire her was because she desired the mac an Og."

"This Queen gets the palm," cried Fergne. "I cry Hola to this Queen, for she is the Pulse of the Heart, and the very Tongue Tip of Wisdom."

"That nobleman," said Maeve to Ailill, "is not only pleasant and courteous and robust, he is also intelligent.

"Where is this girl?" she demanded of Ethal Anbual.

"She is at the Lake of the Dragon's Mouth," he replied sullenly.

19

"Go there," Maeve counselled to Angus Og. "You will find that she is waiting for you, and you will find that she is impatient.

"And now," she said, turning to Ethal Anbual, "I shall return the booty I took from you; that is, the Crown of Bruin, the Mantle of Laery and the Shirt of Dunlaing, for I did not come to sack the Shi, but to give help to the Dagda, and to bring two lovers together."

"You will also return The Whitehorn and The Brown Bull," said Ethal Anbual.

"I shall not give them back," she cried. "You have threatened me about those bulls, and against a threat I will maintain my defiance and my power.

"And now," said she, "I will go back to my own country."

The Dagda then gave her three kisses, and it was thus Maeve of Cruachan went into and out of Faery on that occasion.

From *In the Land of Youth*

Cuchulain

By W. B. YEATS
(1865–1939)

Among the feasting kings Cuchulain dwelt,
And his young sweetheart close beside him knelt,
Stared on the mournful wonder of his eyes,
Even as spring upon the ancient skies,
And pondered on the glory of his days;
And all around the harp-strings told his praise,
And Concubar, the Red Branch King of Kings,
With his own fingers touched the brazen strings.

Cuchulainn is still the greatest hero of ancient Irish legend. Today the statue of the dying Cuchulainn, by Oliver Sheppard, R.H.A., stands in Dublin's General Post Office, whence so many of the 1916 heroes went to their deaths.

Cuchulainn

By J. J. CAMPBELL
(1910–   )

. . . In the morning Lu had vanished, but Dechtire sat in the midst of the maidens with a baby son in her arms . . . Conor said that his sister Finnchoem should rear the child. But immediately there was a dispute . . . And Morann's judgment was that all should share in the training of the boy, for he was destined for greatness, and for the valiant defence of Ulster: his name was destined to be in the mouths of all men: he would win the love of many: he would avenge all wrongs. Morann's judgment was accepted, and Finnchoem and Amergin took him to Dun Breth in the plain of Muirtheimhne. And the name given him was Setanta.

The truth of Morann's prophecy became clear as the boy grew. All the feats and knowledge of boyhood he learned long before the normal age, and he was only about five years old when he decided that he would go to Emain Macha. For he had just heard of the Boy Corps at Conor's court, and how Conor would divide his day into three parts, so that in one part he would watch the boys of the corps at their games, especially hurling, in the second part would

21

play chess, in the third part would feast and listen to music and lays of the bards.

"I will go," said Setanta, "and match myself against the boys of the corps in their games."

"It is too soon yet," said his mother. "You are not old enough in years, and you must have a champion to protect you and ensure your safety with the boys of the corps."

"I cannot wait," said the boy, "until my years are deemed enough for that. Let you but tell me in what direction is Emain, so that I may go now."

His mother knew him, and without further argument pointed the way to him, over Sliabh Fuaid northwards. He took his hurling stick of bronze and ball of silver, his toy spear and sports javelin, and he shortened the way for himself with them: for first he would hurl the ball, then he would throw the hurling stick after it and hit it far from him, then he would throw the javelin and the spear, and in a quick spurt would catch the stick and the ball and the javelin, and lastly the spear by its tip, before they touched the ground.

Thus he made his way to Emain Macha, where he found the boys of the corps, three fifties in number, playing at hurling and games of warfare, with Conor's son Folloman at their head. He ran in amongst them at the hurling and guiding the ball before him, drove it along so that it went no higher than his knee and no lower than his ankle, until he passed the goal with it. And none could stop him or take it from him.

Folloman looked in amazement at the little lad.

"He has no guarantee for his safety amongst us," he said. "He has interfered in our game. He is surely the son of some unknown. All this is to invite attack and revenge. We shall kill him."

They all attacked him with their hurling sticks, but he parried all their blows, and they could not harm him. The same with the balls from which he defended himself with hands and arms alone. The same with their toy spears which he caught on his toy shield. Then he turned to the attack and laid low one fifty of them. He was pursuing five of them past the place where Conor sat watching when Conor called:

"Stop, stop, boy. You are dealing very roughly with the boys of the corps."

22

"And I have good reason," said Setanta. "I came from a great distance to join in their games, and they attacked me. That is not a gentle way to treat a guest."

Conor explained that it was customary for a newcomer to the corps to obtain pledges of protection from the boys before entering amongst them. Setanta said he did not know of this: had he known he would have conformed to custom; for it would be easy for him to obtain pledges. He told Conor then who he was.

Conor called on the boys to give pledges of protection to Setanta.

"We grant it," the boys answered.

Setanta then returned to the play and in a short time a fifty of the boys were laid out on the green, so that their fathers thought they were dead. But in reality they had found the play so strenuous since the little lad joined them that they took refuge from it by lying down on the green.

"He is still playing too roughly," said Conor and called out, "Boy, what are you at?"

"They attacked me," replied Setanta, "until pledges for my protection were given by them. I will ease my attack when they ask pledges of me for their protection."

They all placed themselves at once under his protection.

The following year the smith Culann invited Conor to a banquet, and asked him to bring only a few of his companions, as he had neither the space nor the means for a grand entertainment. Conor accepted, and, before he set out, he went as was his custom to see and say farewell to the boys of the corps.

He watched them at four games. In the first Setanta kept goal against all the three fifties, and they could not score; yet when they all kept goal together, he scored against them as he wished. In the second Setanta guarded the hole, and though each of the hundred and fifty balls came to the edge of the hole, not one did he let in; yet when they all guarded together, he had no difficulty in getting the ball past them into the hole. The third game was the tearing off of mantles: Setanta tore all the hundred and fifty mantles off in a trice; they could not as much as touch his brooch. In the fourth game they wrestled, and with all the corps against him Setanta

23

stood firm on his feet, yet when he turned to the attack he left not one standing.

Conor said to Fergus, who stood with him, "If that lad's deeds when he is full-grown are in keeping with his deeds today, we are a lucky land to have him."

"Is there any reason to believe," said Fergus, "that his prowess, alone of all, will not increase with the years?"

But Conor said, "Let him come with us to Culann's feast. He is worthy."

"I cannot go just yet," said Setanta.

The king was surprised that the boy did not at once leave everything for the opportunity of going to a banquet with the select royal party.

"Why so?" he asked.

"Because the boys are not finished playing," said Setanta, "and I cannot leave until the games are finished."

"We cannot wait so long," said Conor.

"You need not wait. I shall follow you."

"You do not know the way."

"I shall follow the tracks of your chariots."

That was agreed. And Conor's party arrived at Culann's house, where they were welcomed to the feast which was ready laid for them. Culann said to Conor when the company was settling to the feast:

"Before we begin, tell me, is this all the company? There is none to follow?"

"None," said Conor, "all are here." He had already forgotten about Setanta.

"The reason I ask," said Culann, "is that I have a magnificent hound, which is my watchdog, and only myself can handle him or exact obedience from him; and none dare approach the neighbourhood when I loose him to guard the house. And I should like to loose him now before we begin."

"You may loose the hound," said Conor. The hound was loosed, and he made a circuit of the place and sat down with his head on his paws, a huge, fearsome guard.

Meanwhile the six-year-old boy had left his fellows of the boy-corps of Emain Macha, and was on his way to the house of Culann, the smith. He had no arms of defence, but passed the time of the

24

journey with his hurling stick and ball. The hound bayed a fearsome challenge as he came to the house, but the boy continued his play until the hound sprang at him. Then he hurled the ball so that with terrific force it went right down the hound's throat, past the great open jaws and teeth, and as the hound reared back with the force of the blow and the pain, he grasped it by the hind legs and smashed its head to pulp on the stones of the yard.

At the sound of the hound's baying Conor had leaped to his feet remembering the boy. They all rushed out, certain Setanta was being torn by the hound, and were overjoyed to see him alive—all except Culann, who was filled with sorrow as he gazed on the hound.

"It was an unlucky day I made a banquet for Conor," he said. He turned to the boy. "You are welcome, boy, for your father's and mother's sake but not for your own. You have slain the only guard and protector of my house and my substance, of my flocks and my herds."

"Do not grieve," said the boy. "I shall see you are none the worse for what has happened."

"How can that be?" asked Culann, looking at the six-year-old boy.

"If there is a whelp of that dog's siring in all Ireland," said Setanta, "I shall rear and train it until it is able to guard and protect you as well as its sire; and until then I myself will guard your house and your property, even as your hound did."

"That is fair," said Conor.

"And you will be Cu Chulainn, the Hound of Culann, in the meantime," said Cathbhad the druid. "And that shall be your name, Cuchulainn."

"Indeed, I prefer my own name, Setanta, son of Sualtam," said the boy.

"But the name Cuchulainn will be on the lips of all the men of Ireland and the world, and their mouths will be full of its praise," said the druid.

"For that I would accept any name," said the boy; and from that time he was known as Cuchulainn.

Cuchulain has killed kings,
Kings and sons of kings,
Dragons out of the water,
And witches out of the air,
Banachas and Bonachas and people of the woods.

W. B. Yeats

The Death of Cuchullin

By EILEEN O'FAOLAIN
(1905–   )

For seven years after the routing of her armies by Cuchullin and the Ulstermen, at the time of the Cattle Raid of Cooley, Maeve did not once raise a hand against Ulster. But the proud Queen never forgot the disgrace put on her at that time by Cuchullin, when he held back the Men of Erin all through the long winter when there was not a warrior in Ulster who could have lifted a spear against her. She knew, too, that as long as Cuchullin was alive she could never go against her ancient enemies in the North. So she set to work to bring him to his death.

She first gathered around her as allies all Cuchullin's foes, men whose fathers or brothers he had slain, and men who were jealous or envious of him or of Ulster. She sent secret messengers from one end of the country to the other, seeking these enemies of Cuchullin, whispering revenge in their ears, and promising great rewards and spoils to any man who would help her to destroy him.

As well as these mortal warriors who joined Maeve in her vengeful schemes were the six children of Celatin the wizard, whom Cuchullin had slain with his twenty-seven sons when he was keeping Maeve's army out of Ulster. This monstrous brood of six—three sons and three daughters—were born at one birth to Celatin's wife when she heard that Cuchullin had killed her husband. Maeve took the six ill-shapen, evil looking beings and reared them herself for her own ends, and kept them by her until they were of an age to travel. Then she sent them east to Babylon, and to Alba and throughout the wide world to learn magical arts and spells so as to destroy Cuchullin. They studied from dawn till dark and from dark till dawn with all the famous wizards of the East, and even made their way to the fearful realm of the underground, where they met Vulcan. Vulcan, with his own hand forged and tempered for them three spears, three swords and three knives. Into these he put all the cruel venom and poison known to him, and so deadly were they that no one could escape death if they but touched his skin and drew one drop of his blood.

"Take these weapons," said Vulcan to the children of Celatin, "and guard them well; for three kings will die by them, and one of the kings will be that king among warriors, among champions, among heroes, that king of bravery who was never yet defeated, that hard-hitting, noble youth known to you as 'The Hound of Ulster.' "

So at last, with loud and raucous shouts of delight, the misshapen brood sat up on the lap of the East Wind and set off on the long voyage to Erin, until at Samain time, when summer's end had come, they floated down on the broad ramparts of Maeve's palace at Cruachan.

Maeve, seeing her six hideous servants, opened her casements and bade them enter. With joy she heard them give an account of their seven years of learning among the wizards of the East. She heard how they could make the leaves and the wisps of hay, blown along the ground by the autumn wind, take on the appearance of an invading army; of how they could fill the land with smoke and fire and with the clash and noise of battle; and how in the calm of a summer's day they could raise up the appearance of a storm on dry land with mountainous seas threatening to swallow all before them. Lastly they drew out from under their capes the deadly knives and spears and swords that Vulcan had fashioned for them, showed them to Maeve, and told her that in each one the smithy of the underworld had put the killing of a king; and in particular he had put the killing of that hateful hewer and hacker of Connachtmen —"The Hound of Ulster".

"That is well indeed," said Maeve. "Go forth and destroy him."

Seating themselves once more high up on the lap of the wind, the six monstrous goblins flew up over Ulster, and they peered and

27

pried into every dun and palace, until they found Cuchullin, who was at this time at home in Dun Dealgan, with Emir, his wife. Seeing him they at once set about filling the land of Muirthemne, Cuchullin's own patrimony, with the smoke and noise of war and hostings, the clashing of steel on steel, the neighing of horses and the screams and cries of women, in order to draw the champion of Ulster out to battle for his province.

But at the first sign of the witchery of Celatin's brood, Emir, his wife, and Cathbad the druid and Niav the wife of Cuchullin's best warrior friend, Conal of the Victories, and all his other good friends gathered around him and prayed him not to be lured out to his destruction by these sights and sounds of war, which, they told him, were but the spells and visions raised up around him by his enemies. Instead they persuaded him to go with them to the Glen of the Deaf, in Donegal, where these sounds and allurements could not reach him. There, in this lonely and peaceful glen, his friends kept him company, and he gave his word to Niav that he would not leave them without her permission. Then they sang songs and played sweet music to soothe his spirit and to bring him forgetfulness; and in playing chess and telling old tales they passed the time pleasantly till the power of the children of Celatin would be at an end. For Cuchullin's friends knew that this power of raising up magical visions around him could only last for three days.

All this time the goblin brood, knowing that their three days were running out, were sailing on the wind up over Ulster, searching for Cuchullin. They peered into every glen and wooded place where he might be hiding, but nowhere could they see any sign of him, until on the third day one of the goblin women wafted herself up on to the highest cloud in the heavens, from where she could cast her eye over the whole of Ulster's land. As she peered and searched, it seemed to her that the sounds of lutes and the joyous laughter of maidens came to her ears from the farthest dim tip of the land. Changing herself at once into a raven, she flew straight to the lonely mountain valley. There, in a fold among the high mountains, she saw a beautiful summer palace, and on the sunny bawn in front of the palace she saw Cuchullin seated among his musicians, his dancing maidens and his men of poetry.

Once again she changed her shape—this time she took on the form of one of Niav's handmaidens. In this disguise she drew a little

28

near to the group around Cuchullin, and calling her mistress aside, on some clever pretext, sent her into a nearby wood, where she put a spell of straying on her. Then, taking on the shape of Niav herself, she went back to Cuchullin and told him that the Men of Erin were invading his country, and were at that very moment burning Dun Dealgan and driving off his cattle and herds, and she begged him to go before it was too late and drive them out.

At once Cuchullin rose up, and taking his arms ordered Laegh his charioteer to get his horses and to prepare his chariot. At this his friends all crowded around him and began to plead with him not to be drawn out by the magical visions made by his enemies, and Cathbad the druid made a pledge to him that if he would stay with them but one more day he would be free for ever from the spells of Celatin's brood. But madness had seized Cuchullin's brain, and he believed now that his enemies were ravaging the province and that he must rush forth at once to defend it. So he thrust his friends aside.

Then Emir came to him and begged him not to be deluded by these visions: "These phantom armies that you see now around the ramparts of the palace are nothing but the dry leaves of autumn blown by the wind."

But Cuchullin bade her not to hold him back from his fate.

"Fame outlasts life," he told her, "and life itself would be but a poor thing if it were bought with my dishonour. For dishonoured I would be if I did not go forth now and defend Ulster against my enemies."

Laegh then went to yoke Cuchullin's steed, the Grey of Macha, but the horse fled both from him and from Cuchullin, and when at last they captured him and led him to the chariot, great tears of blood trickled from his eyes. It was another sign of doom that when Cuchullin mounted his chariot, his foot had no sooner touched the floor than all his weapons fell from their wonted places and crashed around his feet. And Laegh turned pale to see them fall.

Cuchullin now drove off southward, and as he drove, it seemed to him that out before him, line after line, his enemies were drawn up in battle array, and the clash and din of warfare on every side deafened his ears and clouded his brain. He thought, too, that he saw the palace of Emain covered with a pall of smoke, and lit up by huge tongues of flame, and that from the ramparts he saw the

29

burning corpse of Emir tossed out headless before him. In another vision he saw his own fort, Dun Dealgan, destroyed by fire, while shrieking women fled helpless from its flaming towers. And in all the countryside he saw the Men of Erin burning, killing and destroying, and no hand raised to stop them.

On their way they passed over a stream. There they saw a maiden kneeling by a ford, washing the clothes and fighting gear of a warrior, and as she washed, the water ran red with blood. Seeing Cuchullin she drew a bloodstained corslet out of the water, and held it up. Looking at it he knew it for his own.

"Who is this woman?" he asked his charioteer.

"That is the Washer of the Ford, O Cuchullin," said Laegh. "She is the daughter of the goddess of war, and she washes the garments and armour of those about to die. O Cuchullin, let us turn aside while there is yet time, for it seems to me that it is thy sword and thy corslet that dyes the water red."

But Cuchullin answered, "I would gladly toss my life to the goddess of war if once again I could work havoc on the Men of Erin, and drive them out of Ulster."

Then he drove on till he came to the enemy hosts that Maeve had collected near the border for the invasion of the North. Three times he drove through them, cutting them down and leaving them in little heaps on each side of his tracks. Then he performed his three Thunder Feats, rushing through them in his roaring chariot till their bones flew apart and with the lightning of his blades scattered them broadcast on the wide plain of Muirthemne, like the sands of the sea or the stars in the frosty heavens. And his wheels and his horses' hooves ground them like hailstones under a millstone.

Twice the Men of Erin broke under the fury of his attack. Twice Erc son of Cairpre rallied them again. Then, like a god, his charges breathing fire, his sword white-hot in his hand, Cuchullin drove at the enemy for the third time, and this time they fled beyond recall, for neither Erc, nor Luga, nor Curoi, Cuchullin's bitterest foes, could halt them as they fled before his onset. But at the very moment when the rout was at its height there came a noise of screaming down the wind, as the six children of Celtain entered into the fight with their hideous cries. They thrust Vulcan's deadly weapons into the hands of Erc and Luga and Curoi and

30

bade them put an end to their enemy.

Erc eagerly took the weapons of death. He turned and faced Cuchullin. He took careful aim. Then he threw the venomous spear. It glanced off Cuchullin and plunged its head deep into the breast of his faithful charioteer. Cuchullin tore at the spear to rend it from the flesh of his friend, but no strength could stir the barb one hairsbreadth from its deadly grip. Heedless of his enemies, each with his spear poised to strike, Cuchullin bent over the dying Laegh, and bidding him a tender farewell gently laid him down.

Again he turned to the hosts and, fury-driven, he hacked and hewed around him in savage revenge for Laegh. But now Luga unloosed another barb upon him, and this time it pierced the Grey of Macha and sent the horse stumbling to the ground. Unyoking him, Cuchullin sent him aside from the thick of the fighting, and he galloped off with Vulcan's spear stuck deep in his flesh.

For the third time Cuchullin faced his enemies on the great Plain of Muirthemne. Once more he dashed at them and mowed down great swathes in their lines; and once more they fled before him. And then the goblin brood of Celatin shrieked at Curoi to use the third spear of Vulcan before it would be too late.

"A king," they shrieked, "must fall by that spear."

"I heard you say a king would fall by the spear of Erc this morning," he answered them.

"It is true," they intoned. "Two kings have already fallen by Vulcan's spears—Laegh the King of Charioteers, and the Grey of Macha, the King of Steeds. By this one will fall the King of Champions, Ulster's glorious Hound."

Curoi raised his spear, and taking long and careful aim he threw it at Cuchullin. The bright steel flew up into the air. In the sun it flashed its blue wing. Then down it drove straight for Cuchullin's side, and sank itself deep in his flesh until his blood gushed out upon the floor of the chariot. As Cuchullin fell, his one remaining horse, the Black Sainglend, broke away and fled, with the wrecked chariot hanging from his gory back.

Cuchullin now sank slowly to the ground. Seeing him stretched, with his lifeblood flowing from him in a stream, the enemy hosts stealthily crept back. They stood in a wide circle around him, their weapons grounded, and in silence they watched the champion die.

Then Cuchullin spoke to his enemies, saying, "I would fain

31

quench my thirst at the lakeside."

To this the Men of Erin answered that they gave him leave to go. So, rising to his feet and with his hands holding the great wound in his side to halt the blood, he went to the brink of the lake and drank, and washing himself in the water, he prepared himself to die. A little way from the lake he saw a standing pillar, and going to it he stood up straight with his back against it, facing his enemies, and throwing his girdle around the stone behind him, he tied it around his breast, so that he might die standing upright.

All the while his enemies stood around him in a wide circle, still afraid to come too near while life remained in him.

The hero's blood had by this formed a channel down into the lake; as Cuchullin watched it flow he saw an otter creep out from some nearby bushes and timidly lap his blood. Tugging the spear shaft from his wound he threw it at the beast, and sent him scampering away. Then a raven stealthily hopped up and dipped its beak in the stream of his blood; but so greedy was it to drink that its claws got entangled in some weed, and it fell head foremost into the red pool. Cuchullin laughed a loud and hearty laugh, for he knew it would be the last laugh he would ever give.

His head now sank slowly on his breast. And at the last, as he stood there facing his enemies, on the Great Plain of Muirthemne, his lifeblood trickling from him, the great sky of Ireland over him, the Hero Light about his head grew dim and slowly died. At that the last bright ray of life went out of Cuchullin, and he gave a sigh so deep and strong that it split the pillar-stone behind him.

It was then that Luga, seeing the Hero Light fade and die, drew near to Cuchullin, and made to take the hero's head from his body. But as he did so, the sword fell from the champion's upraised arm, and struck the hand of Luga to the ground.

This is part of the story of Deirdre Of The Sorrows, in the ancient times, when King Conchubor reigned in Ireland. Before she was born, a Druid predicted that she would cause great sorrow and suggested that she should not be allowed to live. But the King decreed that she should grow up in utter seclusion, so that she could cause no harm. She was very beautiful and he intended to marry her as soon as she grew up. But one day she accidentally met a young prince called Naisi. They instantly fell in love. Knowing how angry the King would be when he found out about this, Deirdre, Naisi and his two brothers, Ainnle and Ardan, fled to Scotland, where they lived happily for a long time. At length they grew homesick. The King was very old. Emissaries said that he had forgiven and forgotten the past. Deirdre, her husband and his two brothers returned full of joy to their native land. But no sooner had Naisi, Ainnle and Ardan set foot inside Conchubor's territory than he had them slain.

Bronze "latchet" brooch of 1st Century B.C., *in the National Museum of Ireland.*

The Death of the Sons of USNA

By JOHN MILLINGTON SYNGE
(1871–1909)

(*Tumult.* DEIRDRE *crouches down on* NAISI'S *cloak.*
CONCHUBOR *comes in hurriedly.*)

CONCHUBOR. They've met their death—the three that stole you,
Deirdre, and from this out you'll be my queen in Emain.
(*A keen of men's voices is heard behind.*)

DEIRDRE (*Bewildered and terrified*). It is not I will be a queen.

CONCHUBOR. Make your lamentation a short while if you will, but
it isn't long till a day'll come when you begin pitying a man is
old and desolate, and High King also . . . Let you not fear me,
for it's I'm well pleased you have a store of pity for the three
that were your friends in Alban.

DEIRDRE. I have pity, surely . . . It's the way pity has me this
night, when I think of Naisi, that I could set my teeth into the
heart of a king.

CONCHUBOR. I know well pity's cruel, when it was my pity for my
own self destroyed Naisi.

DEIRDRE (*more wildly*). It was my words without pity gave Naisi
a death will have no match until the ends of life and time. (*Breaking out into a keen*) But who'll pity Deirdre has lost the lips of
Naisi from her neck and from her cheek for ever? Who'll pity
Deirdre has lost the twilight in the woods with Naisi, when
beech-trees were silver and copper, and ash trees were fine gold?

CONCHUBOR (*bewildered*). It's I'll know the way to pity and care
you, and I with a share of troubles has me thinking this night it
would be a good bargain if it was I was in the grave, and Deirdre
crying over me, and it was Naisi who was old and desolate.
(*Keen heard*)

34

DEIRDRE (*wild with sorrow*). It is I who am desolate; I, Deirdre, that will not live till I am old.

CONCHUBOR. It's not long you'll be desolate, and I seven years saying, "It's a bright day for Deirdre in the woods of Alban"; or saying again, "What way will Deidre be sleeping this night, and wet leaves and branches driving from the north?" Let you not break the thing I've set my life on, and you giving yourself up to your sorrow when its joy and sorrow do burn out like straw blazing in an east wind.

DEIRDRE (*turning on him*). Was it that way with your sorrow, when I and Naisi went northward from Slieve Fuadh and let raise our sails for Alban?

CONCHUBOR. There's one sorrow has no end surely—that's being old and lonesome. (*With extraordinary pleading*) But you and I will have a little peace in Emain, with harps playing, and old men telling stories at the fall of the night. I've let build rooms for our two selves, Deirdre, with red gold upon the walls and ceilings that are set with bronze. There never was a queen in the east had a house the like of your house, that's waiting for yourself in Emain.

SOLDIER (*running in*). Emain is in flames. Fergus has come back, and is setting fire to the world. Come up, Conchubor, or your state will be destroyed!

CONCHUBOR (*angry and regal again*). Are the Sons of Usna buried?

SOLDIER. They are in their grave, but no earth is thrown.

CONCHUBOR. Let me see them. Open the tent!

      (SOLDIER *opens back of tent and shows grave.*)

Where are my fighters?

SOLDIER. They are gone to Emain.

CONCHUBOR (*to* DEIRDRE). There are none to harm you. Stay here until I come again.

    (*Goes out with* SOLDIER. DEIRDRE *looks round for a moment, then goes up slowly and looks into grave. She crouches down and begins swaying herself backwards and forwards, keening softly. At first her words are not heard, then they become clear.*)

DEIRDRE. It's you three will not see age or death coming—you that were my company when the fires on the hilltops were put out and the stars were our friends only. I'll turn my thoughts back from this night, that's pitiful for want of pity, to the time it was your rods and cloaks made a little tent for me where there'd be a birch-tree making shelter and a dry stone; though from this day my own fingers will be making a tent for me, spreading out my hairs and they knotted with the rain.

(LAVARCHAM *and* OLD WOMAN *come in stealthily on right.*)

DEIRDRE (*not seeing them*). It is I, Deirdre, will be crouching in a dark place; I, Deirdre, that was young with Naisi, and brought sorrow to his grave in Emain.

OLD WOMAN. Is that Deirdre broken down that was so light and airy?

LAVARCHAM. It is, surely, crying out over their grave. (*She goes to* DEIRDRE.)

DEIRDRE. It will be my share from this out to be making lamentation on his stone always, and I crying for a love will be the like of a star shining on a little harbour by the sea.

LAVARCHAM (*coming forward*). Let you rise up, Deirdre, and come off while there are none to heed us, the way I'll find you shelter and some friend to guard you.

DEIRDRE. To what place would I go away from Naisi? What are the woods without Naisi or the sea shore?

LAVARCHAM (*very coaxingly*). If it is that way you'd be, come till I find you a sunny place where you'll be a great wonder they'll call the queen of sorrows; and you'll begin taking a pride to be sitting up pausing and dreaming when the summer comes.

DEIRDRE. It was the voice of Naisi that was strong in summer—the voice of Naisi that was sweeter than pipes playing, but from this day will be dumb always.

LAVARCHAM (*to* OLD WOMAN). She doesn't heed us at all. We'll be hard set to rouse her.

OLD WOMAN. If we don't the High King will rouse her, coming down beside her with the rage of battle in his blood, for how could Fergus stand against him?

LAVARCHAM (*touching* DEIRDRE *with her hand*). There's a score of woman's years in store for you, and you'd best choose will you start living them beside the man you hate, or being your own mistress in the west or south?

DEIRDRE. It is not I will go on living after Ainnle and after Ardan. After Naisi I will not have a lifetime in the world.

36

OLD WOMAN (*with excitement*). Look, Lavarcham! There's a light leaving the Red Branch. Conchubor and his lot will be coming quickly, with a torch of bog deal for her marriage, throwing a light on her three comrades.

DEIRDRE (*startled*). Let us throw down clay on my three comrades. Let us cover up Naisi along with Ainnle and Ardan, they that were the pride of Emain. (*Throwing in clay*). There is Naisi was the best of three, the choicest of the choice of many. It was a clean death was your share, Naisi; and it is not I will quit your head, when it's many a dark night among the snipe and plover that you and I were whispering together. It is not I will quit your head, Naisi, when it's many a night we saw the stars among the clear trees of Glen da Ruadh, or the moon pausing to rest her on the edges of the hills.

OLD WOMAN. Conchubor is coming, surely. I see the glare of flames throwing a light upon his cloak.

LAVARCHAM (*eagerly*). Rise up, Deirdre, and come to Fergus, or be the High King's slave for ever!

DEIRDRE (*imperiously*). I will not leave Naisi, who has left the whole world scorched and desolate. I will not go away when there is no light in the heavens, and no flower in the earth under them, but is saying to me that it is Naisi who is gone for ever.

CONCHUBOR (*behind*). She is here. Stay a little back.

(LAVARCHAM *and* OLD WOMAN *go into the shadow on left
as* CONCHUBOR *comes in. With excitement, to* DEIRDRE)

Come forward and leave Naisi the way I've left charred timber and a smell of burning in Emain Macha, and a heap of rubbish in the storehouse of many crowns.

DEIRDRE (*more awake to what is round her*). What are crowns and Emain Macha, when the head that gave them glory is this place, Conchubor, and it stretched upon the gravel will be my bed tonight?

CONCHUBOR. Make an end with talk of Naisi, for I've come to bring you to Dundealgan since Emain is destroyed.

(CONCHUBOR *makes a movement towards her.*)

DEIRDRE (*with a tone that stops him*). Draw a little back from Naisi, who is young for ever. Draw a little back from the white bodies I am putting under a mound of clay and grasses that are withered—a mound will have a nook for my own self when the end

37

is come.

CONCHUBOR (*roughly*). Let you rise up and come along with me in place of growing crazy with your wailings here.

DEIRDRE. It's yourself has made a crazy story, and let you go back to your arms, Conchubor, and to councils where your name is great, for in this place you are an old man and a fool only.

CONCHUBOR. If I've folly I've sense left not to lose the thing I've bought with sorrow and the deaths of many. (*He moves towards her.*)

DEIRDRE. Do not raise a hand to touch me.

CONCHUBOR. There are other hands to touch you. My fighters are set round in among the trees.

DEIRDRE. Who'll fight the grave, Conchubor, and it opened on a dark night?

LAVARCHAM (*eagerly*). There are steps in the wood. I hear the call of Fergus and his men.

CONCHUBOR (*furiously*). Fergus cannot stop me. I am more powerful than he is, though I am defeated and old.

FERGUS (*comes in to* DEIRDRE; *a red glow is seen behind the grave*). I have destroyed Emain, and now I'll guard you all times, Deirdre, though it was I, without knowledge, brought Naisi to his grave.

CONCHUBOR. It's not you will guard her, for my whole armies are gathering. Rise up, Deirdre, for you are mine surely.

FERGUS (*coming between them*). I am come between you.

CONCHUBOR (*wildly*). When I've killed Naisi and his brothers, is there any man that I will spare? And is it you will stand against me, Fergus, when it's seven years you've seen me getting my death with rage in Emain?

FERGUS. It's I, surely, will stand against a thief and traitor.

DEIRDRE (*stands up and sees the light from Emain*). Draw a little back with the squabbling of fools when I am broken up with misery. (*She turns round.*) I see the flames of Emain starting upward in the dark night; and because of me there will be weasels and wild cats crying on a lonely wall where there were queens and armies and red gold, the way there will be a story told of a ruined city and a raving king and a woman will be young for ever. (*She looks round.*) I see the trees naked and bare, and the moon shining. Little moon, little moon of Alban,

38

it's lonesome you'll be this night, and tomorrow night, and long nights after, and you pacing the woods beyond Glen Laoi, looking every place for Deirdre and Naisi, the two lovers who slept so sweetly with each other.

FERGUS (*going to* CONCHUBOR's *right and whispering*). Keep back, or you will have the shame of pushing a bolt on a queen who is out of her wits.

CONCHUBOR. It is I who am out of my wits, with Emain in flames, and Deirdre raving, and my own heart gone within me.

DEIRDRE (*in a high and quiet tone*). I have put away sorrow like a shoe that is worn out and muddy, for it is I have had a life that will be envied by great companies. It was not by a low birth I made kings uneasy, and they sitting in the halls of Emain. It was not a low thing to be chosen by Conchubor, who was wise, and Naisi had no match for bravery. It is not a small thing to be rid of grey hairs, and the loosening of the teeth. (*With a sort of triumph*) It was the choice of lives we had in the clear woods, and in the grave we're safe, surely . . .

CONCHUBOR. She will do herself harm.

DEIRDRE (*showing* NAISI's *knife*). I have a little key to unlock the prison of Naisi you'd shut upon his youth for ever. Keep back, Conchubor; for the High King who is your master has put his hands between us. (*She half turns to the grave.*) It was sorrows were foretold, but great joys were my share always; yet it is a cold place I must go to be with you, Naisi; and it's cold your arms will be this night that were warm about my neck so often . . . It's a pitiful thing to be talking out when your ears are shut to me. It's a pitiful thing, Conchubor, you have done this night in Emain; yet a thing will be a joy and triumph to the ends of life and time.

> (*She presses knife into her heart and sinks into the grave.*
> CONCHUBOR *and* FERGUS *go forward. The red glow fades,*
> *leaving stage very dark.*)

FERGUS. Four white bodies are laid down together; four clear lights are quenched in Ireland. (*He throws his sword into the grave.*) There is my sword that could not shield you—my four friends that were the dearest always. The flames of Emain have gone out: Deirdre is dead and there is none to keen her. That is the fate of Deirdre and the Children of Usna, and for this night, Conchubor, our war is ended. (*He goes out.*)

LAVARCHAM. I have a little hut where you can rest, Conchubor; there is a great dew falling.

CONCHUBOR (*with the voice of an old man*). Take me with you. I'm hard set to see the way before me.

OLD WOMAN. This way, Conchubor.

(*They go out.*)

LAVARCHAM (*beside the grave*). Deirdre is dead, and Naisi is dead; and if the oaks and stars could die for sorrow, it's a dark sky and a hard and naked earth we'd have this night in Emain.

(*Curtain*)

From *Deirdre of the Sorrows*

The Great Breath

By GEORGE RUSSELL (AE)
(1867–1935)

Its edges foamed with amethyst and rose,
Withers once more the old blue flower of day;
There where the ether like a diamond glows
    Its petals fade away.

A shadowy tumult stirs the dusky air;
Sparkle the delicate dews, the distant snows;
The great deep thrills, for through it everywhere
    The breath of Beauty blows.

I saw how all the trembling ages past,
Moulded to her by deep and deeper breath,
Neared to the hour when Beauty breathes her last
    And knows herself in death.

40

Untitled

His harp was carved and cunning,
    As the Celtic craftsman makes,
Graven all over with twisted shapes
    Like many headless snakes.

His harp was carved and cunning,
    His sword was prompt and sharp,
And he was gay when he held the sword,
    Sad when he held the harp.

                    G. K. Chesterton

*O*isin, *who was born in the days when history was still passed down through the ages by word of mouth, lived until the times of written history, and so might, in a way, be said to be the link between the two.*

Oisin in the Land of the Ever Young

By EILEEN O'FAOLAIN

One morning in the early summer Finn and the Fianna were hunting in the woods around Loch Lene near Killarney. Mists covered the glens and were draped around the tops of the mountains, but soon the rising sun shot diamond spears down through the clouds, and turned the lakes into twinkling jewels in the dark bed of the glen. Waiting for the mists to clear, Finn and his companions sat on a hillside, but Oisin, his son, stood gazing down on the lakes and rivulets of silver, for Oisin was the poet of the Fianna and he loved the beauty of the lakes, the bogs and the mountains, and the creatures of the forest and the sea. Now he called to his comrades to look at the sun lighting up one misty valley and lake and rivulet after the other, and he reminded them that it was

41

here, in these jewelled and shining ravines, hundred of years before their time, that Len the mighty smithy and armourer to the Gods of Erin had his anvil. And it was here he beat out the magic spears and swords and javelins for Lugh of the Long Arm, and for Nuada of the Silver Hand, for Manannan Mac Lir, the sea-god, and for all the warriors of the People of Dana. And so much magic did he beat into them that, like the famous spear of Lugh, they had to be kept steeping in a pot of poppy seeds to soothe them and keep them quiet, so thirsty were they for blood. As Len worked he made around him sparkling rainbows and fiery dews that falling to the ground made the lakes and silver streams, and the sunshot mist that ever since plays around Loch Lene.

The Fians looked down on the lakes beneath them as Oisin was telling them of Len, and as they looked they saw a small cloud of mist come out of the valley, and waft up the hill towards where they sat. When it drew near it broke in two and out from it stepped a milk white steed and a rider clad in scarlet and gold.

"Tis Len himself who rides towards us," said Finn.

But as the steed came nearer, the Fianna saw that its rider was not Len, but a maiden of great beauty, and she was clad in the raiment of a queen. On her head she wore a crown of gold, and the bridle in her hand was studded with glittering jewels. Her steed was shod with shoes of pure gold, and silver bells adorned his harness of white bronze and red leather. Pulling up the steed, the maiden spoke to Finn, and said:

"Finn, son of Cool, I am Niav of the Golden Hair, daughter of the King of the Land of the Ever Young, and I have crossed the seas for love of your son Oisin, the poet and music maker of the Fianna."

Then she looked at Oisin and asked him if he would return with her to the Land of the Ever Young. And in a voice like a gentle summer breeze playing over silver bells, she sang to him of the beauties of her father's kingdom.

Delightful is the land beyond all dreams!
    Beyond what seems to thee most fair—
    Rich fruit abound the bright year round
    And flowers are found of hues most rare.

Unfailing there the honey and wine
    And draughts divine of mead there be,

42

No ache nor ailing night or day—
Death or decay thou ne'er shalt see!

The mirthful feast and joyous play
And music's sway all blest, benign—
Silver untold and store of gold
Undreamt by the old shall all be thine!

A hundred swords of steel refined,
A hundred cloaks of kind full rare,
A hundred steeds of proudest breed,
A hundred hounds—thy meed when there!

A hundred maidens young and fair
Of blithesome air shall tend on thee.
Of form most meet, as fairies fleet,
And of song more sweet than the wild thrush free!

As they listened to the maiden's song, the Fianna stood stock still, as men under a spell, so bewitched were they with her beauty and with her sweet-sounding voice. And while she sang no bird called out, nor bee was heard to buzz, nor stream to murmur, but over all a silence and a stillness seemed to steal, until the song was ended. Then, finishing her lay, she raised a lily-white arm and waved Oisin to a seat by her side on the white steed.

Gently, like one in a dream, Oisin moved towards her, and mounting the fairy steed he sat by the side of Niav of the Golden Hair. And as the steed wheeled around to go, Oisin for a moment rested his dream-laden eyes on Finn, who was calling out in anguish to see him leave. Then as they galloped off down the hill he looked back once and waved a languid arm in farewell.

They went like the wind over bog and mountain, and soon Oisin could no longer hear the wails and lamentations of his comrades. Then they came to the rocky coast of Kerry, and the fairy steed pranced lightly over the crests of the waves and made out to sea. As they passed over the sun-dazzled floor of the ocean they seemed to enter a land of golden light and pearly dew, a land of rainbow and sunshine, where on either side of them, as they went, they saw rise up the tall pinnacles of mansions and castles shimmering and shining over lawns of softest green and banks of brilliant flowers.

43

Over their heads, embosomed in the clouds, were cities of marble and gold, that seemed to disappear before a second glance. Once a yellow fawn chased by a pure white hound with one red ear went by, and then a beautiful maiden riding on a bay, and holding a golden apple in her hand. After them again they saw a young knight in flowing purple cloak, and in his hand a flashing sword of gold, riding past them mounted on a pure white steed.

Oisin wondered at all these strange and wonderful sights, but Niav bade not to notice these visions, as there was nothing of real beauty to be seen until they reached the Land of the Ever Young.

Then they left the region of sun and brightness, and now dark thunderclouds rolled over them; and daggers of rain and arrows of lightning shot around their heads. But they rode on through the tempest, going as quickly as leaves before the wind, until at last they left the storm behind them. Now they saw a land of great splendour rise up before them out of the sun-kissed ocean.

Their steed faced for this sunny land, and soon was riding up over a silvery strand and on to lawns of sweet smelling clover shaded by giant beech trees, where the song of many birds mingled with the hum and buzz of a myriad bees. Here Oisin saw the people leave their houses and come out to welcome him and Niav, some on foot and others riding steeds as richly caparisoned as their own, and all were young and beautiful and gay.

"What lovely land is this?" asked Oisin of Niav.

For answer Niav smiled and led Oisin through a noble gateway into a palace bawn, where a hundred riders on black steeds, and a hundred on white were drawn up for their reception. Out from the rows of horsemen rode the King of the Land of the Ever Young, and in a loud voice, so all could hear, he welcomed them to this kingdom:

"Welcome, Oisin son of Finn! Welcome to this land where we honour poets, where there is neither age nor sorrow nor death. Where time does not wither away and every day brings only joy! Take Niav for thy bride, live with us for ever, and speak poems of love, life, of beauty and of joy, and of youth that never grows old!"

Then the King of the Land of the Ever Young led Oisin into his palace and presented him to the Queen. And that day Oisin was wedded to Niav, and he sat beside her at the royal banquet that

44

was made in honour of their wedding. There he ate off plates of purest gold, while minstrels played strangely soothing strains on harps of silver, and men of poetry sang joyous and lovely songs, and all the while from the open casements blossom-fragrant winds played around their heads, and brought to their ears the song of birds from the deep, cool woods.

So from one delight to another, day followed day till Oisin knew not whether he lived in one long lovely dream where bliss was unending. He had only to wish for something and it came to pass, and all the delights of his old life with the Fianna, the hunt, the ale feast, the horse races and the sports, he savoured over again—only now they were more perfect, more delightful and more joyful than those of his mortal home.

But at night in his dreams Oisin visited Erin again, and once more took up his old life with Fenian comrades, hunting deer or the wild boar in the great forests of the South, fishing in the great lakes and waterfalls of the Shannon, or horse racing in the great plain of Kildare. Then with the power of longing for his old life he would awaken from his sleep, and stride up and down his chamber in strange unease and still half asleep. But before his full waking came to him Niav, ever watchful of his happiness, would be by his side to read his wish and to bring back his content.

"I thought to be chasing over Ben Eader's heathery side after the fleetest deer that ever ran, and Finn was by my side, and Keelta Mac Ronan and Dermot of the Beautiful Women, and Finn's dogs, Bran, Sgeolaun and Lomair . . ." he would tell her.

And Niav, seeing the longing and sadness in his dream-laden eyes, would quickly order the horses and dogs to be got ready, and before Oisin could have time for one other regretful thought, he would be riding down a woodland avenue on his black steed, on his way to the hunt with Niav and other joyous youths and maidens. And as the woods rang with the winding of the hunting horn, the pounding of a hundred hoofbeats, the belling of stags and the musical clamouring of hounds, Oisin's dream and longing would melt away and be banished for ever from his mind.

But one day, Oisin, riding away from Niav and his companions in the hunt, found himself on the border of a bleak and desolate land. And as he stood and looked around him, trying to discover his way back to the hounds, he thought he heard the sound of the

Dord Fianna, Finn's hunting horn, faintly echoing away among distant hills in the bleak land before him. He listened again, and as he heard the faint sound, once more his dreams of hunting with the Fianna came back to his mind. Closing his eyes he saw the sun-warmed, honey-fragrant heather on which they lay—Finn, Dermot, Keelta, Conan the Bald and Goll son of Morna—and at Finn's feet stretched out, with loving eye and lolling tongue, his favourite hounds, Bran and Sgeolaun. Now all the forest had gone still around him and only the bees in the treetops made a sound. Slowly Oisin turned his horse's head towards the dim hills in the bleak land before him, and with eager desire he pressed on and on, to where he still fancied he heard the dim echo of the Fianna's Horn.

Soon he reached a region of bare rock and trackless boggy mountain, up which his steed scrambled with fear and reluctance. Gone now were all sight of leafy summer woods, and lawns of sweet-smelling clover. Up and up horse and rider pressed until they reached a land where steely icicles clung to the black rocks, and drifts of snow hid chasm and miry dangerous places before them. Inky thunderclouds pressed down around them, while the wind shrieked with horrible, demon-like fury. Up and up over an ever-steep icy mountain they went, the steed clinging with clever hooves to the slippery and dangerous rocks, till at last, high among the mists and clouds, they reached a dreary, foggy plain. And here, among floating drifts of the wind's icy breath, there loomed an ugly black fortress, ancient and battle-scarred.

Oisin dismounted, and drawing his sword he walked towards the great iron-studded door. At the side of the door he saw a deep cave, and in its dark depths a maiden of the fairest face he had ever seen, and she was chained to two ancient eagles. As he drew near, the maiden called out to Oisin to beware, and dragging on her rusty chains she came to the mouth of the cave and spoke to him.

She told him that the castle he saw before him was the castle of the Fomor, a monster and a giant of such strength that no champion in the world could conquer him, for she said he was "as strong as a mountain, as crafty as the fitful winds, and as lasting as the salt sea that eats away the world." She told him, too, that she had been imprisoned here for so long that she had lost count of the centuries, and that many bold warriors had come from the Eastern and the Western worlds to rescue her, but all had been made an end of by

46

the Fomar. He was so evil and so frightful, she told him, that he put the demons screaming and jabbering at night, with fear of him, and these were demons that he had put in prison for growing lax in their evildoing.

"Go while you may from this evil and horrible place," she begged of him, "for there is no chance that you will not be put to death by the Fomor." And while she spoke her rusty chains clanged around her, and the old eagles winked their steel-sharp eyes.

For answer Oisin strode up to the mighty door of the castle and with his sword struck three heavy blows that resounded down the dark and vasty corridors, causing a chorus of shrieks and inhuman horrible wails from the captive demons in the deep dungeons within.

Slowly the rusty door groaned open, and a horrible monster of evil countenance came out fully clad for battle, carrying shield and sword and a giant iron-spiked club. With a roar like the rolling of thunder between high mountains he rushed at Oisin, and swinging his great club over his head he thought to bring it down on Oisin's skull and shatter it to pieces. But Oisin leaped nimbly out of the way, and before the slow-witted and cumbrous Fomor had recovered from his surprise at his opponent's swiftness, Oisin leaped on him and thrust his sword deep into his breast. Forth gushed a spout of blackish-brown blood as Oisin withdrew his blade from the Fomor's chest, and now that the first blood was spilt the fight became fierce and quick. The Fomor rushed at Oisin, and his iron club danced around his head and body with such speed that no eye could see where it was going to fall. So Oisin closed with the giant, and for many bouts blows were given and received that could not be counted. Then at last the Fomor gave a mighty blow with his club that glanced off Oisin's head and crashed on his shield with a stunning and thunderous noise. Oisin staggered, but recovered himself quickly, and turning on the giant, who thought to have felled him, drove his sword right through his shoulder and sent him reeling to the ground.

Out from the shadows servitors of the Fomor now rushed to bear their master away to safety, and to apply healing oils and unguents to his many wounds. From the shadows, too, came Niav, gliding to the side of Oisin, and together they withdrew into the cave where the maiden was chained to the two ancient eagles. As he lay on a pallet of otter skins, Niav, with healing oils and sweet smelling balm distilled from rose petals and water lilies, soothed and healed his many gashes and wounds, and gently chiding him for leaving the Land of the Ever Young, she put a restful slumber on him, and he slept for many hours. But as the first ray of the dawn crept in through the mouth of the cave he leaped to his feet once more and got ready to fight the Fomor. The Fomor, too, healed by magic oils and balms, arose strong and ready to renew the struggle.

And so for seven days they fought, and at the end of each day no one could say whether Oisin or the Fomor was the victor. But each evening as Oisin came back to have his wounds healed, and to seek restful slumber in the cave, he saw that one chain less was binding the beautiful captive to her eagle jailors. Then at the end of seven days, when he put forth all his strength, Oisin leaped at his enemy in an unguarded moment and ran his sword right through his heart. Down sank the giant, and as his lifeblood ebbed away in a murky stream across the castle yard the last of the rusty chains that bound her to the ancient eagles dropped from the waist of the beautiful maiden, and she was free, and with much rejoicing she went out toward Oisin and led him in to his rest and healing. Then taking a steed from the Fomor's stables she left for her own land and her own people, whom she had not seen for many hundred years.

Then, too, Niav and Oisin mounted their steeds, and with a speed that outraced the wind they left the dark region of the Fomor forever, and turned their faces towards that land of gladness and joy—the Land of the Ever Young. As they passed over the confines of that cold shadowland of the Fomor they came to a great dim lake that, deep in moss-quiet woods, stretched out to far unknown shores. As they passed by its leaf-hidden waters Niav urged on her steed more quickly, but something drew Oisin's eye to where the driftwood bobbed on the dark ripple by the stony shore, and caused him to start and pull up his racing steed. Quickly dismounting, he went to the edge of the water, and there picked out from among the floating leaves and straws a spear shaft washed up from mortal shores, a spear shaft made of the wood of the ash, such a one as the Fianna used to have.

For a long time Oisin stood by the lakeshore and gazed at the

48

broken shaft, and never spoke a word to Niav, who now stood questioning by his side. For, as he looked, he saw the hand that had fashioned it, and the woodland by the side of Allen's heathery slopes where it had grown. Then he looked around him at the woods by the lake shore that now were fragrant with bluebells and white hawthorn—the flowers of Maytime. And he thought, "In Erin now the Fianna will be putting out long fishing lines, for the mayfly are hanging in murmurous haze over stream and river, and the shining trout will be leaping, and the splash of the salmon will be making bright the dim forest pools."

Then he said to Niav that he would return to Erin for a short visit to see Finn and the Fianna once again, and to tell them of his life in the Land of the Ever Young. But Niav grew sorrowful at the thought of Oisin leaving her for the land of the mortals, where, she said, the leaf dies on the bough, and the songbirds are silenced by the winter's chilly blast, and the young and the beautiful are withered by age.

But Oisin answered that if the leaf dies, and the birds are muted by winter's cold, their coming with the spring is all the more beautiful when hope is born anew, and if the young and the beautiful grow old, they grow, too, in wisdom. And then he pleaded with her to give him leave to go.

"Let me go, if only for one short day in Erin, that I may grasp the hand of Finn and Dermot and Oscar once again, and tell them my story of the Land of the Ever Young, and then I shall return to your side and dwell with you forever in your blissful country."

And Niav answered, "Go, Oisin, since you so desire to see your land and your people once again, but I warn you most earnestly not to dismount from your steed, or let your foot once touch the soil of Erin, or you shall never again see the Land of the Ever Young."

So Oisin mounted his horse and faced for the Land of Erin. It was on a May morning just as when he left that he returned again to his own country. The sun was breaking out through the light summer clouds when he felt the soil of Erin under his horse's hooves. As they rode along, Oisin's eyes eagerly scanned the hills and the valleys for any sign of the Fianna, and he strained his ears for the sound of their hunting horns. But no sign or sound of the Fianna could he see or hear, and on his journey through the land he passed by many strange new buildings, high and strong and built of stone, and from their towers a sound like that of great cymbals floated out over the countryside. He watched some churls building one such tower, and, as he watched them, great was his surprise at their smallness. And the churls greatly wondered at the giant size of Oisin and at the richness of his attire, and seeing him pass they laid aside the mallets and leaned on their spades, and called out to their fellows to come and see "one of the gods of old that now again visits the earth."

Then Oisin asked them if they knew in what part of Erin Finn and the Fianna were hunting at the present time. And one among them, who was in command—a druid, as it appeared to Oisin from his robes and his shaven head—called out that he should well know that Finn and his Fianna had gone from the world these three hundred years. But Oisin took him for a jealous, power-grasping druid, and spurred on his steed to Finn's chief dun on the Hill of Allen.

On through the broad oak forests in the middle of the country he sped, and never drew rein till he reached the side of the heathery Hill of Allen, rising out of the great bog around Kildare. Here it was that Finn's great household was, in the high dun on the hilltop, its lime-white mansions gleaming in the sun and plainly seen from many leagues away. But now the floating May morning mist obscured it from Oisin's view, or so he thought until he came out of the oak wood and climbed the hill, and then no mist or cloud was hiding the ruin of rath and hall, or the riotous nettles and elders and docks that covered the ramparts and banqueting hall of that once great dwelling.

Oisin pulled up his steed and looked wonderingly around him. No sound broke the awesome silence of desolation.

"No enemy that put his hand to this would live to finish it so fully for Finn would have him killed before he had half begun," thought Oisin.

"Could it be that Finn has left Allen and built himself a larger dun nearer Tara?" he mused.

Or could it be . . . and he remembered the words that the churlish druid had called out to him—that Finn and the Fianna had come to their end.

Frenzy seized Oisin at this thought, and, quickly turning his

50

steed, he faced northwards to Tara of the Kings to seek news of Finn and the Fianna from the High King himself.

His way lay by the mountains that skirt the eastern sea, and as he went by the Valley of the Thrushes he saw a band of churls on the hillside toiling and sweating in the efforts to lift a slab of granite out of a quarry. Greatly marvelling at the sad change that had come over the race of men since his days in Erin—"Even the slaves were twice their size and four times their strength," he thought to himself as he watched them—full of pity for their weakness he stretched out his arm, and, stooping across them, lifted the slab right out of the rock face.

The churls gazed at him with wonder and admiration, and sent up a shout of praise for the strength of the beautiful god that, they believed, had come among them. But the next minute their cheering changed to cries of terror as they fled in confusion at what they now beheld. For, in bending over to lift the slab, Oisin had broken his saddle girth and had fallen to the ground. The minute he touched the ground the noble and powerful young warrior changed into a miserably aged old man, whose beard and hair were thin and white, and his arms, which he now stretched out for help, were as bony and fleshless as a skeleton's. Gone, too, was the royal purple mantle and the gold-bordered red silk tunic, and as for his steed with the golden hooves and the gem-studded trappings, all that was left of that was a white wisp of mist floating away over the brow of the hill.

Oisin had now become a mortal once more, and could never again return to the Land of the Ever Young. And the weight of three hundred years fell on him as he lay, and thinking of his wondrous life with Niav and with the Fianna of old the life went out of him, and he sank to the ground.

The Rune of St. Patrick
(373–493?)

"The Faedh Fiada," or "The Cry of the Deer"

At Tara to-day in this fateful hour
I place all Heaven with its power,
And the sun with its brightness,
And the snow with its whiteness,
And fire with all the strength it hath,
And lightning with its rapid wrath,
And the winds with their swiftness along their path,
And the sea with its deepness,
And the rocks with their steepness,
And the earth with its starkness;
    All these I place,
    By God's almighty help and grace,
Between myself and the powers of darkness.

52

432 A. D.

ST. PATRICK
AND THE COMING
OF CHRISTIANITY

Celtic stone cross at Ahenny, Co. Tipperary, 8th Century.

Brother Jarlath's Story

By HELEN O'CLERY
(1910–   )

"Once upon a time," Brother Jarlath began, "in the far distant past, when our people were still pagan, there was a warlike king in Ireland called Niall of the Nine Hostages. He wasn't always warlike. Sometimes he stayed at home quite peacefully, hunting and fishing, listening to his bards and playing with his children, talking to his wife and playing chess. In fact, doing all the peaceful things which any man enjoys.

"Every now and then, however, the sea called him. Or so he said. And as soon as he got that idea, trouble began.

"Ships were built, armour was made, swords and spears were fashioned. Soldiers practised feats of arms. Sail-makers made sails. Oarsmen strengthened their muscles for pulling, so that, calm or storm, they could launch their great ships at a moment's notice.

"As the day for the voyage approached, men deserted their fields and thronged to the waterside. Peaceful men grew warlike and warlike men grew fierce. The hunting horn was put aside for the trumpet. Bards forgot their soft, sweet music and sang wild battle songs. Excitement grew and grew amongst the men, but the women were sorrowful.

"One day the Queen came to the shore where the King was teaching his soldiers methods of attack.

" 'Niall, my beloved,' she said, 'what has come over you? We have all the riches we want. Our people are peaceful and happy, when you leave them alone. So why do you stir them up to deeds of war? Why do you urge them to plunder and burn some foreign land, where the people are peaceful and happy?'

"The King smiled at her and said, 'My beloved, you are the

54

most wonderful woman in all the world and I love you dearly. But you are only a woman and so you do not understand such matters.' With that he kissed her on both cheeks and went on with his preparations for the expedition.

"The sailors launched their ships. They all sailed away into the east, leaving the women wailing and wringing their hands on the shore.

"The women did not wail for long. There was too much work to be done; now that the men had gone. Soon they were busy tilling the fields, tending the horses, as well as doing their housework. Time passed quickly, till one fine morning a great shout went up from children who had gone to the shore to dig for cockles.

"Everyone trooped to the water's edge and stared. On the horizon dozens of specks gleamed in the sunlight.

" 'It's our fathers coming home!' the children cried delightedly. But their mothers shook their heads and all stood silently watching. Nearer and nearer came the long, low craft; till the crews were clearly seen. Then fiery red beards and horned helmets of the pirate Norsemen could no longer be mistaken. The women fled from the beach, dragging their children with them.

"The invaders, surprised to find no one to fight, gloried in unchecked plunder. They burned the beautiful white cottages down to the ground. They stole ornaments, jewels and household treasures. They even carried any animals they could catch down to their ships, while the women watched from their hiding places in the woods.

"At last, the Norsemen sailed away. The women came back and wandered among the ruins. They were so angry with their men for raiding foreign lands while enemies raided their own, that they did not notice more ships on the horizon. The children were again the first to see them and trooped warily down to the shore.

"This time it really was their fathers, bringing treasures, riches and hundreds of slaves. The children went wild with excitement. They climbed on the warriors' shoulders and were carried up the hill cheering and chattering. But the women sulked and would not come to meet their husbands.

"This did not worry either Niall, or his followers. They were so pleased with themselves and their plunder that they sang and feasted and enjoyed themselves. The slaves were set to rebuild the

55

houses. The women were given jewels, ornaments and foreign clothes. They were teased, coaxed and bullied till they *had* to laugh and be merry with the rest. So they forgave their husbands.

"The Queen alone remained sad. She was no longer angry with Niall. She could not blame him for what was the custom of the times. And she knew his followers thought he was the best King who had ever lived. So she just sighed and went for long walks by herself in the woods, thinking matters over. She wondered if men always, in all places and all ages, were so warlike.

"One day, the Queen met a slave boy driving sheep into the hills. He too looked sad, so she stopped to talk to him, hoping to cheer him up. To her surprise she learned that it was not loneliness or hardship which made this noble-faced youth so sorrowful, but a wish to teach the people of Ireland gentler ways. He told her he was a Christian. She listened to him for hours while he explained the teachings of Christ.

"Then, surprised that he spoke as one of noble birth, she asked him how he had become a slave. He told her he had been stolen from his home by King Niall. But that he would escape and return to his own country to complete his education. And then, he said, he would return to Ireland, a free man, to teach Christianity throughout the country.

"The Queen was happy from that day out. No matter what the warriors did, she wasn't worried, for she knew that sooner or later the boy would keep his promise and teach her people that all men are brothers. As, in time he did. The boy's name was Patrick . . . and you all know how in the year 432 he returned to Ireland and, as a bishop, preached so well that he won the entire country over to the Christian faith."

56

The Return

ANONYMOUS

When he returned to Ireland
   Some came to greet him
Tall youths nearing manhood
   Came to meet him.

They knelt to kiss his ring,
   Receive his blessing;
He knew them not,
   Forgetfulness confessing.

"We were the children.
   Many years ago
When you were slave to Miliuc
   You taught us what we know."

"But why the shamrock
   On your tunics gay?"
"*You* used it as a symbol,
   Showing us the way
Of the true Cross
   And the Trinity."

St. Patrick

By P. W. JOYCE
(1827–1914)

. . . The saint and his little company arrived at the hill of Slane on
Easter Eve, A.D. 433. Here he prepared to celebrate the festival;
and towards nightfall, as was then the custom, he lighted the
Paschal fire on the top of the hill. It so happened that at this very
time the king and his nobles were celebrating a festival of some
kind at Tara; and the attendants were about to light a great fire on
the hill, which was part of the ceremonial. Now there was a law
that while this fire was burning no other should be kindled in the
country all round on pain of death; and accordingly, when the
king and his courtiers saw the fire ablaze on the hill of Slane, nine
miles off, they were much astonished at such an open violation of
the law. The monarch instantly called his druids and questioned
them about it and they said, "If that fire which we now see be not
extinguished tonight, it will never be extinguished, but will over-
top all our fires; and he that has kindled it will overturn thy kingdom." Whereupon the king, in great wrath, instantly set out in
his chariot with a small retinue, nine chariots in all; and having
arrived near Slane, he summoned the strangers to his presence. He
had commanded that none should rise up to show them respect;
but when they presented themselves, one of the courtiers, Erc the
son of Dego, struck with the saint's commanding appearance, rose
from his seat and saluted him. This Erc was converted, and became
afterwards bishop of Slane; and to this day there is, on the bank
of the Boyne near Slane, a little ruined oratory called from him
St. Erc's Hermitage. The result of this interview was what St.
Patrick most earnestly desired: he was directed to appear next day
at Tara and give an account of his proceeding before the assembled court. On the summit of the hill of Slane, at the spot where
Patrick lighted his Paschal fire, there are still the ruins of a monastery erected in commemoration of the event.

The next day was Easter Sunday. Early in the morning Patrick
and his companions set out for the palace, and on their way they
chanted a hymn in the native tongue—an invocation for protection

58

against the dangers and treachery by which they were beset; for they had heard that persons were lying in wait to slay them. This noble and beautiful hymn was long held in great veneration by the people of this country, and we still possess copies of it in a very old dialect of the Irish language. In the history of the spread of Christianity, it would be difficult to find a more singular and impressive scene than was presented at the court of King Laegaire on that memorable Easter morning. Patrick was robed in white, as were also his companions; he wore his mitre, and carried his crosier in his hand; and when he presented hmself before the assembly, Dubthach (Duffa), Laegaire's chief poet, rose to welcome him, contrary to the express commands of the king. The saint, all aflame with zeal and unawed by the presence of king and court, explained to the assembly the leading points of the Christian doctrine, and silenced the king's druids in argument. Dubthach became a convert, and thenceforward devoted his poetical talents to the service of God; and Laegaire gave permission to the strange missionaries to preach their doctrines throughout his dominions. The king himself however was not converted; and for the remaning thirty years of his life he remained an unbeliever, while the paganism of the whole country was rapidly going down before the fiery energy of the great missionary.

Scholars

ANONYMOUS (9th Century)

Translated from the Irish
By FRANK O'CONNOR

Scholars, regrettably, must yell
In torments on the hob of hell
While louts that never learned their letters
Are perched in Heaven among their betters.

Oisin, who had lived in the Land of Youth for hundreds of years, remembered the good old fighting pagan days. Although he was now a feeble old man, he was not prepared to accept Saint Patrick's peaceful Christian creed without an argument.

The Arguments

By LADY GREGORY
(1852–1932)

And St. Patrick took in hand to convert Oisin, and to bring him to baptism; but it was no easy work he had to do, and everything he would say, Oisin would have an answer for it. And it is the way they used to be talking and arguing with one another, as it was put down afterwards by the poets of Ireland:—

PATRICK. Oisin, it is long your sleep is. Rise up and listen to the Psalm. Your strength and your readiness are gone from you, though you used to be going into rough fights and battles.

OISIN. My readiness and my strength are gone from me since Finn has no armies living; I have no liking for clerks, their music is not sweet to me after his.

PATRICK. You never heard music so good from the beginning of the world to this day; it is well you would serve an army on a hill, you that are old and silly and grey.

OISIN. I used to serve an army on a hill, Patrick of the closed up mind; it is a pity you to be faulting me; there was never shame put on me till now.

I have heard music was sweeter than your music, however much you are praising your clerks: the song of the blackbird in Leiter Laoi, and the sound of the Dord Fiann; the very sweet thrush of the Valley of the Shadow, or the sound of the boats striking the strand. The cry of the hounds was better to me than the noise of your schools, Patrick.

60

Little Nut, little Nut of my heart, the little dwarf that was with Finn, when he would make tunes and songs he would put us all into deep sleep.

The twelve hounds that belonged to Finn, the time they would be let loose facing out from the Siuir, their cry was sweeter than harps and than pipes.

I have a little story about Finn. We were but fifteen men. We took the King of the Saxons of the feats, and we won a battle against the King of Greece.

We fought nine battles in Spain, and nine times twenty battles in Ireland. From Lochlann and from the eastern world there was a share of gold coming to Finn.

My grief! I to be stopping after him, and without delight in games or in music; to be withering away after my comrades; my grief it is to be living. I and the clerks of the Mass books are two that can never agree.

If Finn and the Fianna were living, I would leave the clerks and the bells; I would follow the deer through the valleys, I would like to be close on his track.

Ask Heaven of God, Patrick, for Finn of the Fianna and his race; make prayers for the great man; you never heard of his like.

PATRICK. I will not ask heaven for Finn, man of good wit that my anger is rising against, since his delight was to be living in valleys with the noise of hunts.

OISIN. If you had been in company with the Fianna, Patrick of the joyless clerks and of the bells, you would not be attending on schools or giving heed to God.

PATRICK. I would not part from the Son of God for all that have lived east or west; O Oisin, O shaking poet, there will harm come on you in satisfaction for the priests.

OISIN. It was a delight to Finn the cry of his hounds on the mountains, the wild dogs leaving their harbors, the pride of his armies, those were his delights.

PATRICK. There was many a thing Finn took delight in, and there is not much heed given to it after him; Finn and his hounds are not living now, and you yourself will not always be living now, Oisin.

OISIN. There is a greater story of Finn than of us, or of any that

61

have lived in our time; all that are gone and all that are living, Finn was better to give out gold than themselves.

PATRICK. All the gold you and Finn used to be giving out, it is little it does for you now; he is in hell in bonds because he did treachery and oppression.

OISIN. It is little I believe of your truth, man from Rome with the white books, Finn the openhanded head of the Fianna to be in the hands of devils or demons.

PATRICK. Finn is in bonds in hell, the pleasant man that gave out gold; in satisfaction for his disrespect to God, he is under grief in the house of pain.

OISIN. If the sons of Morna were within it, or the strong men of the sons of Baiscne, they would take Finn out of it, or they would have the house for themselves.

PATRICK. If the five provinces of Ireland were within it, or the strong seven battalions of the Fianna, they would not be able to bring Finn out of it, however great their strength might be.

OISIN. If Faolan and Goll were living, and brown-haired Diarmuid and brave Osgar, Finn of the Fianna could not be held in any house that was made by God or devils.

PATRICK. If Faolan and Goll were living, and all the Fianna that ever were, they could not bring out Finn from the house where he is in pain.

OISIN. What did Finn do against God but to be attending on schools and on armies? Giving gold through a great part of his time, and for another while trying his hounds.

PATRICK. In payment for thinking of his hounds and for serving the schools of the poets, and because he gave no heed to God, Finn of the Fianna is held down.

OISIN. You say, Patrick of the Psalms, that the Fianna could not take out Finn, or the five provinces of Ireland along with them.

I have a little story about Finn. We were but fifteen men when we took the King of Britain of the feasts by the strength of our spears and our own strength.

We took Magnus the great, the son of the King of Lochlann of the speckled ships; we came back no way sorry or tired, we put our rent on far places.

O Patrick, the story is pitiful, the King of the Fianna to be under locks; a heart without envy, without hatred, a heart hard in earning victory.

It is an injustice, God to be unwilling to give food and riches; Finn never refused strong or poor, although cold hell is now his dwelling place.

It is what Finn had a mind for, to be listening to the sound of Druim Dearg; to sleep at the stream of Ess Ruadh, to be hunting the deer of Gallimh of the bays.

The cries of the blackbird of Leiter Laoi, the wave of Rudraighe beating the strand, the bellowing of the ox of Magh Maoin, the lowing of the calf of Gleann da Mhail.

The noise of the hunt on Slieve Crot, the sound of the fawns round Slieve Cua, the scream of the sea gulls there beyond on Iorrus, the screech of the crows over the battle.

The waves vexing the breasts of the boats, the howling of the hounds at Druim Lis; the voice of Bran on Cnoc-an-Air, the outcry of the streams about Slieve Mis.

The call of Osgar going to the hunt; the voice of the hounds on the road of the Fianna, to be listening to them and to the poets, that was always his desire.

A desire of the desires of Osgar was to listen to the striking of shields; to be hacking at bones in a battle, it is what he had a mind for always.

We went westward one time to hunt at Formaid of the Fianna, to see the first running of our hounds.

It was Finn was holding Bran, and it is with myself Sceolan was; Diarmuid of the Women had Fearan, and Osgar had lucky Adhnuall.

Conan the Bald had Searc; Caoilte, son of Ronan, had Daol; Lugaidh's Son and Goll were holding Fuaim and Fothran.

That was the first day we loosed out a share of our hounds to a hunting; and Och! Patrick, of all that were in it, there is not one left living but myself.

O Patrick, it is a pity the way I am now, a spent old man without sway, without quickness, without strength, going to Mass at the altar.

Without the great deer of Slieve Luchra; without the hares of Slieve Cuilinn; without going into fights with Finn; without listening to the poets.

Without battles, without taking of spoils; without playing at

63

nimble feats; without going courting or hunting, two trades that were my delight.

PATRICK. Leave off, old man, leave your foolishness; let what you have done be enough for you from this out. Think on the pains that are before you; the Fianna are gone, and you yourself will be going.

OISIN. If I go, may yourself not be left after me, Patrick of the hindering heart; if Conan, the least of the Fiana, were living, your buzzing would not be left long to you.

Or if this was the day I gave ten hundred cows to the headless woman that came to the Valley of the Two Oxen; the birds of the air brought away the ring I gave her, I never knew where she went herself from me.

PATRICK. That is little to trouble you, Oisin; it was but for a while she was with you; it is better for you to be as you are than to be among them again.

OISIN. O Son of Calphurn of the friendly talk, it is a pity for him that gives respect to clerks and bells; I and Caoilte my friend, we were not poor when we were together.

The music that put Finn to his sleep was the cackling of the ducks from the lake of the Three Narrows; the scolding talk of the blackbird of Doire an Cairn, the bellowing of the ox from the Valley of the Berries.

The whistle of the eagle from the Valley of Victories, or from the rough branches of the ridge by the stream; the grouse of the heather of Cruachan; the call of the otter of Druim-re-Coir.

The song of the blackbird of Doire an Cairn indeed I never heard sweeter music, if I could be under its nest.

My grief that I ever took baptism; it is little credit I got by it, being without food, without drink, doing fasting and praying.

PATRICK. In my opinion it did not harm you, old man; you will get nine score cakes of bread, wine and meat to put a taste on it; it is bad talk you are giving.

OISIN. This mouth that is talking with you, may it never confess to a priest, if I would not sooner have the leavings of Finn's house than a share of your own meals.

PATRICK. He got but what he gathered from the banks, or whatever he could kill on the rough hills; he got hell at the last because of his unbelief.

64

OISIN. That was not the way with us at all, but our fill of wine and of meat; justice and a right beginning at the feasts, sweet drinks and every one drinking them.

It is fretting after Diarmuid and Goll I am, and after Fergus of the True Lips, the time you will not let me be speaking of them, O new Patrick from Rome.

PATRICK. We would give you leave to be speaking of them, but first you should give heed to God. Since you are now at the end of your days, leave your foolishness, weak old man.

OISIN. O Patrick, tell me as a secret, since it is you have the best knowledge, will my dog or my hound be let in with me to the court of the King of Grace?

PATRICK. Old man in your foolishness that I cannot put any hounds to, your dog or your hound will not be let in with you to the court of the King of Power.

OISIN. If I had acquaintance with God, and my hound to be at hand, I would make whoever gave food to myself give a share to my hound as well.

One strong champion that was with the Fianna of Ireland would be better than the Lord of Piety, and than you yourself, Patrick.

PATRICK. O Oisin of the sharp blades, it is mad words you are saying. God is better for one day than the whole of the Fianna of Ireland.

OISIN. Though I am now without sway and my life is spent to the end, do not put abuse, Patrick, on the great men of the sons of Baiscne.

If I had Conan with me, the man that used to be running down the Fianna, it is he would break your head within among your clerks and your priests.

PATRICK. It is a silly thing, old man, to be talking always of the Fianna; remember your end is come and take the Son of God to help you.

OISIN. I used to sleep out on the mountain under the grey dew; I was never used to go to bed without food, while there was a deer on the hill beyond.

PATRICK. You are astray at the end of your life between the straight way and the crooked. Keep out from the crooked path of pains, and the angels of God will come beneath your head.

65

OISIN. If myself and openhanded Fergus and Diarmuid were to-gether now on this spot, we would go in every path we ever went in, and ask no leave of the priests.

PATRICK. Leave off, Oisin; do not be speaking against the priests that are telling the work of God in every place. Unless you leave off your daring talk, it is great pain you will have in the end.

OISIN. When myself and the leader of the Fianna were looking for a boar in the valley, it was worse to me not to see it than all your clerks to be without their heads.

PATRICK. It is pitiful seeing you without sense; that is worse to you than your blindness; if you were to get sight within you, it is great your desire would be for Heaven.

OISIN. It is little good it would be to me to be sitting in that city, without Caoilte, without Osgar, without my father being with me.

The leap of the buck would be better to me, or the sight of badgers between two valleys, than all your mouth is promising me, and all the delights I could get in Heaven.

PATRICK. Your thoughts are foolish, they will come to nothing; your pleasure and your mirth are gone. Unless you will take my advice tonight, you will not get leave on this side or that.

OISIN. If myself and the Fianna were on the top of a hill today drawing our spearheads, we would have our choice of being here or there in spite of books and priests and bells.

PATRICK. You were like the smoke of a wisp, or like a stream in a valley, or like a whirling wind on the top of a hill, every tribe of you that ever lived.

OISIN. If I was in company with the people of strong arms, the way I was at Bearna da Coill, I would sooner be looking at them than at this troop of the crooked croziers.

If I had Scolb Sceine with me, or Osgar, that was smart in battles, I would not be without meat tonight at the sound of the bell of the seven tolls.

PATRICK. Oisin, since your wits are gone from you be glad at what I say; it is certain to me you will leave the Fianna and that you will receive the God of the stars.

OISIN. There is wonder on me at your hasty talk, priest that has travelled in every part, to say that I would part from the Fianna,

66

a generous people, never niggardly.

PATRICK. If you saw the people of God, the way they are settled at feasts, every good thing is more plentiful with them than with Finn's people, however great their name was.

Finn and the Fianna are lying now very sorrowful on the flag-stone of pain; take the Son of God in their place; make your repentance and do not lose Heaven.

OISIN. I do not believe your talk now, O Patrick of the crooked staves, Finn and the Fianna to be there within, unless they find pleasure being in it.

PATRICK. Make right repentance now, before you know when your end is coming; God is better for one hour than the whole of the Fianna of Ireland.

OISIN. That is a daring answer to make to me, Patrick of the crooked crozier; your crozier would be in little bits if I had Osgar with me now.

If my son Osgar and God were hand to hand on the Hill of the Fianna, if I saw my son put down, I would say that God was a strong man.

How could it be that God or his priests could be better men than Finn, the King of the Fianna, a generous man without crookedness.

If there was a place above or below better than the Heaven of God, it is there Finn would go, and all that are with him of his people.

You say that a generous man never goes to the hell of pain; there was not one among that Fianna that was not generous to all.

Ask of God, Patrick, does He remember when the Fianna were alive, or has He seen east or west any man better than themselves in their fighting.

The Fianna used not to be saying treachery; we never had the the name of telling lies. By truth and the strength of our hands we came safe out of every battle.

There never sat a priest in a church, though you think it sweet to be singing psalms, was better to his word than the Fianna, or more generous than Finn himself.

If my comrades were living tonight, I would take no pleasure in your crooning in the church; as they are not living now, the

67

rough voice of the bells has deafened me.

Och! in the place of battles and heavy fights, where I used to have my place and to take my pleasure, the crozier of Patrick being carried, and his clerks at their quarreling.

Och! slothful, cheerless Conan, it is great abuse I used to be giving you; why do you not come to see me now? You would get leave for making fun and reviling through the whole of the niggardly clerks.

Och! where are the strong men gone that they do not come together to help me! O Osgar of the sharp sword of victory, come and free your father from his bonds!

Where is the strong son of Lugaidh? Och! Diarmuid of all the women! Och! Caoilte, son of Ronan, think of our love, and travel to me!

PATRICK. Stop your talk, you withered, witless old man; it is my King that made the Heavens, it is He that gives blossom to the trees, it is He made the moon and the sun, the fields and the grass.

OISIN. It was not in shaping fields and grass that my king took his delight, but in overthrowing fighting men, and defending countries, and bringing his name into every part.

In courting, in playing, in hunting, in baring his banner at the first of a fight; in playing at chess, at swimming, in looking around him at the drinking-hall.

O Patrick, where was your God when the two came over the sea that brought away the queen of Lochlann of the Ships? Where was He when Dearg came, the son of the King of Lochlann of the golden shields? Why did not the King of Heaven protect them from the blows of the big man?

Or when Tailc, son of Treon, came, the man that did great slaughter on the Fianna; it was not by God that champion fell, but by Osgar, in the sight of all.

Many a battle and many a victory was gained by the Fianna of Ireland; I never heard any great deed was done by the King of Saints, or that He ever reddened His hand.

It would be a great shame for God not to take the locks of pain off Finn; if God Himself were in bonds, my king would fight for His sake.

Finn left no one in pain or in danger without freeing him by

68

silver or gold, or by fighting till he got the victory. For the strength of your love, Patrick, do not forsake the great men; bring in the Fianna unknown to the King of Heaven.

It is a good claim I have on your God, to be among his clerks the way I am; without food, without clothing, without music, without giving rewards to poets.

Without the cry of the hounds or the horns, without guarding coasts, without courting generous women; for all that I have suffered by the want of food, I forgive the King of Heaven in my will.

My story is sorrowful. The sound of your voice is not pleasant to me. I will cry my fill, but not for God, but because Finn and the Fianna are not living.

The Warrior

ANONYMOUS (14th Century)

Translated from the Irish
By FRANK O'CONNOR
(1903–   )

Patrick, you chatter too loud
   And lift your crozier too high;
Your stick would be kindling soon
   If my son Osgar stood by.

If my son Osgar and God
   Wrestled it out on the hill,
And I saw Osgar go down
   I would say your God fought well.

But how could the Lord you praise
    Or his mild priests singing a tune
Be better than Fionn the swordsman,
    Generous, faultless Fionn?

By the strength of their hands alone
    The Fenians' battles were fought,
With never a spoken lie,
    Never a lie in thought.

There never sat priest in church,
    A tuneful psalm to raise
Better-spoken than they,
    Scarred by a hundred frays.

Whatever your monks have called
    The law of the King of Grace,
That was the Fenians' law;
    His home is their dwelling place.

If happier house than Heaven
    There be, above or below,
'Tis there my master Fionn
    And his fighting men will go.

Ah, priest, if you saw the Fenians,
    Filling the strand beneath,
Or gathered in streamy Naas,
    You would praise them with every breath.

Patrick, ask of your God
    Does he remember their might,
Or has he seen east or west
    Better men in a fight?

Or known in his own land,
    Above the stars and the moon,
For wisdom, courage, and strength
    A man the like of Fionn?

70

The Student

ANONYMOUS (16th Century)

Translated from the Irish
By FRANK O'CONNOR

The student's life is pleasant,
  And pleasant is his labour;
Search all Ireland over,
  You'll find no better neighbour.

Nor lords nor petty princes
  Dispute the student's pleasure;
Nor chapter stints his purse
  Nor stewardship his leisure.

None orders early rising,
  Calf-rearing nor cow-tending,
Nor nights of toilsome vigil;
  His time is his for spending.

He takes a hand at draughts,
  Or plucks a harp string bravely,
And fills his nights with courting
  Some golden-haired light lady.

And when springtime is come
  The ploughshaft's there to follow—
A fistful of goosequills
  And a straight, deep furrow!

H. *V. Morton came to this country "In Search of Ireland." In his book of this name he describes how pilgrims, even to this day, climb to the top of the mountain named Croagh Patrick, where tradition tells that the saint wrestled with the angels for the freedom of his land and for his own spiritual jurisdiction over his people.*

Ardagh chalice, in the National Museum of Ireland, 8th Century.

Croagh Patrick

By H. V. MORTON
(1892–   )

When Lent came in the year A.D. 449, St. Patrick retired to a great mountain in Connaught to commune with God. He fasted there for forty days and forty nights, weeping so it is said, until his chasuble was wet with tears.

The medieval monks possessed detailed accounts of St. Patrick's fast. They said that to the angel, who returned to him every night with promises from God, the saint said:

"Is there aught else that will be granted to me?"

"Is there aught else thou wouldst demand?" asked the angel.

"There is," replied St. Patrick, "that the Saxons shall not abide in Ireland by consent or perforce so long as I abide in heaven."

"Now get thee gone," commanded the angel.

"I will not get me gone," said St. Patrick, "since I have been tormented until I am blessed."

"Is there aught else thou wouldst demand?" asked the angel once more.

St. Patrick requested that on the Day of Judgment he should be judge over the men of Ireland.

"Assuredly," said the angel, "that is not got from the Lord."

"Unless it is got from Him," replied the determined saint, "departure from this Rick shall not be got from me from today until Doom; and, what is more, I shall leave a guardian there."

The angel returned with a message from heaven:

"The Lord said, 'There hath not come, and there will not come from the Apostles, a man more admirable, were it not for thy hardness. What thou has prayed for thou shalt have . . . and there will be a consecration of the men of the folk of Ireland, both living and dead.'"

St. Patrick said, "A blessing on the bountiful King who hath given; and the Rick shall now be departed therefrom."

As he arose and prepared to descend from the mountain mighty birds flew about him so that the air was dark and full of the beating of wings. So St. Patrick stood, like Moses on Sinai, and round him all the Saints of Ireland, past, present and to come.

In this we can see the Irish belief in the inflexible determination of their saint, "a steady and imperturbable man." And it was said that while upon this mountain in Connaught, St. Patrick banished all snakes from Ireland.

This mountain, Croagh Patrick—or Patrick's Hill—lifts its magnificent cone 2,510 feet above the blue waters of Clew Bay. It is Ireland's Holy Mountain. Once a year in July a pilgrimage is made to the little chapel on the crest. Atlantic liners drop anchor in Galway Bay, bringing Irish-Americans who wish to ascend the mountain for the good of their souls. As many as 40,000 pilgrims have climbed the mountain in one day; and many of the more devout remove their shoes and socks and take the hard path barefoot.

From *In Search of Ireland*

M*r. and Mrs. Liam de Paor are archeologists, who have made a special study of early Christian Ireland.*

The Monasteries

By MAIRE & LIAM DE PAOR
(1925–)   (1926–)

. . . Many of the great monasteries of Ireland have left little visible trace. Of Clonard, which numbered its monks, its scholars, and its students in thousands, no faintest relic of church or cell is now to be seen. The literature, however, especially the lives of saints, gives abundant evidence of the character of the monastery. The settlement was usually in a large rath or ring fort, i.e. a circular enclosure bounded by a stone or earthen bank with a ditch outside. Within the enclosure the most important building was the church or oratory, a rectangular structure of oaken planks or of

74

wattle and daub. In spite of its importance this building seems rarely to have been of even moderate size. The cellae or huts (usually of wickerwork) of the monks were dispersed about the enclosure, one or two monks usually, but sometimes more, to a cell. The other buildings of importance were the guesthouse (tech n-oiged) and the refectory (praindtech), and if the monastery was of any importance there was also a school. . . .

. . . There is a famous seventh-century description (by Cogitosus) of the church of St. Brigid's monastery at Kildare; a many windowed building, divided by screens into three parts, ornamented with paintings and linen hangings and with an ornate door. Several of the tenth-century High Crosses have tops comprising carvings in solid stone of little wooden oratories with steep-pitched roofs, gable finials, and roof-coverings of tiles or shingles . . .

. . . at the beginning of the seventh century, but incidentally, as it were, the monasteries of Ireland became centres not only of prayer and penance, but of learning. The learning was Latin: classical and late Roman. There is some evidence, but only a little, for the study of Greek, while the evidence for the study of the Latin authors is abundant. Let us take, for example, St. Columbanus, who lived in Ireland until in middle age he went to found monasteries on the Continent; from his extant writings it seems that he was acquainted with the works of Virgil, Horace, Ovid, Prudentius, . . . Gildas, Fortunatus, Gregory the Great, and perhaps of Statius, Persius, Juvencus and Lucan, as well as with the Scriptures. He wrote an excellent Latin, both in prose and verse, and dealt confidently with questions of philosophy and theology. Columbanus was an exceptional man, but he was a product of the Irish schools of the sixth century. The same monastic schools attracted not only Irishmen but students from other lands in great numbers. The pages of Bede are full of reference to such travellers to Ireland in search of learning, and he tells us, "All these the Scots received kindly and cheerfully, giving them not only their board and their learning free but books also to learn in."

A monk teacher.

1014

BRIAN BORU
AND THE OVERTHROW
OF THE VIKINGS

So-called "Brian Boru" harp, in Library of Trinity College, Dublin, 15th Century.

The Scholar and His Cat

ANONYMOUS (c. 850)

Translated from the Irish

By FRANK O'CONNOR

Each of us pursues his trade,
I and Pangur, my comrade;
His whole fancy on the hunt
And mine for learning ardent.

More than fame I love to be
Among my books, and study;
Pangur does not grudge me it,
Content with his own merit.

When—a heavenly time!—we are
In our small room together,
Each of us has his own sport
And asks no greater comfort.

While he sets his round sharp eye
On the wall of my study,
I turn mine—though lost its edge—
On the great wall of knowledge.

Now a mouse sticks in his net
After some mighty onset,
Then into my store I cram
Some difficult, darksome problem.

When a mouse comes to the kill
Pangur exults—a marvel!
I have, when some secret's won,
My hour of exultation.

Though we work for days or years
Neither the other hinders;
Each is competent and hence
Enjoys his skill in silence.

Master of the death of mice,
He keeps in daily practice;
I, too, making dark things clear,
Am of my trade a master.

Remember the Glories of Brian the Brave

By THOMAS MOORE
(1779–1852)

Remember the glories of Brian the brave,
   Tho' the days of the hero are o'er;
Tho' lost to Mononia, and cold in the grave,
   He returns to Kincora no more!
That star of the field, which so often has pour'd
   Its beam on the battle, is set;
But enough of its glory remains on each sword
   To light us to victory yet!

Mononia! When Nature embellished the tint
   Of thy fields and thy mountains so fair,
Did she ever intend that a tyrant should print
   The footstep of slavery there?
No! Freedom, whose smile we shall never resign,
   Go, tell our invaders the Danes,
That 'tis sweeter to bleed for an age at thy shrine
   Than to sleep but a moment in chains.

Forget not our wounded companions, who stood
   In the day of distress by our side;
While the moss of the valley grew red with their blood,
   They stirred not, but conquered and died!
The sun that now blesses our arms with his light,
   Saw them fall upon Ossory's plain:
Oh! Let him not blush when he leaves us tonight
   To find that they fell there in vain!

Ireland had many centuries of comparative peace in which her monasteries became centers of European learning. But in time the Danes who were still pagans, came periodically to raid and plunder these rich, peaceful setlements. The Irish were unable to put a stop to these devastating "smash and grab" raids until the coming of Brian Boru.

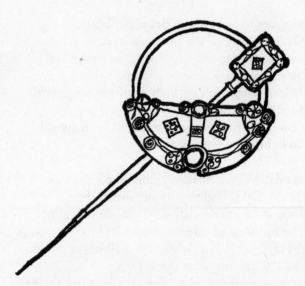

Silver ring-brooch from Killamery, Co. Kilkenny, in the National Museum of Ireland, c. 850 A.D.

Brian Boru

By P. W. JOYCE

. . . Brian devoted his mind to works of peace, like the great Alfred of England. His palace, which was named Kincora, was situated on the high ridge over the Shannon now occupied by the town of Killaloe. He rebuilt the monasteries that had been destroyed by the Danes, and erected bridges and fortresses all over the country. He founded and restored schools and colleges, repressed evildoers, and caused the laws to be obeyed, so that the country was less disturbed and more prosperous than it had been for a long time before. The bright picture handed down to us of the state of Ireland during the dozen years that elapsed from his accession to the battle of Clontarf, is illustrated by the well-known legend, that a beautiful young lady richly dressed, and bearing a gold ring of great value on her wand, traversed the country alone from north to south without being molested: a fiction which Moore has embalmed in the beautiful song "Rich and rare were the gems she wore."

Rich and Rare

By THOMAS MOORE

Rich and rare were the gems she wore,
And a bright gold ring on her wand she bore;
But oh, her beauty was far beyond
Her sparkling gems and snow-white wand;
But oh, her beauty was far beyond
Her sparkling gems and snow-white wand.

"Lady! dost thou not fear to stray,
So lone and lovely, thro' this bleak way?
Are Erin's sons so good or so cold
As not to be tempted by woman or gold?"

81

"Sir Knight! I feel not the least alarm:
No son of Erin will offer me harm,
For, tho' they love woman and golden store,
Sir Knight, they love honour and virtue more."

On she went, and her maiden smile
In safety lighted her round the green isle;
And blest for ever was she who relied
Upon Erin's honour and Erin's pride.

Early Christian Ireland

By MAIRE & LIAM DE PAOR

. . . Brian Boru was remarkable in the Ireland of his time because he seems to have thought in terms of the feudal organization which had already developed in Europe rather than in terms of the primitive and unstable kingship system of Ireland. He must have seen his own career as an image of that of Charlemagne, whose life and exploits were a "mirror for princes" in the later centuries of Dark Age Europe, and when he visited the ecclesiastical capital of Ireland in 1004 he had his scribe enter in the Book of Armagh "Brian, Imperator Scottorum." Brian in winning his way to power had on occasion availed himself of alliances with Norsemen, but the basis of his whole career was opposition to the foreigners and his life ended in 1014 on the field of the battle in which, as High King of Ireland, he faced a last rally of the Vikings, of Dublin, of Man and the Isles, and of Scandinavia itself, together with their Irish allies, outside the walls of Dublin. This was the battle of Clontarf, celebrated in Scandinavian and Irish literature for the breaking of the power of the Vikings in Ireland.

82

The Battle of Clontarf

By L. M. McCRAITH
(1870–   )

. . . Circumstances curious and varied fixed the great contest for
Good Friday, April 23, 1014. The Njal Saga says that the apostate
Brodir found out, by the sorcery for which he had renounced
Christianity, "that if the fight were on Good Friday, King Brian
would fall, but win the day; but if fought before, they all would
fall who were against him." The Danes hung back, therefore, until
the fateful day. Brian had many premonitions of his approaching
end. The Banshee of the Dalcais, Aibell, the Woman of the Grey
Rock, warned him. On the night before the fight, Woden himself,
the old Norse God of War, rode up through the dusk, in the sea
mists, on a dapple-grey horse—so men whispered—halberd in hand,
and took counsel with his champions.

By the sea shore at Clontarf on that April morning, the two great
armies met and engaged. A mighty host had assembled under the
great Danish banner of the Black Raven. It had been woven with
heathen spells in such a fashion that, when the wind blew it forth
unfurled, it seemed as though the bird of omen flapped his black
wings for flight. The old king addressed his warriors before the
battle, crucifix in one hand, sword in the other. "Was it not on this
day the Christ Himself suffered for you?" he said, as he reminded
them of the sacrileges and cruelties of the Galls, and he bade them
fight for faith, as well as country. Then Brian retired to his tent,
leaving the command in his son Murrough's hands, to pass the
hours of battle in prayer, and the repetition of the Psalter. Murrough had with him as well as his young step-brother Donough,
his own son Turlough, a promising young soldier.

The struggle went on from dawn till dusk. The swords of the
men of Ireland grew blunt, then blunter. Their battle-axes were

83

clogged with human hair and blood. Here is the description that Maelseachlinn sent to Clan Colman a month after the battle: "I never beheld with my eyes, nor read in history an account of a sharper and bloodier fight than this memorable action; nor if an angel from heaven would descend and relate the circumstances of it could you, without difficulty, be induced to give credit to it. I withdrew with the troops under my command, and was no other concerned than as a spectator, and stood at no greater distance from the field than the breadth of a fallow field and a ditch. When both the powerful armies engaged, and grappled in close fight, it was dreadful to behold how the swords glittered over their heads, being struck with the rays of the sun, which gave them an appearance of a numerous flock of white sea gulls, flying in the air; the strokes were so mighty, and the fury of the combatants so terrible that great quantities of hair, torn or cut off their heads by their sharp weapons, were driven far off by the wind, and their spears and battle-axes were so encumbered by hair cemented together with clotted blood that it was scarce possible to clean or bring them to their proper brightness."

The tide flowed in and out again, yet still the fight went on. Then, as it flooded in again, the foreigners began to give way. Back they were pressed into "their natural inheritance"—as the chronicler calls the incoming sea—and took refuge in their ships, or retreated inside the walls of Dublin.

Murrough fought his way to the Danish standard, and cut down two mail-clad standard bearers. All day he performed the feats of "a hero among heroes." But as the day wore on, the Norwegian prince Anrud encountered Murrough, whose arms had become paralysed by fatigue. Murrough's great strength enabled him to seize his foe and fling him to the ground, and he ran his sword through Anrud's body. But even as he inflicted Anrud's death wound, Murrough received a mortal blow from the dagger of the Dane, and both fell together.

From his tent the old king sent his attendants to watch the battle, while he prayed. Constantly he enquired how the battle went, and the position of his eldest son's standard. "As long as that standard is erect," he said, "it shall go well with the men of Erin." After a time came reports of a thinning field—"all the brushwood is now burned, and the wood is on fire." It was the time of cham-

84

pion's single combats. Then came grievous tidings, Murrough's standard had fallen. "Alas!" said Brian, "Erin has fallen with it! Why should I survive such losses, even should I attain the sovereignty of the world?" He began to give directions as to his will and funeral. He had been warned, and he felt sure that death drew nigh, although he did not realize that he was to die in the arms of victory.

The foreigners were at last in full retreat, led by "God's Bastard," Brodir. As he fled, the apostate caught sight of the old king on his knees in the tent. At first he supposed him to be merely a priest, and scarcely would have stayed to wreak vengeance on one of the class to which he himself once belonged. Then someone shouted that this was no priest, but the Ard-Righ himself. Brodir paused in his flight, and struck a great blow at the kneeling king. The old warrior's hand and arm had not altogether lost their strength and cunning. One last mighty brandish of his great sword swept both Brodir's legs from under his body, while, at the same time, Brodir's blade cleft that kingly, mighty brain.

So died the greatest of Irish heroes. Thus ended the great ideal of a United Ireland.

Visions and Portents

By P. W. JOYCE

. . . The battle of Clontarf was the last great struggle between Christianity and heathenism. The news resounded through all Europe, and brought dismay and terror to every Norse household from the Baltic shore to their furthest settlements in the South. The Nial Saga—the Danish chronicle—relates the whole story of the battle as a great defeat, and tells of fearful visions and portents seen by the Scandinavian people in their homes in the North, on that fatal Good Friday. It ought to be remembered that in the very year of this great battle, Sweyn the Dane overran and mastered England; and that after his death three Danish kings ruled the country in succession . . .

Kincora

Translated from the Irish
By JAMES CLARENCE MANGAN
(1803–1849)

O, where, Kincora! is Brian the Great?
  And where is the beauty that once was thine?
O, where are the princes and nobles that sate
  At the feast in thy halls, and drank the red wine?
                Where, O, Kincora?

They are gone, those heroes of royal birth,
  Who plundered no churches, and broke no trust;
'Tis weary for me to be living on earth
  When they, O Kincora, be low in the dust!
                Low, O, Kincora!

1167

STRONGBOW

*Tomb of Strongbow, in Christ Church Cathedral,
Dublin.*

All through the flourishing days of the monasteries, from about the fifth to the tenth century, Ireland was divided into four separate kingdoms, each with its own king subject to the High King who reigned in Tara. These kings sometimes had small wars against each other, but they were little more than skirmishes till, in the year 1168, Dermot MacMurrogh committed the unforgivable crime of inviting the English to come and fight on his side against another Irish king.

Dermot MacMurrogh

By P. W. JOYCE

Dermot MacMurrogh, king of Leinster . . . is described by Cambrensis as "a tall man of stature, and of a large and great bodie, a valiant and bold warrior in his nation; and by reason of his continuall halowing and crieng (in battle) his voice was hoarse: he rather choce to be feared than to be loved: a great oppressor of his nobilitie, but a great advancer of the poore and weake. To his owne people he was rough and greevous, and hatefull to strangers; he would be against all men, and all men against him" (Old translation). He was a headstrong and passionate man, and was as much hated in his own day as his memory has been hated ever since. Yet with all his evil qualities he founded many churches and encouraged learning. In 1152 he carried off Dervorgilla, the wife of Ternan O'Ruarc prince of Brefney, while O'Ruarc himself was absent from home; and she took away all she had brought to her husband as dowry . . .

. . . At last Dermot's conduct becoming unbearable, he was deposed and banished by King Roderick O'Conor, O'Ruarc, and others (A.D. 1166); whereupon, breathing vengeance, he fled across the sea, resolved to seek the aid of the great King Henry II of England.

Many years before this time, Pope Adrian IV, an Englishman, influenced by an unfair and exaggerated account of the evil state of

88

religion in Ireland, given to him by an envoy of King Henry, issued a bull authorising the king to take possession of Ireland. Some writers have questioned the issue of this bull. But the evidence is so strong on the other side as to leave no good reason to doubt that the pope really did issue it, believing that it would be for the advancement of religion and for the good of Ireland.

Dermot presented himself before the king at Aquitaine, and prayed him for help against his enemies, offering to acknowledge him as lord and master. The king eagerly accepted the offer; but being then too busy with the affairs of his own kingdom to go to Ireland himself, he gave permission to any of his British or French subjects that pleased to join the Irish king. Dermot immediately proceeded to Bristol, where he engaged the services of Richard de Clare, Earl of Pembroke, better known by the name of Strongbow; who agreed to help him on condition that he should get Dermot's daughter Eva in marriage, and should succeed him as King of Leinster . . .

Iron sword, 12th Century.

The English, now that they had got a foothold in Ireland, refused to go home. This was the beginning of the long struggle which went on almost incessantly from 1169 till 1922. Dermot MacMurrogh, who had brought the enemy to our shores, was never forgiven. Tradition tells us that a curse was put upon him and that he and his lover, Dervorgilla, are doomed to wander over the hills of Ireland, ghosts who can neither be at peace nor come together till even one Irishman forgives them. This is the theme of the following play.

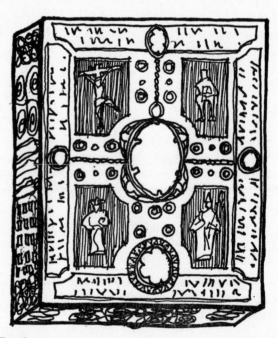

Book shrine of Stowe. Missal written at Tallaght, Co. Dublin, about 800 A.D.; Shrine, mid-11th Century. In the National Museum of Ireland.

The Dreaming of the Bones

By W. B. YEATS

Persons in the Play:

THREE MUSICIANS (*their faces made up to resemble masks*)
A YOUNG MAN
A STRANGER (*wearing a mask*)
A YOUNG GIRL (*wearing a mask*)

Time—1916

The stage is any bare place in a room close to the wall. A screen, with a pattern of mountain and sky, can stand against the wall, or a curtain with a like pattern hung upon it, but the pattern must only symbolize or suggest. One MUSICIAN *enters and then two others; the first stands singing, as in preceding plays, while the others take their places. Then all three sit down against the wall by their instruments, which are already there—a drum, a zither, and a flute. Or they unfold a cloth as in "At the Hawk's Well," while the instruments are carried in.*

(*Song for the folding and unfolding of the cloth*)
FIRST MUSICIAN (*or all* THREE MUSICIANS, *singing*).

> Why does my heart beat so?
> Did not a shadow pass?
> It passed but a moment ago.
> Who can have trod in the grass?
> What rogue is night-wandering?
> Have not old writers said

91

That dizzy dreams can spring
From the dry bones of the dead?
And many a night it seems
That all the valley fills
With those fantastic dreams.
They overflow the hills,
So passionate is a shade,
Like wine that fills to the top
A gray-green cup of jade,
Or maybe an agate cup.

(*The* THREE MUSICIANS *are now seated by the drum, flute and zither at the back of the stage. The* FIRST MUSICIAN *speaks.*)

The hour before dawn and the moon covered up;
The little village of Abbey is covered up;
The little narrow trodden way that runs
From the white road to the Abbey of Corcomroe
Is covered up; and all about the hills
Are like a circle of agate or of jade.
Somewhere among great rocks on the scarce grass
Birds cry, they cry their loneliness.
Even the sunlight can be lonely here,
Even hot noon is lonely. I hear a footfall—
A young man with a lantern comes this way.
He seems an Aran fisher, for he wears
The flannel bawnee and the cowhide shoe.
He stumbles wearily, and stumbling prays.

(*A* YOUNG MAN *enters, praying in Irish.*)

Once more the birds cry in their loneliness.
But now they wheel about our heads; and now
They have dropped on the gray stone to the northeast.

(*A* STRANGER *and a* YOUNG GIRL, *in the costume of a past time, come in. They wear heroic masks.*)

92

YOUNG MAN (*raising his lantern*). Who is there? I cannot see what
    you are like.
    Come to the light.
STRANGER. But what have you to fear?
YOUNG MAN. And why have you come creeping through the dark?

(*The* GIRL *blows out lantern.*)

    The wind has blown my lantern out. Where are you?
    I saw a pair of heads against the sky
    And lost them after; but you are in the right,
    I should not be afraid in County Clare;
    And should be, or should not be, have no choice,
    I have to put myself into your hands,
    Now that my candle's out.
STRANGER. You have fought in Dublin?
YOUNG MAN. I was in the Post Office, and if taken
    I shall be put against a wall and shot.
STRANGER. You know some place of refuge, have some plan
    Or friend who will come to meet you?
YOUNG MAN. I am to lie
    At daybreak on the mountain and keep watch
    Until an Aran coracle puts in
    At Muckanish or at the rocky shore
    Under Finvara, but would break my neck
    If I went stumbling there alone in the dark.
STRANGER. We know the pathways that the sheep tread out,
    And all the hiding places of the hills,
    And that they had better hiding places once.
YOUNG MAN. You'd say they had better before English robbers
    Cut down the trees or set them upon fire
    For fear their owners might find shelter there.
    What is that sound?
STRANGER. An old horse gone astray.
    He has been wandering on the road all night.
YOUNG MAN. I took him for a man and horse. Police
    Are out upon the roads. In the late Rising
    I think there was no man of us but hated
    To fire at soldiers who but did their duty

And were not of our race, but when a man
Is born in Ireland and of Irish stock,
When he takes part against us—
STRANGER. I will put you safe,
No living man shall set his eyes upon you;
I will not answer for the dead.
YOUNG MAN. The dead?
STRANGER. For certain days the stones where you must lie
Have in the hour before the break of day
Been haunted.
YOUNG MAN. But I was not born at midnight.
STRANGER. Many a man that was born in the full daylight
Can see them plain, will pass them on the highroad
Or in the crowded marketplace of the town,
And never know that they have passed.
YOUNG MAN. My Grandam
Would have it they did penance everywhere;
Some lived through their old lives again.
STRANGER. In a dream;
And some for an old scruple must hang spitted
Upon the swaying tops of lofty trees;
Some are consumed in fire, some withered up
By hail and sleet out of the wintry North,
And some but live through their old lives again.
YOUNG MAN. Well, let them dream into what shape they please
And fill waste mountains with the invisible tumult
Of the fantastic conscience. I have no dread;
They cannot put me into gaol or shoot me;
And seeing that their blood has returned to fields
That have grown red from drinking blood like mine,
They would not if they could betray.
STRANGER. This pathway
Runs to the ruined Abbey of Corcomroe;
The abbey passed, we are soon among the stone
And shall be at the ridge before the cocks
Of Aughanish or Bailevelehan
Or gray Aughtmana shake their wings and cry.

(They go round the stage once.)

94

FIRST MUSICIAN (*speaking*). They've passed the shallow well and
    the flat stone
  Fouled by the drinking cattle, the narrow lane
  Where mourners for five centuries have carried
  Noble or peasant to his burial;
  An owl is crying out above their heads.

(*singing*)

    Why should the heart take fright?
    What sets it beating so?
    The bitter sweetness of the night
    Has made it but a lonely thing.
    Red bird of March, begin to crow!
    Up with the neck and clap the wing,
    Red cock, and crow!

(*They go round the stage once. The* FIRST MUSICIAN *speaks.*)

And now they have climbed through the long grassy field
And passed the ragged thorn trees and the gap
In the ancient hedge; and the tomb-nested owl
At the foot's level beats with a vague wing.

(*singing*)

    My head is in a cloud;
    I'd let the whole world go;
    My rascal heart is proud
    Remembering and remembering.
    Red bird of March, begin to crow!
    Up with the neck and clap the wing,
    Red cock, and crow!

STRANGER. We're almost at the summit and can rest.
  The road is a faint shadow there; and there
  The Abbey lies amid its broken tombs.
  In the old days we should have heard a bell
  Calling the monks before day broke to pray;

And when the day had broken on the ridge,
The crowing of its cocks.
YOUNG MAN. Is there no house
Famous for sanctity or architectural beauty
In Clare or Kerry, or in all wide Connacht,
The enemy has not unroofed?
STRANGER. Close to the altar
Broken by wind and frost and worn by time
Donough O'Brien has a tomb, a name in Latin,
He wore fine clothes and knew the secrets of women,
But he rebelled against the King of Thomond
And died in his youth.
YOUNG MAN. And why should he rebel?
The King of Thomond was his rightful master.
It was men like Donough who made Ireland weak—
My curse on all that troop, and when I die
I'll leave my body, if I have any choice,
Far from his ivy rod and his owl. Have those
Who, if your tale is true, work out a penance
Upon the mountaintop where I am to hide,
Come from the Abbey graveyard?
YOUNG GIRL. They have not that luck,
But are more lonely; those that are buried there
Warred in the heat of the blood; if they were rebels
Some momentary impulse made them rebels
Or the commandment of some petty king
Who hated Thomond. Being but common sinners,
No callers-in of the alien from oversea,
They and their enemies of Thomond's party
Mix in a brief dream-battle above their bones;
Or make one drove; or drift in amity;
Or in the hurry of the heavenly round
Forget their earthly names. These are alone,
Being accursed.
YOUNG MAN. But if what seems is true
And there are more upon the other side
Than on this side of death, many a ghost
Must meet them face to face and pass the word
Even upon this gray and desolate hill.

96

YOUNG GIRL. Until this hour no ghost or living man
    Has spoken, though seven centuries have run
    Since they, weary of life and of men's eyes,
    Flung down their bones in some forgotten place,
    Being accursed.
YOUNG MAN. I have heard that there are souls
    Who, having sinned after a monstrous fashion,
    Take on them, being dead, a monstrous image
    To drive the living, should they meet its face,
    Crazy, and be a terror to the dead.
YOUNG GIRL. But these
    Were comely even in their middle life
    And carry, now that they are dead, the image
    Of their first youth, for it was in that youth
    Their sin began.
YOUNG MAN. I have heard of angry ghosts
    Who wander in a wilful solitude.
YOUNG GIRL. These have no thought but love, nor any joy
    But that upon the instant when their penance
    Draws to its height, and when two hearts are wrung
    Nearest to breaking, if hearts of shadows break,
    His eyes can mix with hers; nor any pang
    That is so bitter as that double glance,
    Being accursed.
YOUNG MAN. But what is this strange penance—
    That when their eyes have met can wring them most?
YOUNG GIRL. Though eyes can meet, their lips can never meet.
YOUNG MAN. And yet it seems they wander side by side.
    But doubtless you would say that when lips meet
    And have not living nerves, it is no meeting.
YOUNG GIRL. Although they have no blood, or living nerves,
    Who once lay warm and live the livelong night
    In one another's arms, and know their part
    In life, being now but of the people of dreams,
    Is a dream's part; although they are but shadows,
    Hovering between a thorn tree and a stone,
    Who have heaped up night on wingéd night; although
    No shade however harried and consumed
    Would change his own calamity for theirs,

Their manner of life were blessed could their lips
A moment meet; but when he has bent his head
Close to her head, or hand would slip in hand,
The memory of their crime flows up between
And drives them apart.

YOUNG MAN. The memory of a crime—
He took her from a husband's house, it may be,
But does the penance for a passionate sin
Last for so many centuries?

YOUNG GIRL. No, No;
The man she chose, the man she was chosen by,
Cared little and cares little from whose house
They fled towards dawn amid the flights of arrows,
Or that it was a husband's and a king's;
And how, if that were all, could she lack friends,
On crowded roads or on the unpeopled hill?
Helen herself had opened wide the door
Where night by night she dreams herself awake
And gathers to her breast a dreaming man.

YOUNG MAN. What crime can stay so in the memory?
What crime can keep apart the lips of lovers
Wandering and alone?

YOUNG GIRL. Her king and lover
Was overthrown in battle by her husband,
And for her sake and for his own, being blind
And bitter and bitterly in love, he brought
A foreign army from across the sea.

YOUNG MAN. You speak of Diarmuid and Dervorgilla
Who brought the Norman in?

YOUNG GIRL. Yes, yes, I spoke
Of that most miserable, most accursed pair
Who sold their country into slavery; and yet
They were not wholly miserable and accursed
If somebody of their race at least would say,
"I have forgiven them."

YOUNG MAN. O, never, never,
Shall Diarmuid and Dervorgilla be forgiven.

YOUNG GIRL. If some one of their race forgave at last
Lip would be pressed on lip.

98

YOUNG MAN. O, never, never
    Shall Diarmuid and Dervorgilla be forgiven.
    You have told your story well, so well indeed
    I could not help but fall into the mood
    And for a while believe that it was true,
    Or half believe; but better push on now.
    The horizon to the east is growing bright.

(*They go round stage once. The* MUSICIANS *play.*)

So here we're on the summit. I can see
    The Aran Islands, Connemara Hills,
    And Galway in the breaking light; there too
    The enemy has toppled roof and gable,
    And torn the panelling from ancient rooms;
    What generations of old men had known
    Like their own hands, and children wondered at,
    Has boiled a trooper's porridge. That town had lain,
    But for the pair that you would have me pardon,
    Amid its gables and its battlements
    Like any old admired Italian town;
    For though we have neither coal, nor iron ore,
    To make us wealthy and corrupt the air,
    Our country, if that crime were uncommitted,
    Had been most beautiful. Why do you dance?
    Why do you gaze, and with so passionate eyes,
    One on the other, and then turn away,
    Covering your eyes, and weave it in a dance?
    Who are you? what are you? you are not natural.
YOUNG GIRL. Seven hundred years our lips have never met.
YOUNG MAN. Why do you look so strangely at one another,
    So strangely and so sweetly?
YOUNG GIRL. Seven hundred years.
YOUNG MAN. So strangely and so sweetly. All the ruin,
    All, all their handiwork is blown away
    As though the mountain air had blown it away
    Because their eyes have met. They cannot hear,
    Being folded up and hidden in their dance.
    The dance is changing now. They have dropped their eyes,

99

They have covered up their eyes as though their hearts
Had suddenly been broken—never, never
Shall Diarmuid and Dervorgilla be forgiven.
They have drifted in the dance from rock to rock.
They have raised their hands as though to snatch the sleep
That lingers always in the abyss of the sky
Though they can never reach it. A cloud floats up
And covers all the mountain head in a moment;
And now it lifts and they are swept away.

(*The* STRANGER *and the* YOUNG GIRL *go out.*)

I had almost yielded and forgiven it all—
Terrible the temptation and the place!
(*The* MUSICIANS *begin unfolding and folding a black
cloth. The* FIRST MUSICIAN *comes forward to the front
of the stage, at the centre. He holds the cloth before him.
The other two come one on either side and unfold it.
They afterwards fold it up in the same way. While it is
unfolded, the* YOUNG MAN *leaves the stage.*)

(*Songs for the unfolding and folding of the cloth.*)

THE MUSICIANS (*singing*).

I

At the gray round of the hill
Music of a lost kingdom
Runs, runs and is suddenly still.
The winds out of Clare-Galway
Carry it: suddenly it is still.

I have heard in the night air
A wandering airy music;
And moidered in that snare
A man is lost of a sudden,
In that sweet wandering snare.

What finger first began
Music of a lost kingdom?
They dream that laughed in the sun.
Dry bones that dream are bitter,
They dream and darken our sun.

Those crazy fingers play
A wandering airy music;
Our luck is withered away,
And wheat in the wheatear withered,
And the wind blows it away.

II

My heart ran wild when it heard
The curlew cry before dawn
And the eddying cat-headed bird;
But now the night is gone.
I have heard from far below
The strong March birds a-crow.
Stretch neck and clap the wing,
Red cocks, and crow!

(*Curtain*)

1607

THE FLIGHT
OF THE
EARLS

The Shilling of JAMES I.

The Anglo-Norman Colonists

By L. M. McCRAITH

. . . The Anglo-Norman colonists had settled down by degrees in Ireland. They married Irish wives, and their children were reared by foster-parents according to the Irish custom, which created a tie stronger even than that of blood. The wars of the Bruces were ended by the desperate battle of Faughard, near Dundalk, in which Edward Bruce was killed. Little heed was paid to Ireland by the three successive Edwards, Kings of England, who sought their laurels of victory chiefly in Wales, and in France. The native chiefs, seeing that England scarcely supported the English settlers in Ireland, gradually repossessed themselves of their old land, and authority . . .

Still all might have been well, if Prince Lionel of England had not come to Ireland to see what was going on. He decided that the Irish chieftains had regained too much power. He then set about putting them in what he considered to be their place.

The Statute of Kilkenny 1366 A. D.

By P. W. JOYCE

. . . But there were also direct attempts made to keep the English and Irish people asunder, especially by a law known as the "Statute of Kilkenny." . . .

"The Statute of Kilkenny" was intended to apply only to the English, and was framed entirely in their interests. Its chief aim was to withdraw them from all contact with the "Irish enemies," as the natives are designated all through the act; to separate the two races for evermore.

104

According to this law, intermarriage, fosterage, gossipred, traffic, and close relations of any kind with the Irish were forbidden as high treason: punishment, death.

If any man took a name after the Irish fashion, used the Irish language or dress, rode a horse without a saddle, or adopted any other Irish custom, all his lands and houses were forfeited, and he himself was put into jail till he could find security that he would comply with the law. The Irish living among the English were forbidden to use the Irish language under the same penalty: that is, they were commanded to speak English, a language they did not know. To use the Brehon law—as many of the English, both high and low, were now doing—or to exact coyne and livery was treason.

No Englishman was to make war on the Irish without the special permission of the government, who would carry on all such wars, "so that," as the Act expresses it, "the Irish enemies shall not be admitted to peace until they be finally destroyed or shall make restitution fully of the costs and charges of that war."

No native Irish clergyman was to be appointed to any position in the church within the English district, and no Irishman was to be received into any English religious house in Ireland.

It was forbidden to receive or entertain Irish bards, pipers, storytellers, or mowers, because, as the Act said, these and such like often came as spies on the English.

But this new law, designed to effect so much, was found to be impracticable, and became after a little while a dead letter. It would require a great army to enable the governor to carry it out: and he had no such army. Coyne and livery continued to be exacted from the colonists by the three great earls, Kildare, Desmond, and Ormond; and the Irish and English went on intermarrying, gossiping, fostering, dressing, speaking Irish, riding horse without saddle, and quarreling on their own account, just the same as before.

Let Erin Remember the Days of Old

By THOMAS MOORE

Let Erin remember the days of old,
Ere her faithless sons betrayed her,
When Malachi wore the collar of gold,
Which he won from her proud invader;
When her kings, with standard of green unfurled,
Led the Red-Branch Knights to danger,
Ere the emerald gem of the western world
Was set in the crown of a stranger.

On Lough-Neagh's bank, as the fisherman strays,
When the clear cold eve's declining,
He sees the round towers of other days
In the wave beneath him shining!
Thus shall Memory often, in dreams sublime,
Catch a glimpse of the days that are over;
Thus, sighing, look through the waves of Time
For the long faded glories they cover!

*D*espite England's determination to rule Ireland as she thought fit, there were still many parts of the country, remote from the east coast, which were quite unsubdued and which carried on in their old way of life.

Lady Margaret

By P. W. JOYCE

. . . It is pleasant to be able to record that the native people still retained all their kindly hospitality and their ancient love of learning. This is shown by what we read of Margaret, the wife of O'Conor of Offaly, a lady celebrated for her benevolence. Twice in one year (about 1450) she invited to a great banquet the learned men of Ireland and Scotland: poets, musicians, brehons, historians, etc. The first meeting was held at Killeigh, near Tullamore, when 2700 guests were present; and the second at Rathangan in Kildare, to which were invited all who had been absent from the first. Lady Margaret herself was present, and she sat like a queen high up in the gallery of the church in view of the assembly, clad in robes of gold, surrounded by her friends and by the clergy and brehons. All were feasted in royal style, seated according to rank, after which each learned man was presented with a valuable gift: and the names of all present were entered on a roll by Mac Egan, chief brehon to the lady's husband.

By the fifteenth century the Anglo-Normans had in fact become Anglo-Irish. An English writer of this time complained that "the Norman settlers had become more Irish than the Irish themselves." A parliament convened in Dublin in 1449, at the instigation of the Anglo-Irish, asserted that the Irish legislature was henceforth independent and that the country was free from all laws except those passed by the Lords and Commons of Ireland. But forty years later the English decided that no parliament might be held in Ireland unless all the acts it intended to pass were sanctioned by the English king. This was called Poynings's Law.

Processional Cross of 15th Century, which was found in a quarry at Sheephouse, Co. Meath, now in the National Museum of Ireland.

The Reformation

By CAMILLE BOURNIQUEL

Translated by John Fisher

But the Statutes of Kilkenny and Poynings's Law were merely stepping stones. The real drama, the outrageous scandal, began only with the Reformation. From that time on abuses could be cloaked with a hypocritical excuse: they were necessary for dismantling this stronghold of popery and for imposing the new religion, by force, if need be. The Protestants were the faithful subjects, the others outcasts without status of any kind. "The English Law," as a Lord Chancellor said later, "does not suppose any such person to exist as an Irish Roman Catholic." From this day, the Ireland of the faithful was a land beyond the pale . . .

. . . In 1588, the disaster of the Armada merely strengthened the position of the English. Ulster, however, remained intact. One last chance remained to Ireland in 1595, when the two Hughs, O'Neill and O'Donnell, after their victories at Clontibret and Yellow Ford, succeeded in unifying the country for the last time and endangered the whole conquest. Essex, the queen's favourite, preferred to negotiate with them rather than fight; for that he was recalled to London and executed. He was replaced by Mountjoy, who landed in 1600 with 20,000 well-armed men. Mountjoy savagely repressed the Munster revolt, destroying farms and flocks everywhere and spreading famine. A Spanish landing was decisively defeated at Kinsale (1601). Hugh O'Donnell was forced to flee to Spain, where he is believed to have died of poison. Hugh O'Neill fled to Tyrone and had to sue for pardon.

In the end he and the successor of Hugh O'Donnell, Rory O'Donnell, were welcomed in London by James Stuart. After their return to Ireland they felt themselves under strict surveillance and fled secretly into exile. This was the famous Flight of the Earls which marked the final reverse and closed the long-drawn-out Gaelic era (1607).

Queen Elizabeth I, hoping to win the Irish chieftains to her side, invited them to her court, where she showered honors upon them. Many of them she knighted, and henceforth any suspicion of rebellion on their parts was called treason—an excuse for her government to imprison or execute them. Her successors made good use of this policy.

The Flight of the Earls

By L. M. McCRAITH

. . . the Government, without anything definite to charge O'Neill with, suspected, or chose to suspect, that he was organising a fresh rebellion. Incriminating letters were written—or forged— and dropped in a convenient place—outside the door of the Council in Dublin. There were conversations in the Fitzgerald's garden at Maynooth, between Rory O'Donnell and Lord Delvin, which Delvin repeated. There was Rory's supposed plot to capture the Lord Deputy and the Council. More besides was said and done. O'Neill sent a list of his grievances—undoubtedly great and real— to London. O'Cahan made more trouble, and O'Neill was unwisely enraged. It is all a sad and tangled tale.

Then O'Neill was summoned to London to state his case, and answer the charges against him. But information was conveyed to Hugh by his son Henry—an officer in the Spanish army in the Netherlands—through the Maguires that, could he be lured to London, his arrest was intended. By means of the Maguires a ship was sent from Brussels to Rathmullen, and O'Neill was warned to escape, and bring all he held dear along with him, especially the O'Donnell and his family.

Rightly or wrongly, the Earls of Tyrone and of Tyrconnell decided to fly. Tyrone was at Slane with the Lord Deputy when the news reached him that the ship had come, and he seems to have made his decision very hastily. The action of Hugh and Rory suggests not premeditated rebellion, but alarmed innocence. On September 4th (old style), 1607, ninety persons embarked from Rathmullen on Lough Swilly in a little craft of eighty tons.

110

"It was on the Festival of Holy Cross in Harvest they embarked in the ship," wrote the Four Masters. "That was a distinguished company for one ship. For it is most certain that the sea has not borne, nor the wind wafted from Ireland in latter times a party in any one ship more eminent, illustrious, and noble than they were in point of genealogy, or more distinguished for great deeds and renowned feats of arms and valorous achievements; and would that God had granted them to remain in their patrimonies until their youths should attain to the age of manhood. Woe to the heart that meditated, woe to the mind that conceived, woe to the council that decided on the project of their setting out on this voyage, without knowing that they should ever return to their native principalities or patrimonies to the end of the world!"

Here, as far as Irish history is concerned, ends the career of the great Hugh O'Neill.

The pathos, the romance, the heroism—heroism of a new kind—begins with the story of the closing fourteen years of O'Neill's life. We see the little over-loaded ship, with its miserable accommodation, buffeted by terrible weather, all but wrecked by unparalleled storms, barely escaping English interception. Only after fourteen days' tossing did the wretched passengers, drenched, starved, and thirsty, shelter in the estuary of the Seine. We see them hounded on out of France, for all that Henry IV answered the English Ambassador—who demanded that they should be sent to London—that "France was a free country, and no guest of France shall be molested, least of all those driven from their homes for their religion." Wearily, the party travelled on to Amiens, to Arras, to Douay, where Irish seminarists welcomed the great O'Neill, who had often sheltered such as they.

Desolation

Translated from the Irish
By ROBIN FLOWER
(1881–1946)

This night sees Eire desolate!
    Her chiefs are cast out of their state,
    Her men, her maidens weep to see
    Her desolate that should peopled be.

How desolate is Connla's plain
    Though aliens swarm in her domain;
    Her rich bright soil had joy in these
    That now are scattered overseas.

Man after man, day after day,
    Her noblest princes pass away
    And leave to all the rabble rest
    A land dispeopled of her best.

Men smile at childhood's play no more,
    Music and song, their day is o'er;
    At wine, at Mass the kingdom's heirs
    Are seen no more; changed hearts are theirs.

Her chiefs are gone. There's none to bear
    Her cross, or lift her long despair;
    The grieving lords take ship. With these
    Our very souls pass overseas.

The Earls Abroad

By JAMES GRANT
(1822–1887)

The deeds of the Irish regiments in the Spanish service would fill volumes . . . Owen Roe O'Neil, of Ulster, rose to high rank in the Spanish Imperial service and held an important post in Catalonia. He defended Arras against Louis XIII in 1640, and when forced to surrender, he did so, says Carte, "upon honourable terms; yet his conduct in the defence was such as gave him great reputation, and procured him extraordinary respect even from the enemy;" and the brave O'Sullivan Bearra of Dunboy, who fled in the days of James I, became Governor of Corunna under Philip IV.

Lieutenant-General Don Carlos Felix O'Neile (son of the celebrated Sir Neil O'Neile of Ulster, slain at the battle of the Boyne), was Governor of Havannah and favourite of Charles III of Spain; he died at Madrid in 1791, after attaining the great age of one hundred and ten years.

In 1780, Colonel O'Moore commanded the Royal Walloon Guards of Charles III. In 1799, Field-Marshal Arthur O'Neil was Governor-General of Yucatan under the same monarch, and commanded the flotilla of thirty-one vessels which made an unsuccessful attack on the British settlements in the Bay of Honduras. In the same year, Don Gonzalo O'Farrel was the Spanish ambassador at the Court of Berlin, and in 1808 he was Minister of War for Spain.

In 1797, O'Higgins was Viceroy of Peru, under Charles IV, one of whose best generals was the famous Alexander Count O'Reilly.

Don Pedro O'Daly was Governor of Rosas when it was besieged by Gouvion St. Cyr in 1809; and General John O'Donoghue was chief of Cuesta's staff and one of the few able officers about the person of that indolent and obstinate old hidalgo, whose incapacity nearly caused the ruin of the Spanish affairs at the commencement of the Peninsular War. He died Viceroy of Mexico in 1816.

O'Higgins was Viceroy of Peru under Ferdinand VI and the third and fourth Charles of Spain. He signalized himself with great bravery in the wars with the Araucanos, a nation on the coast of Chili, who were ultimately subdued by him and subjected to the Spanish rule. . . . In 1765, he marched against the Araucanos with a battalion of Chilian infantry and fifteen hundred horse named Maulinians. He was thrice brought to the ground by having three horses killed under him, but the Araucanos were routed, and the Spanish rule extended over all Peru, of which he died Viceroy in the beginning of the present century, after fighting the battles of Rancagua and Talchuana, which secured the independence of Chili.

Few names bear a more prominent place in Spanish history than those of Blake, the Captain-General of the Coronilla, and O'Reilly, a soldier of fortune, who saved the life of Charles III during the revolt at Madrid, and who reformed and disciplined anew the once noble army of Spain.

Alexander Count O'Reilly was born in Ireland about 1735, of Roman Catholic parents, and when young entered the Spanish service as a sub-lieutenant in the Irish regiment with which he served in Italy during the war of the Spanish Succession, and received a wound from which he was rendered lame for the rest of his life. In 1751 he went to serve in Austria, and made two campaigns against the Prussians, under the orders of Marshal Count Lacy, his countryman. Then in 1759 he passed into the service of Louis XV, under whose colours was still that celebrated Irish Brigade whose native bravery so mainly contributed to win for France the glory of Fontenoy.

The Old College of the Irish, Paris

By PADRAIC COLUM
(1881–   )

The Lombards having gone back to their land,
We, who might never flock to native land
Except like birds that fly like fugitives,
Desperately, in a wind across the sea,
We drew our brood to their forsaken nest.
The Lombards' halls became the Irelanders',
And charity was craved for us—'twas given
In names of Almantza and Namur,
Cremona, Barcelona, Charleroi—
Fields that our soldiers bled on for a cause
Not ours, under command not ours.

Our order broken, they who were our brood
Knew not themselves the heirs of noted masters,
Of Columbanus and Erigena:
We strove towards no high road of speculation,
Towards no delivery of gestated dogma,
No resolution of age-long disputes,
Only to have a priest beside the hedges,
Baptising, marrying,
Offering Mass within some clod-built chapel,
And to the dying the last sacrament
Conveying, no more we strove to do—
We, all bare exiles, soldiers, scholars, priests.

115

Apart from the flight of the earls, a great many young Catholics who wished to be educated in their own faith, and could afford to do so, went to Spain. From there Geoffrey Keating wrote home. This nostalgic poem was written, probably during a visit to Spain, while gazing at a letter addressed to Ireland.

Keating to His Letter

By GEOFFREY KEATING
(1570–1644)
Translated from the Irish
By JOHN DALTON
(1792–1867)

"For the sake of the dear little isle where I send you,
  For those who will welcome, and speed, and befriend you;
  For the green hills of Erin, that still hold my heart there,
Tho' stained by the blood of the patriot and martyr.
      My blessing attend you!
      My blessing attend you!

Adieu to her fish rivers, murmuring through rushes!
Adieu to her meadows, her fields, wells, and bushes!
Adieu to her lawns, her moors and her harbours!
Adieu, from my heart, to her forests and arbours,
      All vocal with thrushes!
      All vocal with thrushes!

Adieu to her harvests, for ever increasing!
And her hills of assemblies, all wisdom possessing!
And her people—Ah! where is there braver, or better?
Then go to the Island of Saints, my dear Letter,
      And bring her my blessing!
      And bring her my blessing!"

116

1644

THE CURSE
OF
CROMWELL

One of Cromwell's Armed Soldiers.

If parts allure thee, think how Bacon shined,
The wisest, brightest, meanest of mankind:
Or, ravish'd with the whistling of a name,
See Cromwell, damn'd to everlasting fame!

Alexander Pope
(1688–1744)

Oliver Cromwell 1599-1658

By CLEMENT WALKER
(–1651)

Sunday after Easter day (1649), six preachers militant at White-hall tried the patience of their hearers; one calling up another successively; at last the Spirit of the Lord called up Oliver Cromwell, who standing a good while with lifted up eyes, as it were in a trance, and his neck inclining a little to one side, as if he had expected Mahomet's dove to descend and murmur in his ear; and sending forth abundantly the groans of the Spirit, spent an hour in prayer, and an hour and a half in a Sermon. In his prayer he desired God to take off from him the government of this mighty People of England, as being too heavy for his shoulders to bear: An audacious, ambitious and hypocritical imitation of Moses. It is now reported of him that he pretendeth to Inspirations; and that when any great weighty matter is propounded, he usually retireth for a quarter or half an hour and then returneth and delivereth out the Oracles of the Spirit.

118

Oliver Cromwell declared that the Providence of God had cast upon him the task of executing the English king, Charles I. After the execution of the king on January 30, 1649, he took upon himself the role of Lord Protector of England. Can we be surprised, therefore, at his claim that Providence inspired him to invade Ireland? On Marcrh 30, 1649 he landed, to reconquer Ireland and convert her to Protestantism. He offered two and a half million acres of Irish land to English adventurers in return for their support.

While Cromwell wreaked havoc further north, his henchman, Broghill, reduced Munster to devastation.

Head of Crozier of Cormac MacCarthy, 13th Century, found on the Rock of Cashel, now in the National Museum of Ireland.

The Bishop of Ross

By DR. MADDEN
(1798–1886)

The tramp of the trooper is heard at Macroom;
  The soldiers of Cromwell are spared from Clonmel,
And Broghill—the merciless Broghill—is come
  On a mission of murder which pleases him well.

The wailing of women, the wild ululu,
  Dread tidings from cabin to cabin convey;
But loud though the plaints and the shrieks which ensue,
  The war cry is louder of men in array.

In the park of Macroom there is gleaming of steel,
  And glancing of lightning in looks on that field,
And swelling of bosoms with patriot zeal,
  And clenching of hands on the weapons they wield.

MacEgan, a prelate like Ambrose of old,
  Forsakes not his flock when the spoiler is near.
The post of the pastor's in front of the fold
  When the wolf's on the plain and there's rapine to fear.

The danger is come, and the fortune of war
  Inclines to the side of oppression once more;
The people are brave—but, they fall; and the star
  Of their destiny sets in the darkness of yore.

MacEgan survives in the Philistine hands
  Of the lords of the Pale, and his death is decreed;
But the sentence is stayed by Lord Broghill's commands,
  And the prisoner is dragged to his presence with speed.

"To Carraig-an-Droichid, this instant," he cried,
  "Prevail on your people in garrison there
To yield, and at once in our mercy confide,
  And your life I will pledge you my honour to spare."

"Your mercy! Your honour!" the prelate replied,
  "I well know the worth of: my duty I know,
Lead on to the castle, and there, by your side,
  With the blessing of God, what is meet will I do."

The orders are given, the prisoner is led
  To the castle, and round him are menacing hordes:
Undaunted, approaching the walls, at the head
  Of the troopers of Cromwell, he utters these words:

"Beware of the cockatrice—trust not the wiles
  Of the serpent, for perfidy skulks in its folds!
Beware of Lord Broghill the day that he smiles
  His mercy is murder!—his word never holds.

"Remember, 'tis writ in our annals of blood,
  Our countrymen never relied on the faith
Of truce, or of treaty, but treason ensued—
  And the issue of every delusion was death!"

Thus nobly the patriot prelate sustained
  The ancient renown of his chivalrous race,
And the last of old Eoghan's descendants obtained
  For the name of Ui-Mani new lustre and grace.

He died on the scaffold, in front of those walls
  Where the blackness of ruin is seen from afar;
And the gloom of its desolate aspect recalls
  The blackest of Broghill's achievements in war!

121

Even Oliver Cromwell's soldiers seem to have found their leader's tactics worthy of comment at home.

News From The Cromwellian Front

By ANTHONY Á WOOD
(1632–1695)

. . . being often with his mother and brethren, he would tell them of the most terrible assaulting and storming of Tredagh (Drogheda), wherein he himself had been engaged. He told them that 3,000 at least, besides some women and children, were, after the assailants had taken part, and afterwards all the town, put to the sword on the 11 and 12 Sept., 1649; at which time Sir Arthur Aston, the governor had his brains beat out, and his body hack'd and chop'd to pieces.

He told them, that when they were to make their way up to the lofts and galleries in the church and up to the tower where the enemy had fled, each of the assailants would take up a child and use it as a buckler of defence, when they ascended the steps, to keep themselves from being shot or brain'd. After they had killed all in the church, they went into the vaults underneath where all the flower and choicest of the women and ladies had hid themselves.

Oliver's Advice

By WILLIAM BLACKER
(1777–1855)

The night is gathering gloomily, the day is closing fast;
The tempest flaps his raven wings in loud and angry blast!
The thunder clouds are driving athwart the lurid sky,
But put your trust in God, my boys, and keep your powder dry.

There *was* a day when loyalty was hailed with honor due,
Our banner the protection waved to all the good and true—
And gallant hearts beneath its folds were linked in honour's tie,
We put our trust in God, my boys, and kept our powder dry.

122

They come, whose counsels wrapped the land in foul rebellious
    flame,
Their hearts unchastened by remorse, their cheeks untinged by
    shame.
Be still, be still, indignant heart—be tearless, too, each eye,
And put your trust in God, my boys, and keep your powder dry.

The Power that led His chosen by pillared cloud and flame
Through parted sea and desert waste, that Power is still the same;
He fails not—He, the loyal hearts that firm on Him rely,
So put your trust in God, my boys, and keep your powder dry.

For "happy homes," for "altars free," we grasp the ready sword,
For freedom, truth, and for our God's unmutilated word,
These, these the war cry of our march, our hope the Lord on high;
Then put your trust in God, my boys, and keep your powder dry.

You ask me what I have found, and far and wide I go:
Nothing but Cromwell's house and Cromwell's murderous crew,
The lovers and the dancers are beaten into the clay,
And the tall men and the swordsmen and the horsemen,
Where are they?

W. B. Yeats

Mr. and Mrs. Hall came on frequent visits to Ireland from England, and wrote in collaboration three volumes called "Ireland: Its Scenery and Character." They delved resolutely into the past as they went from town to town. No archives were too dusty for them and no tomb too ivy-grown. This is their report of Oliver Cromwell's tactics.

Siege of Drogheda

By MR. and MRS. HALL
(1800–1889)—(1800–1881)

"A resolution being taken to besiege that place," writes Ludlow, "our army sate down before it, and the Lieutenant-General caused a battery to be erected, by which he made a breach in the wall." The spot from which he first assaulted the town is still known by the name of "Cromwell Fort", and stands on the summit of a hill that completely commands the town.

A third assault, led by the Lieutenant-General in person was successful, though Cromwell himself, in his despatch to the Parliament, admits that the "enemy disputed it very stiffly with us."

Leland asserts that "quarter had been promised to all who should lay down their arms"; but the moment the town was completely reduced, Cromwell issued his "infernal order" for a general and indiscriminate massacre. He himself best tells the horrid story of his butchery, in a letter to the Speaker Lenthall, dated September 17th: "The governor, Sir Arthur Aston, and divers considerable officers, being there, our men getting at them were ordered by me to put them all to the sword, and indeed, being in the heat of action, I forbade them to spare any that were in arms in the town, and I think that night they put to the sword about two thousand men; divers of the officers and men being fled over the bridge into the other part of the town, where about one hundred of them possessed Saint Peter's church steeple, some the west gate, and others a round tower, next the gate, called Saint Sunday's; these being summoned to yield to mercy, refused, whereupon I ordered the steeple of Saint Peter's to be fired, when one of them was heard to say, in the midst of the flames, 'God damn me! God confound me! I burn! I burn!' The next day the other towers were summoned, in one of

124

which was about six or seven score, but they refused to yield themselves, and we knowing that hunger must compel them, set only a good guard to secure them from running away, until their stomachs were come down; from one of the said towers, notwithstanding their condition, they killed and wounded some of our men; when they submitted themselves, their officers were knocked on the head, and every tenth man of the soldiers killed, and the rest shipped for the Barbadoes."

The butcher thus blasphemously sums up the history of his atrocity: "And now give me leave to say how it came to pass, this great work is wrought; it was set upon some of our hearts that a great thing should be done, not by power or might, but by the Spirit of God; and is it not so, clearly, that which caused your men to storm the breach so courageously it was the Spirit of God, who gave your men courage, and took it away again, and gave the enemy courage, and took it away again, and gave your men courage again, and therewith this great success, and therefore it is good that God alone have all the glory."

From the same unquestionable authority—Cromwell himself—we learn that the murders were as cold-blooded as they were extensive; and continued long after the excitement of the contest had subsided. The hideous execution of the savage order for indiscriminate slaughter was continued "during five days, with every circumstance of horror;" it was stayed at length—according to tradition, for history has no record of the fact—in consequence of a touching incident arousing the lingering spark of humanity in the iron heart of Cromwell; walking through the streets, he noticed, stretched along the path, the dead body of a newly-made mother, from whose breast the miserable infant was vainly endeavouring to draw sustenance. A single touch alone is necessary to complete this picture of horrors: the Parliament, on the receipt of the letters of General Cromwell describing the massacre—ordered a day to be set apart as a day of solemn thanksgiving "for the mercy vouchsafed," throughout the whole of the kingdom—and the first day of November was "set apart accordingly."

The storming of Drogheda was but the first act of a terrible tragedy; every step which Cromwell took through Ireland was marked with blood.

From *Hall's Ireland*

125

When Cromwell had had his day and the English monarchy was restored, Ireland had a breathing space until William of Orange and James II decided to fight for the English crown on Irish soil. William was Prostestant, James was Catholic. The descendants of the original English who had been given grants of land in Ireland by the English crown were Protestants and rallied around William. The native Irish, being Catholic, supported James. The first decisive battle was the "battle of the Boyne," and this is how an "Orangeman" describes it.

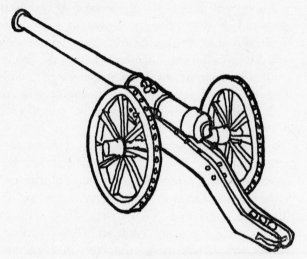

Cannon of the type used in the Battle of the River Boyne.

The Battle of the Boyne

ANONYMOUS

July the First, of a morning fair,
    In sixteen ninety famous,
King William did his men prepare
    To fight with false King Shamus.
King James he pitched his tents between,
    The lines for to retire . . .
But King William threw his bomb-balls in,
    And set them all on fire. . .

126

Thereat revenge the Irish vowed
  Upon King William's forces,
And vehemently with cries did crowd
  To check their forward courses.
A ball from out their battery flew,
  As the King he faced its fire;
His shoulder-knot away it shot,
  Quoth he, "Pray come no nigher!"

Then straight his officers he did call,
  Saying, "Gentlemen, mind your station,
And prove your valour one and all
  Before this Irish nation.
My brazen walls let no man break
  And your subtle foes you'll scatter,
Let us show them today good English play,
  As we go over the water."

Then, horse and foot, we marched amain,
  Resolved their ranks to batter,
But the brave Duke Schomberg he was slain,
  As we went over the water.
Then King William cried, "Feel no dismay
  At the losing of one commander,
For God shall be our King today,
  And I'll be general under."

Then stoutly we Boyne river crossed
  To give the Irish battle;
Our cannon to his dreadful cost
  Like thunderclaps did rattle.
In majestic mien our prince rode o'er;
  The stream ran red with slaughter,
As with blow and shout we put to rout
  Our enemies over the water.

After the disastrous battle of the Boyne, James is said to have declared in Dublin that his Irish allies "fled from the battlefield," to which he got the following reply, "Your Majesty seems to have won the race."

Despite this defeat, the war continued and the Irish still fought for the thankless James under the brilliant leadership of Patrick Sarsfield. The French, a Catholic country, had promised to send shiploads of soldiers to their aid and Ireland's mood of jubilation is expressed in this old song—the words of which have been changed many times in the course of history. The Shan Van Vocht is an old woman who passes on a message, and many a message she passed on under the very ears of her enemies, who never suspected the significance of the gay tune.

The Shan Van Vocht

ANONYMOUS

Oh! the French are on the sea,
   Says the Shan Van Vocht;
The French are on the sea,
   Says the Shan Van Vocht;
Oh! the French are in the Bay,
They'll be here without delay,
And the Orange will decay,
   Says the Shan Van Vocht.

And where will they have their camp?
   Says the Shan Van Vocht;
Where will they have their camp?
   Says the Shan Van Vocht;
On the Curragh of Kildare,
The boys they will be there,
With their pikes in good repair,
   Says the Shan Van Vocht.

128

Then what will the yeomen do?
  Says the Shan Van Vocht;
What will the yeomen do?
  Says the Shan Van Vocht;
What should the yeomen do
But throw off the Red and Blue,
And swear that they'll be true
  To the Shan Van Vocht?

And what colour will they wear?
  Says the Shan Van Vocht;
What colour will they wear?
  Says the Shan Van Vocht;
What colour should be seen
Where our fathers' homes have been,
But our own immortal Green?
  Says the Shan Van Vocht.

And will Ireland then be free?
  Says the Shan Van Vocht;
Will Ireland then be free?
  Says the Shan Van Vocht;
Yes! Ireland shall be free,
From the centre to the sea;
Then hurrah for Liberty!
  Says the Shan Van Vocht.

Fleur-de-lis, 17th Century.

But the French fleet was delayed. It seemed as if they might never come, when, quite unexpectedly, the English offered to sign a treaty on quite favorable terms for the Irish.

The Treaty of Limerick 1691

By COL. CHARLES O'KELLY
(1621–1695)

The Treaty began on the 26th September and continued to the 3rd October, and then it was concluded, to the Satisfaction of some, and to the sensible Affliction of others. But that which raised the Admiration of all People, and began an Astonishment which seemed universall over all Ireland, was the sudden, unexpected, prodigious Change of Sarsfield, who appeared now the most active of all the Commanders to forward the Treaty, and took most pains to persuade the Colonels and Captains to a Complyance; representing that there was but a small Quantity of Provisions left, and noe Expectation of any Supply out of France till next Spring; that if they rejected the conditions now offered, they were to hope for none when their Provisions were all spent; and that therefore, the Necessity to capitulate, at present was absolute and unavoidable. The authority of Sarsfield, and the Opinion which all the World conceived of his untainted Loyalty and Zeal for his Country, expressed uppon several Occasions, made them approve what he expressed or proposed, tho' with a great Deal of Reluctancy, and a Regrett equall thereunto.

And now, alas! the saddest Day is come, that ever appeared above the Horizon of Ireland. The sun was darkened, and covered over with a black cloud, as if unwilling to behold such a wofull spectacle: there needed noe Rain to bedew the Earth, for the Tears of the disconsolate Irish did abundantly moisten their native Soile to which they were that Day, to bid the last Farewell. Those who resolved to leave it never hoped to see it again; and those who made the unfortunate Choise to continue therein, could at the same Time have nothing in Prospect but Contempt and Poverty, Chains and Imprisonment, and, in a Word all the Miserys that a conquered Nation could rationally expect from Power and Malice. . . .

130

What the Reasons might be for these prodigious Transactions, and what performance the conquered Irish (whether living in voluntary Exile abroad, or in a forced Bondage at home) have hitherto received, after soe many large Promises of both sides, must be the Work of another Time, and likely of an other Pen: the publick Calamity of my Countrymen, unfortunate Countrymen in generall, and the Lamentable Condition of some particular friends, added to the Incommodities of old age, rendring me unable to pursue that Remnant of a woful History, that requires Ink mixed with the Writer's Tears; and the Fountain of my weak Eyes hath been drained up already by the too frequent Remembrance of the slaughter at Aughrim and the sad Separation at Limerick.

Sarsfield

By SEUMAS MacMANUS
(1870–1962)

A few days later a French fleet came up the Shannon. It brought men, money, arms, ammunition, stores and clothing. The news reached Sarsfield. Stunned, he remained silent for a few moments. Then: "Too late," he said, "the Treaty is signed. Ireland's and our honour is pledged. Though one hundred thousand Frenchmen offered to aid us now, we must keep our word!"

In his quarters Ginckel heard that the fleet had come. He was alarmed. Would Sarsfield tear up the Treaty? Would the French soldiers land? Would the Irish regiments listed for France, men with their arms, renew the fight? The cautious Dutchman, an honest brave man, himself, feared.

But his anxiety was soon ended. Sarsfield, the unbuyable—Sarsfield, the man of honour—had forbidden the French to land. Instead, their ships were to transport the Irish regiments to France.

Not a man of these saw Ireland again.

131

The Treaty of Limerick, though signed in all good faith by the English leaders, was broken by the English government when Sarsfield and his men had safely sailed away to France where they had promised to aid the French army. Sarsfield himself fell at the battle of Landen. His dying words were, "Oh, that this was for Ireland!" It was as well for Sarsfield that he died just then, for what followed in Ireland would have broken his heart.

The Treaty promised to restore to the Irish Catholics at least a degree of religious freedom. But before five years had passed the iniquitous Penal Code was drawn up, which was a violation both in the spirit and in the letter of the Treaty of Limerick.

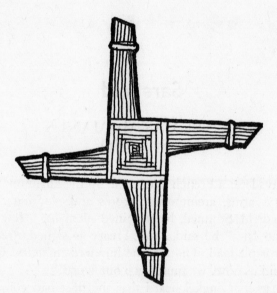

St. Brigid's Cross, made of rushes or straw, and hung up in the house on the Eve of St. Brigid's Day, February 1st.

The Penal Code

1691–1829

The Penal Laws enacted or reenacted in the new era succeeding the siege of Limerick, when under the pledged faith and honour of the English crown, the Irish Catholics were to be "protected in the free and unfettered exercise of their religion," provided amongst other things that:

The Irish Catholic was forbidden the exercise of his religion.

He was forbidden to receive education.

He was forbidden to enter a profession.

He was forbidden to hold public office.

He was forbidden to engage in trade or commerce.

He was forbidden to live in a corporate town or within five miles thereof.

He was forbidden to own a horse of greater value than five pounds.

He was forbidden to purchase land.

He was forbidden to lease land.

He was forbidden to accept a mortgage on land in security for a loan.

He was forbidden to vote.

He was forbidden to keep any arms for his protection.

He was forbidden to hold a life annuity.

He was forbidden to buy land from a Protestant.

He was forbidden to receive a gift of land from a Protestant.

He was forbidden to inherit land from a Protestant.

He was forbidden to inherit anything from a Protestant.

He was forbidden to rent any land that was worth more than thirty shillings a year.

He was forbidden to reap from his land any profit exceeding a third of the rent.

He could not be guardian to a child.

He could not, when dying, leave his infant children under Catholic guardianship.

He could not attend Catholic worship.

He was compelled by the law to attend Protestant worship.

He could not himself educate his child.

He could not send his child to a Catholic teacher.

He could not employ a Catholic teacher to come to his child.

He could not send his child abroad to receive education.

The priest was banned and hunted with bloodhounds. The school master was banned and hunted with bloodhounds.

If he had an unfaithful wife, she, by going through the form of adopting the Protestant religion, compelled from a papist the heaviest annuity that might be squeezed out of him—and would inherit all the property at his death. If he had an unnatural child, that child by conforming to the Established religion, could compel from him the highest possible annuity and inherit all his property at his death—to the total exclusion of all the children who had remained faithful to their father, and their religion.

If he was discovered in the act of having his son educated at home, a ruinous fine and a dungeon awaited him. If he sent his son to be educated abroad, all his property was confiscated—and the child so educated was thereby debarred from all rights and properties in the country, and debarred from inheriting anything.

He was compelled to pay double for the support of the militia. And he was compelled to make good all damages done to the state by the privateers of any Catholic power in which the state was at war.

The law soon came to recognize an Irishman in Ireland only for the purpose of repressing him. Till in the reign of George I, Lord Chancellor Bowes and also Chief Justice Robinson, in their official capacity, pronounced: "The law does not suppose any such person to exist as an Irish Roman Catholic."

FROM SEUMAS MacMANUS' *Story Of The Irish Race*

134

The Dark Days

By SEUMAS MacMANUS

Throughout those dark days the hunted schoolmaster, with price upon his head, was hidden from house to house. And in the summer time he gathered his little class, hungering and thirsting for knowledge, behind a hedge in remote mountain glen—where, while in turn each tattered lad kept watch from the hilltop for the British soldiers, he fed to his eager pupils the forbidden fruit of the tree of knowledge.

Latin and Greek were taught to ragged hunted ones under shelter of the hedges—whence these teachers were known as "hedge schoolmasters." A knowledge of Latin was a frequent enough accomplishment among poor Irish mountaineers in the seventeenth century—and was spoken by many of them on special occasions. And it is authoritatively boasted that cows were bought and sold in Greek, in mountain marketplaces of Kerry.

Throughout these dreadful centuries, too, the hunted priest— who in his youth had been smuggled to the Continent of Europe to receive his training—tended the flame of faith. He lurked like a thief among the hills. On Sundays and feast days he celebrated Mass at a rock, on a remote mountainside, while the congregation knelt on the heather of the hillside, under the open heavens. While he said Mass, faithful sentries watched from all the nearby hilltops, to give timely warning of the approaching priest-hunter and his guard of British soldiers. But sometimes the troops came on them unawares, and the Mass Rock was bespattered with his blood—and men, women and children caught in the crime of worshipping God among the rocks, were frequently slaughtered on the mountainside.

Then, bishops and archbishops, meanly dressed in rough homespuns, trudged on foot among their people—and often dwelt, ate and slept, in holes in the ground.

135

The Hedge Schoolmasters

By SEUMAS MacMANUS

When the night shall lift from Erin's hills, 'twere shame if we
    forget
One band of unsung heroes whom Freedom owes a debt.
When we brim high cups to brave ones then, their memory let
    us pledge
Who gathered their ragged classes behind a friendly hedge.
By stealth they met their pupils in the glen's deep-hidden nook,
And taught them many a lesson was never in English book;
There was more than wordy logic shown to use in wise debate;
Nor *amo* was the only verb they gave to conjugate.
When hunted on the heathery hill and through the shadowy wood,
They climbed the cliff, they dared the marsh, they stemmed the
    tumbling flood;
Their blanket was the clammy mist, their bed the windswept bent;
In fitful sleep they dreamt the bay of bloodhounds on their scent.
Their lore was not the brightest, nor their store, mayhap, the best,
But they fostered love, undying, in each young Irish breast;
And through the dread, dread night, and long, that steeped our
    island then,
The lamps of hope and fires of faith were fed by these brave men.
The grass waves green above them; soft sleep is theirs for aye;
The hunt is over, and the cold; the hunger passed away.
O hold them high and holy! and their memory proudly pledge,
Who gathered their ragged classes behind a friendly hedge.

Evasions

By P. W. JOYCE

. . . It was the governing classes that made those terrible penal
laws; the general body of the Protestant people, whether in England
or Ireland, had no hand in them. And when the laws came into
operation, a large proportion of Irish Protestants, all through the
country, looked upon them with silent disapproval, and did a great

136

deal in a quiet way to protect their Catholic neighbors; . . . it often happened that a dying Catholic, with young children, sent for his Protestant friend and complied outwardly with the law by leaving them to his guardianship, with the secret understanding that they should be educated by some Catholic selected by the family; and there is good reason to believe that guardians thus appointed were generally faithful to their trust: often at great risk to themselves. The enactment about the horse of more than £5 value was taken advantage of only in a very few cases; and Catholic gentlemen continued to hunt and race and drive equipages with valuable horses, among the Protestant gentry, without any molestation during the whole time the law remained in force. . . .

. . . In other ways the operation of these cruel laws was mitigated, and it often turned out that matters were not quite so bad with Catholics as the lawmakers intended. Evasions were very often winked at, even where well-known. Catholic bishops remained all through the country in spite of every effort to discover them, living in huts in remote places under various disguises, and meeting their congregations by night in wild glens and bogs. Young priests who had been educated abroad managed to return, and took up their duties though not registered. But such breaches and evasions were always very dangerous, and might at any moment end in detection and punishment. Then as to education. Many priests kept schoolmasters, who taught in sheds put up in remote glens, or they instructed individual scholars, in a scrappy kind of way, in fields or lanes; which however was only a flickering sort of education, that could not reach the general mass of the people.

. . . making every allowance for kindliness, protection, evasion, and non-enforcement of the law, the Catholic people underwent terrible sufferings for three or four generations; and no one who has not read the detailed history of those times can have any idea of the sort of life they led. . . .

Jonathan Swift, the Protestant Dean of Saint Patrick's Cathedral, Dublin, was one of the Anglo-Irish colony. He held his appointment under the English crown, but never tired of exercising his incomparable wit to aid the Irish cause. A favorite quotation from his sayings is, "Burn everything from England but her coal."

He poked fun at abuses of all sorts and turned many a heavy parliamentary utterance to ridicule.

Bird, after THE BOOK OF KELLS.

A Depending Kingdom?

By JONATHAN SWIFT
(1667–1745)

This gives me the opportunity of explaining to those who are ignorant, another point which has often swelled in my breast. Those who come over hither to us from England, and some weak people among ourselves, whenever in discourses we make mention of liberty and property, shake their heads, and tell us that Ireland is a depending kingdom, as if they would seem by this phrase to intend that the people of Ireland are in some state of slavery or dependence different from those of England; whereas a depending kingdom is a modern term of art, unknown, as I have heard, to all ancient civilians and writers upon government; and Ireland is, on the contrary, called in some statutes, "an imperial crown", as held only from God, which is as high a style as any kingdom is capable of receiving. Therefore, by the expression, "a depending kingdom", there is no more to be understood than that, by a statute made here in the thirty-third year of Henry VIII, the king and his successors are to be kings imperial of this realm, as united and knit to the imperial crown of England. I have looked over all English and Irish statutes without finding any law that makes Ireland depend upon England, any more than England does upon Ireland. We have, indeed, obliged ourselves to have the same king with them, and consequently they are obliged to have the same king with us. For the law was made by our own Parliament, and our ancestors then were not such fools (whatever they were in the preceding reign) to bring themselves under I know not what dependence, which is now talked of, without any ground of law, reason, or common sense . . .

Sinecures

By JONATHAN SWIFT

Besides the prodigious profit which England receives by the transmittal thither of two-thirds of the revenues of this old kingdom, it has another mighty advantage, by making our country a receptacle wherein to disburden themselves of their supernumerary pretenders to office. Persons of second-rate merit in their own country, who, like birds of passage, most of them thrive and fatten here, and fly off when their credit and employments are at an end. So that Ireland may justly say, what Luther said of himself, "POOR Ireland makes many rich!" . . .

. . . Mr. Addison was forced to purchase an old obscure place, called Keeper of the Records in Bermingham's Tower, of £10 a year, and to get a salary of £400 annexed to it, though all the records there are not worth half-a-crown either for curiosity or use . . . But the jest is, that I have known, upon occasion, some of these absent officers as keen against the interest of Ireland, as if they had never been indebted to her for a single groat.

What's the use
Of my abuse?
The world will run
Around the sun
As it has done
Since time begun
When I have drifted to the deuce:
And what's the use
Of my abuse?

James Stephens
(1882–1950)

140

1798

THE DREAD DAYS OF REBELLION

E*dmund Burke, the Irish patriot, was a member of the English House of Commons, where he seized every opportunity to speak on behalf of his fellow countrymen.*

Criticism

By EDMUND BURKE
(1728–1797)

You who have looked deeply into the spirit of the Popery laws, must be perfectly sensible that a great part of the present mischief which we abhor in common (if it at all exists) has arisen from them. Their declared object was to reduce the Catholics in Ireland to a miserable populace, without property, without estimation, without education. The professed object was to deprive the few men who, in spite of those laws, might hold or retain any property amongst them, of all sort of influence or authority over the rest. They divided the nation into two distinct bodies, without common interest, sympathy, or connection. One of these bodies was to possess *all* the franchises, *all* the property, *all* the education; the other was to be composed of drawers of water and cutters of turf for them. Are we to be astonished when, by the efforts of so much violence in conquest, and so much policy in regulation, continued without intermission for nearly a hundred years, we had reduced them to a mob; that whenever they came to act at all, many of them would act exactly like a mob, without temper, measure, or foresight.

1792

John Mitchel was a member of the Young Ireland party and writer in "The Nation" magazine. In 1848 he was arrested for treason because he openly advocated rebellion. He was deported to Tasmania. He subsequently managed to escape and made his way to America. There he lived for many years, writing and editing newspapers, until at length, towards the end of his days, he was allowed to return to Ireland.

While in jail John Mitchel wrote the first part of the book called "Jail Journal." It is not only a diary of day to day events, but it rambles over the history of Ireland, which in confinement he had plenty of time to think about. These are his thoughts on the beginning of the Irish Volunteer Army which rose in rebellion against the English in 1798.

Mitchel Summarizes

By JOHN MITCHEL
(1815–1875)

During that eighteenth century, the Catholics disappear from history and politics. Such sallies of resistance as were made in those years against the encroachment of British power were made by Protestants (Swift, Lucas, Molyneux), in assertion of a Protestant Nationality, and for the independence of a Protestant Parliament. Indeed, when the Protestant Dissenters of England argued for the repeal of the Corporation Act and Test Act, which prevented them from holding certain State offices, Dean Swift, the Irish patriot, wrote a sarcastic petition, as if from the Irish Catholics, praying that *they* might be relieved from their penal disabilities; in order to cast ridicule and discredit on the pretensions of Dissenters, by way of reductio ad absurdum—We will have the very Catholics, said he, coming in next!

We might well expect, by the close of that century, to find Ireland altogether Anglicised—the Catholics all dead or converted—the ruling classes so completely British in their feelings as well as by their extraction that England would never more need to fear the uprising of a hostile Irish Nation. Ireland was to all human appearance dead and buried this time. . . .

143

Yet, before the end of that same century, such vitality is there in the Irish race and the Irish cause, Dublin streets beheld a wonderful spectacle—the Volunteer Army in its brilliant battalions and an Independent Parliament legislating for the Sovereign Kingdom of Ireland! Apparently the conquest of Ireland had not yet been entirely finished.

Theobald Wolfe Tone

Tone, Theobald Wolfe, (1763–1798), Irish rebel, the son of Peter Tone, a Dublin coachmaker, was born in Dublin on June 20, 1763. He entered Trinity college, at twenty-two he married Matilda Witherington, a girl of sixteen, took his degree in 1786 and went to London. He was entered at the Middle Temple, and afterwards read law in Dublin, being called to the Irish bar in 1789. Tone wrote two pamphlets in 1790, one of which, "A Review of the Conduct of Administration," attracted some notice from the Whigs.

Tone made the acquaintance of Thomas Russell (1767–1803), Napper Tandy and others, and the society of the "United Irishmen" was formed (1791). The original purpose of this society was simply the formation of a political union between Roman Catholics and Protestants, to secure parliamentary reform; it was only when that object appeared to be unattainable by constitutional methods, that the majority of the members adopted the more uncompromising opinions which Wolfe Tone held from the first, and conspired to establish an Irish Republic by armed rebellion. Tone desired to root out the popular respect for Charlemont and Grattan, and to transfer to more violent leaders the conduct of the national movement. Grattan was a reformer and a patriot without a tincture of democratic ideas; Wolfe Tone was a revolutionary whose principles were drawn from the French Convention. Grattan's political philosophy was allied to that of Edmund Burke; Tone was a disciple of Danton and Thomas Paine.

In 1794 the United Irishmen, persuaded that their scheme of universal suffrage and equal electoral districts was not likely to be accepted by any party in the Irish Parliament, began to found their hopes on a French invasion. An English clergyman named William Jackson, who had imbibed revolutionary opinions in France, came

144

to Ireland to negotiate between the French Committee of Public Safety and the United Irishmen. For this emissary Tone drew up a memorandum on the state of Ireland, which he described as ripe for revolution; the paper was betrayed to the Government, and in April 1794 Jackson was arrested on a charge of treason. Several of the leading United Irishmen, including Reynolds and Hamilton Rowan, immediately fled the country; the papers of the United Irishmen were seized; and for a time the organization was broken up. Tone, who had not attended meetings of the society since May 1793, remained in Ireland till after the trial and suicide of Jackson in April 1795. He was enabled to make terms with the government, stipulating only that he should not be called on to give evidence against Rowan and the others, and was permitted to emigrate to America, where he arrived in May 1795.

He went to Philadelphia where he met fellow exiles, and the French minister, Adet, who gave him letters of introduction to the Committee of Public Safety in Paris. In February 1796 he arrived in Paris and had interviews with De La Croix and L. N. M. Carnot, who were greatly impressed by his energy, sincerity and ability. A commission was given him as adjutant-general in the French army, which he hoped might protect him from the penalty of treason in the event of capture by the English. He drew up two memorials representing that the landing of a considerable French force in Ireland would be followed by a general rising of the people, and giving a detailed account of the condition of the country. The French directory, which possessed information from Lord Edward Fitzgerald and Arthur O'Connor confirming Tone, prepared to despatch an expedition under Hoche. On December 15, 1796, the expedition, consisting of 43 sail and carrying about 15,000 men, sailed from Brest. Tone, who accompanied it as "Adjutant-General Smith," had the greatest contempt for the seamanship of the French sailors, which was amply justified by the disastrous result of the invasion. The ships were dispersed by a storm off the coast of Kerry.

But the Dutch fleet was delayed by bad weather, and before it put to sea in October, only to be crushed by Duncan in the battle of Camperdown, Tone had returned to Paris; and Hoche, the chief hope of the United Irishmen, was dead. Bonaparte, with whom Tone had several interviews about this time, was much less disposed than Hoche had been to undertake in earnest an Irish expedition; and when the rebellion broke out in Ireland in 1798 he had started for Egypt. When, therefore, Tone urged the directory to send effective assistance to the Irish rebels, all that could be promised was a number of small raids to descend simultaneously on different points of the Irish coast. One of these under Humbert succeeded in landing a force in Killala bay, and gained some success in Connaught before it was subdued by Lake and Cornwallis, Wolfe Tone's brother Matthew being captured, tried by court-martial, and hanged; a second, accompanied by Napper Tandy, came to disaster on the coast of Donegal; while Wolfe Tone took part in a third, under Admiral Bompard, with General Hardy in command of a force of about 3,000 men, which encountered an English squadron near Lough Swilly on October 12, 1798.

Tone, who was on board the "Hoche," refused Bonaparte's offer of escape in a frigate before the action, and was taken prisoner when the "Hoche" was forced to surrender. At his trial by court-martial in Dublin, Tone made a manly straightforward speech, avowing his determined hostility to England and his design "by fair and open war to procure the separation of the two countries," and pleading in virtue of his status as a French officer to die by the musket instead of the rope. He was, however, sentenced to be hanged on November 12; but on the 11th he cut his throat with a penknife, and on Nov. 19, 1798, he died of the wound. He was buried in Bodenstown churchyard.

From *The Encyclopaedia Britannica*

The Harp That Once Through Tara's Halls

By THOMAS MOORE

The harp that once through Tara's halls
The soul of music shed,
Now hangs as mute on Tara's walls
As if that soul were fled:

So sleeps the pride of former days,
    So glory's thrill is o'er;
And hearts, that once beat high for praise,
    Now feel that pulse no more!

No more to chiefs and ladies bright
    The harp of Tara swells:
The chord alone, that breaks at night,
    Its tale of ruin tells.
Thus Freedom now so seldom wakes,
    The only throb she gives
Is when some heart indignant breaks,
    To show that still she lives.

Speech at His Trial

By WOLFE TONE

*An excerpt from Frank
MacDermot's "Wolfe Tone"*

Mr. President and Gentlemen of the Court-martial: I mean not to give you the trouble of bringing judicial proof to convict me legally of having acted in hostility to the Government of His Britannic Majesty in Ireland. I admit the fact. From my earliest youth I have regarded the connection between Ireland and Great Britain as the curse of the Irish nation; and felt convinced that whilst it lasted this country could never be free nor happy. My mind has been confirmed in this opinion by the experience of every succeeding year, and the conclusions which I have drawn from every fact before my eyes. In consequence, I determined to apply all the powers which my individual efforts could move in order to separate the two countries.

That Ireland was not able of herself to throw off the yoke I knew. I therefore sought for aid wherever it was to be found. In honourable poverty I rejected offers, which, to a man in my circumstances, might be considered highly advantageous. I remained faithful to what I thought the cause of my country and sought in the French Republic an ally to rescue three millions of my countrymen from . . .

The President here interrupted the prisoner, observing that this language was neither relevant to the charge nor such as ought to be delivered in a public court. . . .

. . . But I hear it said that this unfortunate country has been a prey to all sorts of horrors. I sincerely lament it. I beg, however, it may be remembered that I have been absent four years from Ireland. To me these sufferings can never be attributed. I designed by fair and open war to procure the separation of the two countries. For open war I was prepared; but if, instead of that, a system of private assassination has taken place, I repeat, whilst I deplore it, that it is not chargeable on me. Atrocities, it seems, have been committed on both sides. I do not less deplore them; I detest them from my heart; and to those who know my character and sentiments I may safely appeal for the truth of this assertion. With them I need no justification.

In a cause like this, success is everything. Success in the eyes of the vulgar fixes its merits. . . .

The Memory of the Dead

By JOHN KELLS INGRAM
(1823–1907)

Who fears to speak of Ninety-eight?
　　Who blushes at the name?
When cowards mock the patriot's fate,
　　Who hangs his head for shame?
He's all a knave, or half a slave,
　　Who slights his country thus;
But a true man, like you, man,
　　Will fill your glass with us.

We drink the memory of the brave,
　　The faithful and the few;
Some lie far off beyond the wave,
　　Some sleep in Ireland, too;
All, all are gone, but still lives on

148

The fame of those who died;
All true men, like you, men,
Remember them with pride.

Some on the shores of distant lands
    Their weary hearts have laid,
And by the stranger's heedless hands
    Their lonely graves were made;
But though their clay be far away,
    Beyond the Atlantic foam,
    In true men, like you, men,
    Their spirit's still at home.

The dust of some is Irish earth,
    Among their own they rest;
And the same land that gave them birth
    Has caught them to her breast;
And we will pray that from their clay
    Full many a race may start
    Of true men, like you, men,
    To act as brave a part.

They rose in dark and evil days,
    To right their native land;
They kindled here a living blaze
    That nothing shall withstand.
Alas! that might can vanquish right!
    They fell and passed away;
    But true men, like you, men,
    Are plenty here today.

Then here's their memory! may it be
    For us a guiding light,
To cheer our strife for liberty,
    And teach us to unite!
Through good and ill, be Ireland's still,
    Though sad as theirs your fate;
    And true men, be you, men,
    Like those of Ninety-eight.

The United Irishmen and 1798

A Letter

from Lord Clare,

to Lord Auckland

(June 5, 1798)

My dear Lord—Our rebellion, I am sorry to say, begins to wear a very serious and formidable aspect. The insurgents are now in possession of nearly the whole of the County of Wexford, and are so strong that I fear the force which has been sent against them is altogether unequal to dislodge them. Yesterday a column of five hundred of the King's troops received a very severe check near Gorey, and lost three pieces of cannon with all their ammunition, breadcarts, etc., etc. This misfortune was altogether owing to the rashness and ignorance of Colonel Walpole who commanded them. General Loftus, who commanded another body of troops which was to have co-operated with Walpole, has fallen back several miles, and, as yet, we have had no accounts from Johnson and Eustace (Useless) who marched from another point against Walpole.

Our situation is critical in the extreme. We know that there has been a complete military organization of the people in three-fourths of the kingdom. In the North nothing will keep the rebels quiet but a conviction that where treason had broken out the rebellion is merely Popish, but even with this impression in their minds, we cannot be certain that their love of republicanism will not outweigh their inveteracy against Popery. In the Capital there is a rebel army organized, and if the garrison was forced out to meet an invading army from the side of Wexford, they would probably on their return, find the Metropolis in possession of its proper rebel troops. In a word, such is the extent of treason in Ireland, that if any one district is left uncovered by troops, it will be immediately possessed by its own proper rebels. Believe me I do not magnify our danger; you know that I have long foreseen the mischief and condemned the imbecility which has suffered it to extend itself.

150

The Wearin' o' the Green

ANONYMOUS

O Paddy dear, an' did ye hear the news that's goin' round?
The Shamrock is by law forbid to grow on Irish ground!
No more St. Patrick's Day we'll keep, his colour can't be seen,
For there's a cruel law agin the wearin' o' the Green!

I met with Napper Tandy, and he took me by the hand,
And he said, "How's poor ould Ireland, and how does she stand?"
She's the most disthressful country that iver yet was seen,
For they're hangin' men an' women there for the wearin' o' the
    Green.

And if the colour we must wear is England's cruel Red,
Let it remind us of the blood that Ireland has shed;
Then pull the shamrock from your hat, and throw it on the sod,
And never fear, 'twill take root there, tho' under foot 'tis trod!

When law can stop the blades of grass from growin' as they grow,
And when the leaves in summertime their colour dare not show,
Then I will change the colour, too, I wear in my caubeen,
But till that day, please God, I'll stick to wearin' o' the Green.

Let Us Be Merry Before We Go

By JOHN PHILPOT CURRAN

If sadly thinking, with spirits sinking,
    Could, more than drinking, my cares compose,
A cure for sorrow from sighs I'd borrow,
    And hope tomorrow would end my woes.
But as in wailing, there's nought availing,
    And Death unfailing will strike the blow,
Then for that reason, and for a season,
    Let us be merry before we go.

To joy a stranger, a wayworn ranger,
    In ev'ry danger my course I've run,
Now hope all ending, and death befriending,
    His last aid lending, my cares are done.
No more a rover, or hapless lover,
    My griefs are over—my glass runs low;
Then for that reason, and for a season,
    Let us be merry before we go.

Although the rebellion of 1798 was crushed, the spirit behind it was not and sporadic risings broke out here and there under one leader and then another.

John Philpot Curran

By PADRAIC COLUM

The sparkling wit, the brilliant orator, the enthusiastic advocate, the extraordinary humourist, the flashing conversationalist was with all one of the most devoted, true-hearted patriots and statesmen ever given birth to. . . .

Curran was more than the advocate of the United Irishmen. He was their friend. Though himself not a separatist, he sympathised with their aspirations, and admired the courage and self-sacrifice with which they devoted themselves to the national cause. . . .

Emmet loved Curran's daughter Sarah. They were engaged to be married.

Curran knew nothing of the facts. He saw Emmet frequently at his house, but suspected nothing. Then the rising came. After its suppression Emmet could have escaped. But he wished to see Sarah Curran once more. He concealed himself in a house near Curran's. He wrote to Sarah—tried to see her. Then his hiding place was discovered. He was arrested. His relations with Sarah became public. Curran's house was searched for papers, and Curran himself had to undergo an examination before his inveterate enemy, Lord Clare. Curran was indignant. He refused to defend Emmet, refused even to see the doomed rebel. . . .

152

Last Words

(before his execution on September 20, 1803)

By ROBERT EMMET
(1778–1803)

My lords, as to why judgement of death and execution should
not be passed on me, according to law, I have nothing to say; but as
to why my character should not be relieved from the imputations
and calumnies thrown out against it, I have much to say. I do not
imagine that your lordships will give credit to what I am going to
utter; I have no hopes that I can anchor my character in the breast
of the court, I only wish your lordships may suffer it to float down
your memories until it has found some more hospitable harbour to
shelter it from the storms with which it is at present buffeted. Was
I to suffer only death, after being adjudged guilty, I should bow in
silence to the fate which awaits me; but the sentence of the law
which delivers over my body to the executioner, consigns my character to obloquy. A man in my situation has not only to encounter
the difficulties of fortune, but also the difficulties of prejudice.
Whilst the man dies, his memory lives; and that mine may not forfeit all claim to the respect of my countrymen, I seize upon this
opportunity to vindicate myself from some of the charges alleged
against me. I am charged with being an emissary of France: it is
false—I am no emissary. I did not wish to deliver up my country to
a foreign power, and least of all, to France. Never did I entertain
the remotest idea of establishing French power in Ireland . . .

Were the French to come as invaders or enemies uninvited by
the wishes of the people, I should oppose them to the utmost of my
strength. Yes! my countrymen, I should advise you to meet them
upon the beach with a sword in one hand and a torch in the other.

My lords, will a dying man be denied the legal privilege of ex-
culpating himself in the eyes of the community from a reproach
thrown upon him during his trial, by charging him with ambition
and attempting to cast away, for a paltry consideration, the liberties
of his country, why then insult me, or rather, why insult justice,
in demanding of me why sentence of death should not be pro-

153

nounced against me? I know, my lords, that the form prescribes that you should put the question; the form also confers a right to answering. This, no doubt, may be dispensed with, and so might the whole ceremony of the trial, since sentence was already pronounced at the Castle before your jury were impaneled. Your lordships are but the priests of the oracle, and I submit, but I insist on the whole of the form.

(*Here Mr. Emmet paused, and the court desired him to proceed.*)

My lords, you are impatient for the sacrifice. The blood which you seek is not congealed by the artificial terrors which surround your victim—it circulates warmly and unruffled through its channels, and in a little time it will cry to heaven—be yet patient! I have but a few words more to say—I am going to my cold and silent grave—my lamp of life is nearly extinguished—I have parted with everything that was dear to me in this life, and for my country's cause with the idol of my soul, the object of my affections. My race is run—the grave opens to receive me, and I sink into its bosom. I have but one request to ask at my departure from this world, it is the charity of its silence. Let no man write my epitaph; for as no man who knows my motives dare now vindicate them, let not prejudice or ignorance asperse them. Let them rest in obscurity and peace, my memory be left in oblivion, and my tomb remain uninscribed, until other times and other men can do justice to my character. When my country takes her place among the nations of the earth, then, and not till then, let my epitaph be written. I have done.

After the Rebellion

By JOHN MITCHEL

The Catholic bishops were bribed by promises of emancipation (which the English delayed to fulfill for thirty years), to deliver over their flocks into the hands of the British.

. . . the year 1800 saw the Act of Union. At one blow, England had her revenge. Ireland, and all Irish produce and industry, were placed totally in her power; and Ireland having but one member in six to what they called the Imperial Parliament, security was taken that the arrangement should never be disturbed.

154

This time, once more, Ireland was fully conquered—never a nation yet took so much conquering and remained unsubdued. For twenty years after the Union the country was as absolutely prostrated in means and in spirit as she seems to be now: and as a matter of course she had her cruel famine every year. Without a famine in Ireland, England could not live as she had a right to expect; and the exact complement of a comfortable family dinner in England is a coroner's inquest in Ireland: verdict, starvation. In 1817 the famine was more desperate than usual, and in the best counties of Ireland, people fed on weeds. In 1822 it was more horrible still. . . .

From Jail Journal

After her lover, Robert Emmet, was executed, Sarah Curran left Ireland, married an Englishman, and died in Sicily at an early age.

She Is Far From the Land

By THOMAS MOORE

She is far from the land where her young hero sleeps,
    And lovers are round her sighing;
But coldly she turns from their gaze and weeps,
    For her heart in his grave is lying!

She sings the wild song of her dear native plains,
    Every note which he loved awaking;
Ah! little they think, who delight in her strains,
    How the heart of the minstrel is breaking!

He had lived for his love, for his country he died;
    They were all that to life had entwined him;
Nor soon shall the tears of his country be dried,
    Nor long will his love stay behind him!

Oh! make her a grave where the sunbeams rest
    When they promise a glorious morrow;
They'll shine o'er her sleep, like a smile from the west,
    From her own loved island of sorrow.

Cathleen Ni Houlihan symbolizes Ireland and is evoked in many songs and stories to lament Ireland's fate or to arouse Irish patriotism, as in this play.

Cathleen Ni Houlihan

By W. B. YEATS

Persons in the play:

PETER GILLANE
MICHAEL GILLANE, his son, going to be married
PATRICK GILLANE, a lad of twelve, Michael's brother
BRIDGET GILLANE, Peter's wife
DELIA CAHEL, engaged to Michael
THE POOR OLD WOMAN
NEIGHBOURS

(*Interior of a cottage close to Killala, in 1798.* BRIDGET *is standing at a table undoing a parcel.* PETER *is sitting at one side of the fire,* PATRICK *at the other.*)

PETER. What is that sound I hear?

PATRICK. I don't hear anything. (*He listens.*) I hear it now. It's like cheering. I wonder what they are cheering about. I don't see anybody.

PETER. It might be a hurling.

PATRICK. There's no hurling today. It must be down in the town the cheering is.

BRIDGET. I suppose the boys must be having some sport of their own. Come over here, Peter, and look at Michael's wedding clothes.

PETER. Those are grand clothes, indeed.

BRIDGET. You hadn't clothes like that when you married me, and no coat to put on of a Sunday more than any other day.

PETER. That is true, indeed. We never thought a son of our own would be wearing a suit of that sort for his wedding, or have so good a place to bring a wife to.

156

PATRICK. There's an old woman coming down the road. I don't know is it here she is coming.

BRIDGET. It will be a neighbour coming to hear about Michael's wedding. Can you see who it is?

PATRICK. I think it is a stranger, but she's not coming to the house. She's turned into the gap that goes down where Maurteen and his sons are shearing sheep. Do you remember what Winny of the Cross-Roads was saying the other night about the strange woman that goes through the country whatever time there's war or trouble coming?

BRIDGET. Don't be bothering us about Winny's talk, but go and open the door for your brother. I hear him coming up the path.

PETER. I hope he has brought Delia's fortune with him safe, for fear the people might go back on the bargain and I after making it. Trouble enough I had making it.

(PATRICK *opens the door and* MICHAEL *comes in.*)

BRIDGET. What kept you, Michael? We were looking out for you this long time.

MICHAEL. I went round by the priest's house to bid him be ready to marry us tomorrow.

BRIDGET. Did he say anything?

MICHAEL. He said it was a very nice match, and that he was never better pleased to marry any two in his parish than myself and Delia Cahel.

PETER. Have you got the fortune, Michael?

MICHAEL. Here it is.

(MICHAEL *puts bag on table and goes over and leans against chimney-jamb.* BRIDGET, *who has been all this time examining the clothes, pulling the seams and trying the lining of the pockets, etc., puts the clothes on the dresser.*)

PETER (*getting up and taking the bag in his hand and turning out the money*). Yes, I made the bargain well for you, Michael. Old John Cahel would sooner have kept a share of this a while longer. "Let me keep the half of it until the first boy is born," says he. "You will not," says I. "Whether there is or is not a boy, the

157

whole hundred pounds must be in Michael's hands before he brings your daughter to the house." The wife spoke to him then, and he gave in at the end.

BRIDGET. You seem well pleased to be handling the money, Peter.

PETER. Indeed, I wish I had had the luck to get a hundred pounds, or twenty pounds itself, with the wife I married.

BRIDGET. Well, if I didn't bring much I didn't get much. What had you the day I married you but a flock of hens and you feeding them, and a few lambs and you driving them to the market at Ballina? (*She is vexed and bangs a jug on the dresser.*) If I brought no fortune I worked it out in my bones, laying down the baby, Michael that is standing there now, on a stook of straw, while I dug the potatoes, and never asking big dresses or anything but to be working.

PETER. That is true, indeed. (*He pats her arm.*)

BRIDGET. Leave me alone now till I ready the house for the woman that is to come into it.

PETER. You are the best woman in Ireland, but money is good, too. I never thought to see so much money within my four walls. We can do great things now we have it. We can take the ten acres of land we have the chance of since Jamsie Dempsey died, and stock it. We will go to the fair at Ballina to buy the stock. Did Delia ask any of the money for her own use, Michael?

MICHAEL. She did not, indeed. She did not seem to take much notice of it, or to look at it at all.

BRIDGET. That's no wonder. Why would she look at it when she had yourself to look at, a fine, strong young man? It is proud she must be to get you; a good steady boy that will make use of the money, and not be running through it or spending it on drink like another.

PETER. It's likely Michael himself was not thinking much of the fortune either, but of what sort the girl was to look at.

MICHAEL. Well, you would like a nice comely girl to be beside you, and to go walking with you. The fortune only lasts for a while, but the woman will be there always.

PATRICK. They are cheering again down in the town. Maybe they are landing horses from Enniscrone. They do be cheering when the horses take the water well.

MICHAEL. There are no horses in it. Where would they be going

158

and no fair at hand? Go down to the town, Patrick, and see what is going on.

PATRICK. Will Delia remember, do you think, to bring the gray-hound pup she promised me when she would be coming to the house?

MICHAEL. She will surely. (PATRICK *goes out, leaving the door open.*)

PETER. It will be Patrick's turn next to be looking for a fortune, but he won't find it so easy to get it and he with no place of his own.

BRIDGET. I do be thinking sometimes, now things are going so well with us, and the Cahels such a good back to us in the district, and Delia's own uncle a priest, we might be put in the way of making Patrick a priest some day, and he so good at his books.

PETER. Time enough, time enough. You have always your head full of plans, Bridget.

BRIDGET. We will be well able to give him learning, and not to send him tramping the country like a poor scholar that lives on charity.

MICHAEL. They're not done cheering yet.

(*He goes over to the door and stands there for a moment, putting up his hand to shade his eyes.*)

BRIDGET. Do you see anything?

MICHAEL. I see an old woman coming up the path.

BRIDGET. Who is it, I wonder? It must be the strange woman Patrick saw a while ago.

MICHAEL. I don't think it's one of the neighbours anyway, but she has her cloak over her face.

BRIDGET. It might be some poor woman heard we were making ready for the wedding and came to look for her share.

PETER. I may as well put the money out of sight. There is no use leaving it out for every stranger to look at.

(*He goes over to a large box in the corner, opens it and puts the bag in and fumbles at the lock.*)

MICHAEL. There she is, father! (*An* OLD WOMAN *passes the window*

159

slowly. She looks at MICHAEL *as she passes*.) I'd sooner a stranger not to come to the house the night before my wedding.

BRIDGET. Open the door, Michael; don't keep the poor woman waiting.

(*The* OLD WOMAN *comes in.* MICHAEL *stands aside to make way for her.*)

OLD WOMAN. God save all here!

PETER. God save you kindly!

OLD WOMAN. You have good shelter here.

PETER. You are welcome to whatever shelter we have.

BRIDGET. Sit down there by the fire and welcome.

OLD WOMAN (*warming her hands*). There is a hard wind outside.

(MICHAEL *watches her curiously from the door.* PETER *comes over to the table.*)

PETER. Have you travelled far today?

OLD WOMAN. I have travelled far, very far; there are few have travelled so far as myself, and there's many a one that doesn't make me welcome. There was one that had strong sons I thought were friends of mine, but they were shearing their sheep, and they wouldn't listen to me.

PETER. It's a pity indeed for any person to have no place of their own.

OLD WOMAN. That's true for you indeed, and it's long I'm on the roads since I first went wandering.

BRIDGET. It is a wonder you are not worn out with so much wandering.

OLD WOMAN. Sometimes my feet are tired and my hands are quiet, but there is no quiet in my heart. When the people see me quiet, they think old age has come on me and that all the stir has gone out of me. But when the trouble is on me I must be talking to my friends.

BRIDGET. What was it put you wandering?

OLD WOMAN. Too many strangers in the house.

BRIDGET. Indeed you look as if you'd had your share of trouble.

160

OLD WOMAN. I have had trouble indeed.

BRIDGET. What was it put the trouble on you?

OLD WOMAN. My land that was taken from me.

PETER. Was it much land they took from you?

OLD WOMAN. My four beautiful green fields.

PETER (*aside to* BRIDGET). Do you think could she be the widow Casey that was put out of her holding at Kilglass a while ago?

BRIDGET. She is not. I saw the widow Casey one time at the market in Ballina, a stout fresh woman.

PETER (*to* OLD WOMAN). Did you hear a noise of cheering, and you coming up the hill?

OLD WOMAN. I thought I heard the noise I used to hear when my friends came to visit me.

(*She begins singing half to herself.*)

> I will go cry with the woman,
> For yellow-haired Donough is dead,
> With a hempen rope for a neckcloth,
> And a white cloth on his head,—

MICHAEL. What is it that you are singing, ma'am?

OLD WOMAN. Singing I am about a man I knew one time, yellow-haired Donough that was hanged in Galway. (*She goes on singing much louder.*)

> I am come to cry with you, woman,
> My hair is unwound and unbound;
> I remember him ploughing his field,
> Turning up the red side of the ground,
> And building his barn on the hill
> With the good mortared stone;
> Oh! we'd have pulled down the gallows
> Had it happened in Enniscrone!

MICHAEL. What was it brought him to his death?

OLD WOMAN. He died for love of me: many a man has died for love of me.

PETER (*aside to* BRIDGET). Her trouble has put her wits astray.

161

MICHAEL. Is it long since that song was made? Is it long since he got his death?

OLD WOMAN. Not long, not long. But there were others that died for love of me a long time ago.

MICHAEL. Were they neighbours of your own, ma'am?

OLD WOMAN. Come here beside me and I'll tell you about them. (MICHAEL *sits down beside her on the hearth.*) There was a red man of the O'Donnells from the north, and a man of the O'Sullivans from the south, and there was one Brian that lost his life at Clontarf by the sea, and there were a great many in the west, some that died hundreds of years ago, and there are some that will die tomorrow.

MICHAEL. Is it in the West that men will die tomorrow?

OLD WOMAN. Come nearer, nearer to me.

BRIDGET. Is she right, do you think? Or is she a woman from beyond the world?

PETER. She doesn't know well what she's talking about, with the want and the trouble she has gone through.

BRIDGET. The poor thing, we should treat her well.

PETER. Give her a drink of milk and a bit of the oaten cake.

BRIDGET. Maybe we should give her something along with that, to bring her on her way. A few pence or a shilling itself, and we with so much money in the house.

PETER. Indeed I'd not begrudge it to her if we had it to spare, but if we go running through what we have, we'll soon have to break the hundred pounds, and that would be a pity.

BRIDGET. Shame on you, Peter. Give her the shilling and your blessing with it, or our own luck will go from us.

(PETER *goes to the box and takes out a shilling.*)

BRIDGET (*to the* OLD WOMAN). Will you have a drink of milk, ma'am?

OLD WOMAN. It is not food or drink that I want.

PETER (*offering the shilling*). Here is something for you.

OLD WOMAN. This is not what I want. It is not silver I want.

PETER. What is it you would be asking for?

OLD WOMAN. If any one would give me help he must give me himself, he must give me all.

162

(PETER *goes over to the table staring at the shilling in his hand in a bewildered way, and stands whispering to* BRIDGET.)

MICHAEL. Have you no one to care you in your age, ma'am?

OLD WOMAN. I have not. With all the lovers that brought me their love I never set out the bed for any.

MICHAEL. Are you lonely going the roads, ma'am?

OLD WOMAN. I have my thoughts and I have my hopes.

MICHAEL. What hopes have you to hold to?

OLD WOMAN. The hope of getting my beautiful fields back again; the hope of putting the strangers out of my house.

MICHAEL. What way will you do that, ma'am?

OLD WOMAN. I have good friends that will help me. They are gathering to help me now. I am not afraid. If they are put down today they will get the upper hand tomorrow. (*She gets up.*) I must be going to meet my friends. They are coming to help me and I must be there to welcome them. I must call the neighbours together to welcome them.

MICHAEL. I will go with you.

BRIDGET. It is not her friends you have to go and welcome, Michael; it is the girl coming into the house you have to welcome. You have plenty to do; it is food and drink you have to bring to the house. The woman that is coming home is not coming with empty hands; you would not have an empty house before her. (*To the* OLD WOMAN) Maybe you don't know, ma'am, that my son is going to be married tomorrow.

OLD WOMAN. It is not a man going to his marriage that I look to for help.

PETER (*to* BRIDGET). Who is she, do you think, at all?

BRIDGET. You did not tell us your name yet, ma'am.

OLD WOMAN. Some call me the Poor Old Woman, and there are some that call me Cathleen, the daughter of Houlihan.

PETER. I think I knew some one of that name, once. Who was it, I wonder? It must have been some one I knew when I was a boy. No, no; I remember, I heard it in a song.

OLD WOMAN (*who is standing in the doorway*). They are wondering that there were songs made for me; there have been many songs made for me. I heard one on the wind this morning.

163

Do not make a great keening
When the graves have been dug tomorrow.

Do not call the white-scarfed riders
To the burying that shall be tomorrow.

Do not spread food to call strangers
To the wakes that shall be tomorrow;

Do not give money for prayers
For the dead that shall die tomorrow . . .

They will have no need of prayers, they will have no need of prayers.

MICHAEL. I do not know what that song means, but tell me something I can do for you.

PETER. Come over to me, Michael.

MICHAEL. Hush, father, listen to her.

OLD WOMAN. It is a hard service they take that help me. Many that are red cheeked now will be pale cheeked; many that have been free to walk the hills and the bogs and the rushes will be sent to walk hard streets in far countries; many a good plan will be broken; many that have gathered money will not stay to spend it; many a child will be born and there will be no father at its christening to give it a name. They that have red cheeks will have pale cheeks for my sake, and for all that, they will think they are well paid.

(She goes out; her voice is heard outside singing.)

They shall be remembered forever,
They shall be alive forever,
They shall be speaking forever,
The people shall hear them forever.

BRIDGET (*to* PETER). Look at him, Peter; he has the look of a man that has got the touch. (*Raising her voice*) Look here, Michael, at the wedding clothes. Such grand clothes as these are! You have a right to fit them on now; it would be a pity tomorrow if they did not fit. The boys would be laughing at you. Take them, Michael, and go into the room and fit them on.

(*She puts them on his arm.*)

MICHAEL. What wedding are you talking of? What clothes will I be wearing tomorrow?

BRIDGET. These are the clothes you are going to wear when you marry Delia Cahel tomorrow.

MICHAEL. I had forgotten that.

(*He looks at the clothes and turns towards the inner room, but stops at the sound of cheering outside.*)

PETER. There is the shouting come to our own door. What is it has happened?

(*Neighbours come crowding in,* PATRICK *and* DELIA *with them.*)

PATRICK. There are ships in the Bay; the French are landing at Killala!

(PETER *takes his pipe from his mouth and his hat off, and stands up. The clothes slip from* MICHAEL'S *arm.*)

DELIA. Michael! (*He takes no notice.*) Michael! (*He turns towards her.*) Why do you look at me like a stranger?

(*She drops his arm.* BRIDGET *goes over towards her.*)

PATRICK. The boys are all hurrying down the hillside to join the French.

DELIA. Michael won't be going to join the French.

BRIDGET (*to* PETER). Tell him not to go, Peter.

PETER. It's no use. He doesn't hear a word we're saying.

BRIDGET. Try and coax him over to the fire.

DELIA. Michael, Michael! You won't leave me! You won't join the French, and we going to be married!

165

(*She puts her arms about him, he turns towards her as if about to yield.*)

(*The* OLD WOMAN'S *voice outside*)

They shall be speaking for ever,
The people shall hear them for ever.

(MICHAEL *breaks away from* DELIA, *stands for a second at the door, then rushes out, following the* OLD WOMAN'S *voice.* BRIDGET *takes* DELIA, *who is crying silently, into her arms.*)

PETER (*to* PATRICK, *laying a hand on his arm*). Did you see an old woman going down the path?

PATRICK. I did not, but I saw a young girl, and she had the walk of a queen.

(*Curtain*)

The Minstrel Boy

By THOMAS MOORE

The Minstrel Boy to the war is gone,
    In the ranks of death you'll find him;
His father's sword he has girded on,
    And his wild harp slung behind him.
"Land of song!" said the warrior bard.
"Though all the world betrays thee,
One sword, at least, they rights shall guard,
One faithful harp shall praise thee!"

The Minstrel fell!—but the foeman's chain
    Could not bring that proud soul under;
The harp he loved ne'er spoke again,
    For he tore its chords asunder;
And said, "No chains shall sully thee,
    Thou soul of love and bravery!
Thy songs were made for the pure and free,
    They shall never sound in slavery."

166

Behind the bitter scenes of rebellion, executions and general bloodshed, business was proceeding quietly in the background. In his book entitled "Green and Silver," which deals with the history of the Irish canals, L. T. C. Rolt says, "In 1800, a Board of Directors General of Inland Navigation was appointed 'to promote, complete and control Inland Navigation'." Some years later Charles Lever describes a voyage on the first of these canals to be completed.

Fish, after THE BOOK OF KELLS.

Travel by Grand Canal

By CHARLES LEVER
(1809–1872)

". . . the sedgy banks whose tall flaggers bow their heads beneath the ripple that eddies from the bow . . . the loud bray of the horn . . . the far-off tinkle of a bell. We near Shannon Harbour, and all its bustle and excitement. The large bell at the stern of the boat is thundering away . . . the banks are crowded . . . the track rope is cast off, the weary posters trot away to their stables, and the stately barge floats on to its destined haven without the aid of any visible influence. A prospect more bleak, more desolate, more barren it would be impossible to conceive—a wide river with low and reedy banks, moving sluggishly on its yellow current between broad tracts of bog or callow meadowland; no trace of cultivation, not even a tree to be seen. Such is Shannon Harbour."

Anthony Trollope was not so complimentary when describing canal travel towards the close of its reign. For, from 1834 on, the railways eclipsed both the flyboats on the canals and the stage coaches on the roads as the "last word" in travel.

Another Journey by Grand Canal

By ANTHONY TROLLOPE
(1815–1882)

I hardly know why a journey in one of these boats should be much more intolerable than travelling either outside or inside a coach; for, either in or on the coach, one has less room for motion, and less opportunity for employment. I believe the misery of the canal-boat chiefly consists in a preconceived and erroneous idea of its capabilities. One prepares oneself for occupation—an attempt is made to achieve actual comfort—and both end in disappointment; the limbs become weary with endeavouring to fix themselves in a position of repose, and the mind is fatigued more by the search after, than the want of, occupation.

Canal Barge.

Barges continued to carry cargo along the network of canals long after the railways were built, but Percy French does not seem to have had a high opinion of their efficiency.

The Mary Ann McHugh*

By PERCY FRENCH
(1854–1920)

Come all ye lads who plough the seas and also seize the plough,
The cruise of a canal boat I am telling to ye now.
It was the Mary Ann McHugh that braved the angry surf
And bore away from Mullingar with a terrible load of turf.

And the captain's name was Duff,
His manners they were rough,
  But every cape and headland by its Christian name he knew,
And he issued this command—
  "Keep her well in sight of land!
  Till we make the port of Dublin in the Mary Ann McHugh."

The engine was of one horse-power, propelled wid a blackthorn
    stick,
Wid the wind astarn, and filled with corn, the horse went a terrible
    lick.
We worked her roun' the Hill o'Down, and then Kilcock we
    passed,
And when we seen John Flynn's shebeen, we cried out, "Land at
    last."

But the captain, Jamesy Duff,
Cried "Luff! ye lubbers, luff!
  And don't put in near Johnny Flynn
Whatever else ye do.
  Last time we passed his door
  We forgot to pay his score,

* By kind permission of Messrs. Keith Prowse Music Publishing Co. Ltd.

169

So he's got the polis watching for the Mary Ann McHugh."

Then up and spake an old sailor who had sailed the Irish Sea,
"I pray thee put into yonder port or the crew will mutinee;
To put to sea with the boy and me is a cruel thing, I think,
With water, water everywhere, and never a drop o' drink!"

But the captain, Jamesy Duff,
Said "Enough, my lad, enough!
    No man before the mast shall ever tell me what to do.
Clap on all sail at wance,
For that's our only chance,
    To keep from debt and danger in the Mary Ann McHugh."

With anxious hearts the vessel starts upon her altered course,
The wind and waves they lashed the shore, and the pilot lashed the
        horse,
But all in vain—beneath the strain the rope began to part,
And she ran aground on a lump of coal that wasn't put down in the
        chart!

And the captain, Jamesy Duff,
He caught me such a cuff,
    And then he said, "Go heave the lead," while the flag at half-mast
        flew,
But I had had enough
Of the tyrant Jamesy Duff,
    So I heaved the lead at his head and fled from the Mary Ann
        McHugh.

Hugh Malet in his book called "Voyage In a Bowler Hat", which was published in 1960, describes his journey from England across the Irish Sea, through the Grand Canal from Dublin to the river Shannon with its great network of navigable lakes and rivers. As he and his boat struggle through the long neglected canal, he is amazed to find traces of derelict side canals, harbors, docks and hotels. When his journey was made, the Irish canals were at their lowest ebb.

Canal Travel Today

By HUGH MALET

I passed the Kilbeggan branch which has become overgrown with weed and practically impassable, and battled down through several locks, against a wind which was rushing in unchecked from the open Atlantic, until at length I came in the late evening to the crumbling harbour at Tullamore, nestling under the tall spire of a cathedral.

Tullamore is a town bred from quarries of gray rain and surrounded by the Great Bog. A sinister lightning without thunder flickered on the horizon, and the hunched outline of the Slieve Bloom Mountains was blurred in a lashing rain. At Tullamore as at Llangollen I felt that I had entered another country beyond the Pale of English influence. The harbourmaster, Mr. J. Larkin, told me of the days when the passenger boats were running, for he remembered many old people who had lived and worked along the canal in those far off times, and he said that often enough the canal hotels were so full that they could not accommodate all the passengers. He said that a great bell hung in each hotel; it rang for the first time as a signal for the horses to be harnessed, a second time for the passengers to board the boat, and a third time for the boat to leave. He also said that, according to an ancient by-law, a man could still claim a passage for himself and his horse on the ferry at Shannon Harbour, but the ferryboat had almost vanished into the mud. It was from Mr. Larkin I learned that Tullamore Harbour had once had the peculiar distinction of being a barrack square before the arrival of the canal.

171

The next day one of the typical broad barges of the Grand Canal came into the harbour and the skipper gave me some useful information about my route to Limerick and the rigours of Lough Derg, an inland sea some twenty-four miles long, through which the Shannon flows before it drops down to the great hydro-electric dam at Ardnacrusha. He told me that the waves on the lough are whipped up quickly by the violence of the Atlantic wind, and a barge on tow behind the St. James had been sunk a few years before off Parker's point, and only one of the crew of three managed to reach the shore. The height of the waves made it impossible for the St. James to turn to the rescue.

There was something inestimably sad about Tullamore Harbour, with the weed creeping out from the corners and spreading gradually towards the centre, the warehouses crumbling into decay, and the staff waiting patiently as the cargoes gradually diminished on what was until recently one of the most bustling waterways in these islands. . . . The Great Bog still stretched ahead, but on the far edge of it I saw a series of gleaming pipes and glistening domes, looking like some strange machine destined for outer space, but as I drew closer I realized that it was one of the new peat-burning power stations which are helping to supply the remoter corners of the country with electricity. When I had passed it the bog came to an end at last and the canal wound down through a land of pleasant woods and meadows.

The little village of Shannon Harbour had all the melancholy charm of a place from which industry had departed. Though the houses were neat and trim on either side of the single short street, many of the warehouses had lost their roofs, while others hinted that one might be unwise to venture too close to them in an Atlantic gale. The Canal Hotel, where I had once imagined that I might be able to stay for the night, but where I suppose no visitor has slept for a hundred years or more, dominated the whole place, its roof still intact but its windows hollow like some living thing that had grown old and blind. The floor-joists had been cut away to avoid the payment of the heavy rates, and black stains of rot had spread down the classical facade. Behind it and as far as the eye could see stretched the flooded countryside, dotted with narrow islands of higher ground, and the broad river itself, the longest in the British Isles, its channel among the floods marked by a line of

172

reed. The very remoteness of the place was attractive, but it was also a little frightening in its desolation, and left me wondering whether the world might not have looked like that before man came and whether it might not look like that again when he had gone. I felt that I had come suddenly out of a pleasant countryside to the very edge of Europe.

FROM Voyage In A Bowler Hat 1960

From 1834 on, the railways eclipsed the coaches and the canal passenger boats.

"Are Ye Right There, Michael?" *
A Lay of the Wild West Clare

By PERCY FRENCH

You may talk of Columbus's sailing
  Across the Atlantical sea
But he never tried to go railing
  From Ennis as far as Kilkee.
You run for the train in the mornin',
  The excursion train starting at eight,
You're there when the clock gives the warnin',
  And there for an hour you'll wait.

(*Spoken*):
  And as you're waiting in the train,
  You'll hear the guard sing this refrain:—

"Are ye right there, Michael? are ye right?
Do you think that we'll be there before the night?
  Ye've been so long in startin'
  That ye couldn't say for sartin'—
Still ye might now, Michael, so ye might!"

* By kind permission of Messrs. Keith Prowse Music Publishing Co. Ltd.

173

They find out where the engine's been hiding,
    And it drags you to sweet Corofin;
Says the guard, "Back her down on the siding
    There's the goods from Kilrush comin' in."
Perhaps it comes in in two hours,
    Perhaps it breaks down on the way;
"If it does," says the guard, "be the powers
    We're here for the rest of the day!"

(*Spoken*):
    And while you sit and curse your luck,
    The train backs down into a truck!

"Are ye right there, Michael, are ye right?
Have ye got the parcel there for Mrs. White?
    Ye haven't! Oh, begorra!
    Say it's comin' down tomorra—
And it might now, Michael, so it might!"

At Lahinch the sea shines like a jewel,
    With joy you are ready to shout,
When the stoker cries out, "There's no fuel,
    And the fire's taytotally out.
But hand up that bit of a log there—
    I'll soon have ye out of the fix;
There's a fine clamp of turf in the bog there;
    And the rest go a-gatherin' sticks."

(*Spoken*):
    And while you're breakin' bits of trees,
    You hear some wise remarks like these:—

"Are ye right there, Michael? are ye right?
Do ye think that ye can get the fire to light?"
    "Oh, an hour you'll require,
    For the turf it might be drier—"
"Well, it might now, Michael, so it might!"

174

Kilkee! Oh, you never get near it!
  You're in luck if the train brings you back,
For the permanent way is so queer, it
  Spends most of its time off the track.
Uphill the ould engin' is climbin',
  While the passengers push with a will;
You're in luck when you reach Ennistymon,
  For all the way home is down-hill.

(*Spoken*):
  And as you're wobbling through the dark,
  You hear the guard make this remark:—

  "Are ye right there, Michael? are ye right?
  Do you think that ye'll be home before it's light?"
    " 'Tis all dependin' whether
    The ould engin' howlds together—"
  "And it might now, Michael, so it might!"

Having *deviated from the course of history to see what had become of the once glorious canals, we must go back to where we were and see what Mr. and Mrs. Hall have to say about road travel during one of their frequent visits to Ireland in the years between 1825 and 1842.*

Road Travel (1842)

By MR. and MRS. HALL

Machines for travelling in Ireland are, some of them at least, peculiar to the country. The stage coaches are precisely similar to those in England, and travel at as rapid a rate. They, of course, run upon all the great roads, and are constructed with due regard to safety and convenience. The public cars of M. Bianconi have, however, to a large extent, displaced the regular coaches, and are to be encountered in every district in the south of Ireland. In form they resemble the common outside jaunting car, but are calculated to hold twelve, fourteen, or sixteen persons; they are well horsed, and have cautious and experienced drivers, are generally driven with three horses, and usually travel at the rate of seven Irish miles an hour; the fares averaging about two-pence per mile. They are open cars; but a huge apron of leather affords considerable protection against rain; and they may be described as, in all respects, very comfortable and convenient vehicles. . . .

1829

THE FIGHT FOR

CATHOLIC

EMANCIPATION

GEORGE IV, *from a coin of 1825.*

T ill now George III, who was slightly insane during his later years, had stubbornly refused even to consider such a measure as Catholic Emancipation, and on one occasion when the question was tentatively raised he had declared vehemently, "No, I had rather beg my bread from door to door throughout Europe than consent to such a measure." But now he was dead and his son, George IV, a more tolerant man, was on the throne, so the question could be raised, and raised it was. Daniel O'Connell was its chief Irish exponent, and here is how M. Duvergier, one of many Frenchmen who visited Ireland during this period, wrote in his "Letters On The State of Ireland."

A Frenchman's View

By M. DUVERGIER
(1826)

There is not a country, nor a city, nor a borough, nor a parish, where there are not meetings, to address petitions to the new parliament, to pass votes of thanks to the forty-shilling freeholders, and what is still more to the purpose, to offer assistance and support to those very men, whom their masters have, in consequence of their late conduct, unmercifully ejected from their holdings. O'Connell and Shiel fly from province to province, from meeting to meeting. Everywhere they are received with enthusiasm; everywhere their eloquent declamations rouse in the souls of the old Milesians the stern sense of their strength and their degradation. To enforce obedience, they require neither *gens d'armes* nor soldiers. A word of theirs is of more power than twenty decrees of the Lord Lieutenant; and the delegates of Old England are compelled to tremble before two lawyers. . . .

Emancipation—full, total, and unconditional emancipation, such is at present the unanimous cry of six millions of men. One would be inclined to say that this single word contained within itself the panacea for all the sufferings of Ireland. For the Catholic proprietor, it signifies a place in Parliament; for the lawyer, a silk gown;

178

for the poor, bread. In the midst of this fever of hope, the wise statesman well knows, that the effects of so many ages of oppression are not to be got rid of in a day; but he also knows that without emancipation nothing can be done; and he will give all his support to every exertion which is calculated to obtain it. . . .

The history of the Catholic Association is singular enough. Founded about five years ago, it had already acquired a formidable degree of political power, when last session Parliament decided upon its suppression. It was alleged to be an *imperium in imperio*. Accordingly, Mr. Canning and Mr. Peel, Lord Eldon and Mr. Plunkett, entered into a coalition against it; and a Bill in 15 paragraphs decreed its dissolution. Six months afterwards it reappeared. No means to defeat the provisions of the Bill have been neglected; and the profound wisdom of Parliament has produced no other result than the revival of the old Association; so difficult is it in England to attack the right of meeting and petition—a sacred right, an imprescriptible right, the best pledge and substitute for so many others. France has yet some lessons to learn from her neighbours.

The Association holds its meetings in an oblong hall, surrounded with benches and arranged nearly in the same manner as the House of Commons. The first time I entered it, I saw on his legs a man of about fifty years of age; who, with his hand to his bosom, seemed throwing out his opinions in a negligent manner to about 300 persons, who were listening with the greatest attention around him. This man was Daniel O'Connell, the glory of Kerry and the pride of Munster. In person he is tall; his appearance is imposing; his countenance full of frankness and keenness, though somewhat bordering on the vulgar, and when he speaks, his physiognomy, as changeable as his imagination, expresses, in two minutes, twenty different passions. There is no sort of study either in his gesture or language. If he threatens, his entire figure seems ready to follow the defiance, which he hurls against the power of England; if he indulges in a trait of humour, before it is yet upon his lips an expansive gaiety already radiates from all his features. I know of no living orator who communicates so thoroughly to his audience the idea of profound and absolute conviction . . .

EDITORIALS and LETTERS to the
DUBLIN EVENING MAIL

29th June, 1828

Mr. Daniel O'Connell offers himself to the constituency of Clare, as a candidate for the representation. A contemporary of ours, The Mercantile Advertiser, in announcing this intention yesterday, expresses itself in the following manner:

"This, unquestionably, will be a most extraordinary scene. Mr. O'Connell has all the qualifications necessary—and there is no law which prevents him offering himself to the County—there is no law which prevents his Election. In short, if he should have the majority of the votes, the Sheriff must put him in the return.

"Again, there is no law which will compel Mr. O'Connell to take his seat. If there be not a call of the House, he may hold the representation during the present Parliament, without entering the House of Commons, or wait the passage of an Emancipation Bill . . . It is impossible adequately to describe the sensation that this announcement caused in Dublin yesterday. We suppose that the astonishment that it will create in London will be equal. The eyes of the Empire will, therefore, be very speedily turned to the County of Clare.

"It will be the first time since the Revolution that a Catholic has offered himself to the people of Ireland. We have not time to say any more at present. We must content ourselves, therefore, by referring our readers to Mr. O'Connell's address. The entire of the South of Ireland is in a state of active but peaceable commotion. We are satisfied that the Military and Constabulary forces of the country will not be lent to the rage or the mortification of the landlords of Clare. Notwithstanding the great show, therefore, of Horse, Foot, and Artillery, which is moving upon Ennis and surrounding it, like a beleagured town, we entertain no fears."

DUBLIN EVENING MAIL

5th July, 1828

The event of the Clare election is known to all Ireland and indeed to the whole of the Empire by this time. The return of Mr. O'Connell has produced a sensation in London, and indeed in every part of England, almost as lively as in Ireland itself. The Times, which was adverse at the commencement of the election has changed its tone. The Chronicle observes that the return of Mr. O'Connell "establishes in the most unanswerable manner the power over the electors possessed by the Roman Catholics: and shows them that they have but to remain united and they will compel the Government to do them justice. A whole people cannot be punished; the whole tenantry of a country cannot be deluded. The grand secret has been taught the Irish people; and as well might they attempt to roll back the tides of the ocean, as to think of replacing them in the prostrate condition in which they were."

E*ver since the Penal Code was drawn up in 1691 Irishmen and Englishmen continued to protest, either in arms or in words against its injustice. In 1829 this long struggle is drawing to a close when Robert Peel, then England's Home Secretary and Leader of the House of Commons, said these words:*

Speech in the House of Commons, 1829

By SIR ROBERT PEEL
(1788–1850)

I rise, Sir, in the spirit of peace, to propose the adjustment of the Roman Catholic question—that question which has so long and so painfully occupied the attention of Parliament, and which has distracted the councils of the King for the last thirty years . . . According to my heart and conscience, I believe that the time is come when less danger is to be apprehended to the general interests of the Empire, and to the spiritual and temporal welfare of the Protestant Establishment, in attempting to adjust the Catholic Question than in allowing it to remain any longer in its present state. . . .

Early in 1829 the bill for the emancipation of the Catholics passed its third reading, after a long debate and much bitter opposition. On April 13th it received the Royal assent. But all was not plain sailing for O'Connell. His enemies did not refrain from using any weapon which came to hand, as the following pages show.

Lines on Daniel O'Connell

Mounted on a Premier's back,
Lash the Ministerial pack,
At thy nod they hold their places,
Crack their sinews, grind their faces.
Tho' thy hand had stabbed their mother,
They would fawn and call thee brother. . . .

The Times, London, November 26, 1835.

Daniel O'Connell

By T. C. LUBY
(—1880)

During the years immediately following the Union, he confined himself almost exclusively to a diligent and laborious pursuit of professional reputation. He had far greater difficulties to contend with than those which Protestants of equal abilities had at that time to encounter. Not to speak of the semi-contemptuous manner in which Catholics were still regarded by the potent faction of the Ascendancy, and their necessarily inferior influence with those attorneys who had most briefs to give, it is to be remembered that, till the year 1829, a Catholic was not eligible for the position of King's counsel.

182

D*aniel O'Connell's profession was that of a barrister and he could be as much of a character in the courtroom as in the House of Commons, or on the door step of an objectionable neighbour's shop.*

Dan and Biddy Moriarty

By T. C. LUBY

He had already hit upon an ingenious plan for the terrible Biddy's overthrow. Resolving to take the initiative, our hero thus began his attack:

"What's the price of this walking stick, Mrs. What's-your-name?"

"Moriarty, sir, is my name, and a good one it is; and what have you to say agen it? and one-and-sixpence's the price of the stick. Troth, it's chape as dirt—so it is."

"One-and-sixpence! Whew! Why, you are no better than an imposter, to ask eighteen pence for what cost you twopence."

"Twopence! your grandmother!" replied Biddy, at once waxing irascible. "Do you mane to say that it's cheating the people I am? Imposter, indeed!"

"Ay, imposter; and it's that I call you to your teeth," rejoined O'Connell.

"Come, cut your stick, you cantankerous jackanapes!" quoth Biddy, her face growing redder every moment.

"Keep a civil tongue in your head, you old diagonal!" returned O'Connell, in the calmest possible tone. The effect of this calmness on the excitable nerves of the fair lady was even more irritating than his abuse.

"Stop your jaw, you pug-nosed badger!" exclaimed Mrs. Moriarty, "or by this and that, I'll make you go quicker nor you came."

"Don't be in a passion, my old radius!" said our hero, still preserving the most provoking coolness in his voice and demeanour; "anger will only wrinkle your beauty."

"By the jokey, if you say another word of impudence, I'll tan your dirty hide, you bastely common scrub! And sorry I'd be to soil my fists upon your carcase."

"Whew! boys, what a passion old Biddy is in! I protest, as I'm a

183

gentleman—"

"Jintleman! jintleman! the likes of you a jintleman! Wisha, by gorry, that bangs Banagher! Why, you potato-faced pippin-sneezer! where did a Madagascar monkey like you pick up enough of common Christian dacency to hide your Kerry brogue?"

"Easy, now; easy now," said Dan, with the same look and tone of imperturbable good humour, "don't choke yourself with fine language, you old whisky drinking parallelogram!"

"What's that you call me, you murderin' villain?" shouted Mrs. Moriarty, by this time goaded into perfect fury.

"I call you," answered O'Connell, "a parallelogram; and a Dublin judge and jury will say that it's no libel to call you so."

"Oh, tare-an-ouns! oh, holy Biddy!" screamed Mrs. Moriarty, her eyes flaming like those of a tigress robbed of her whelps, "that an honest woman, like me, should be called a parrybellygrum to her face! I'm none of your parry bellygrums, you rascally gallows-bird! You cowardly sneaking, plate lickin' blaguard!"

"Oh! not you, indeed!" retorted O'Connell. "Why, I suppose you'll deny that you keep a hypotheneuse in your house?"

"It's a lie for you, you bloody robber!" roared the raging virago; "I never had such a thing in my house, you swindling thief!"

"Why, sure your neighbors all know very well that you keep not only a hypotheneuse, but that you have two diameters locked up in your garret, and that you go out to walk with them every Sunday, you heartless old heptagon!"

"Oh, hear that, ye saints in glory! Oh! there's bad language from a fellow that wants to pass for a jintleman! May the divil fly away with you, you micher from Munster, and make celery sauce of your rotten limbs, you mealy-mouthed tub of guts!"

"Ah," persisted her arch-tormenter, "you can't deny the charge, you miserable submultiple of a duplicate ratio!"

"Go," vociferated the half frantic scold, "go rinse your mouth in the Liffy, you nasty tickle-pitcher! After all the bad words you spake, it ought to be filthier than your face, you dirty chicken of Beelzebub!"

"Rinse your own mouth, you wicked-minded old polygon! To the deuce I pitch you, you blustering intersection of a stinking superficies!"

"You saucy tinker's apprentice! if you don't cease your jaw, I'll

184

—" But here Biddy, utterly confounded by Dan's volleyed abuse, fairly gasped for breath. For the first time in her life, her foul-tongued volubility completely failed her. Unable to heave up another word, she stood, purple-visaged and foaming at the mouth like a baffled fury.

At the risk of giving her an immediate fit of apoplexy, our hero now relentlessly pursued his triumph. Without letting her have moment's breathing time, he poured in on the devoted Biddy broadside after broadside of double-shotted scurrility.

"While I have a tongue, I'll abuse you, you most inimitable periphery! Look at her, boys! There she stands, a convicted perpendicular in petticoats! There's contamination in her circumference, and she trembles with guilt down to the extremities of her corollaries. Ah! you're found out, you rectilineal antecedent and equiangular old hag! 'Tis with you the devil will fly away, you porter-swiping similitude of the bisection of a vortex!"

Astounded and overwhelmed with this cataract of vituperation, which, in being utterly incomprehensible to her, only "bothers" her the more, Biddy stands speechless, as though she were struck dumb by palsy. Still albeit worsted, she is game to the last. Suddenly snatching up a saucepan, she aims it as the head of our hero. But, ere it flies from her hand, he very wisely contrives to beat a hasty retreat.

There can be little doubt that on this occasion, at all events, "discretion was the better part of valour."

O'Connell's Last Case

By PADRAIC COLUM
(1881–   )

A thrilling account of Daniel O'Connell's last case, that of the "Doneraile Conspiracy," is here given: An unpopular Irish magistrate had been murdered and the resulting investigation unearthed a conspiracy to kill a number of oppressive local magnates. One hundred and fifty persons were indicted, and were to be tried in three batches.

In the defence of the first batch, Daniel O'Connell was not engaged, and they were all convicted and sentenced, lads and aged men together, to execution within the week. The remaining prisoners and their friends, seized with panic, sent an urgent messenger from Cork to Derrynane, ninety miles away, and O'Connell hastened to the rescue.

There was not a moment to spare, as the judge had refused to delay the opening of the second trial for his arrival. Traveling in a light gig with relays of horses, and scarcely stopping for rest or food, O'Connell traversed the frightful Kerry roads at full speed, and at length arrived in the courthouse square flogging his exhausted horse, which dropped dead between the shafts as he descended, hailed by a crowd of thousands with wild shouts: "He's come! He's come!"

Amid a frantic uproar of cheers, he was swept into the courtroom, where the opposing lawyer, Mr. Doherty, was addressing the jury.

The solicitor general turned white. The cloud of despair lifted from the faces of the prisoners in the dock. O'Connell at once bowed to the judges, and apologized for not appearing in wig and gown. He also craved permission to refresh himself in court. A bowl of bread and milk was brought, and as he ate, a young barrister on either side of him poured into each ear an account of all that had been done, and how the case stood.

It was a contrast, the big, massive counsellor snatching his hasty breakfast, and the graceful, aristocratic Mr. Doherty, talking in the most refined way to the court. As he laid down a doctrine of law, O'Connell, with marked contempt, cried out, with his mouth full of bread and milk: "That's not law!"

Again and again he interrupted, but always the decision of the judges upheld him and affirmed the error of his antagonist. He was still more successful when the witnesses fell into his hands for cross-examination. They told or tried to tell the same story on which the former prisoners had been convicted; but O'Connell so badgered, tripped, and terrified them that their evidence went hopelessly to pieces.

"Wisha, thin," cried one of them hysterically, visibly trembling, "God knows 'tis little I thought I'd meet you here this day, Counsellor O'Connell! May the Lord save me from you!"

The jury could not agree, though locked up and starved for a day and a half. Nor were the accused tried again, for the third

186

batch having received meanwhile a full acquittal, the government despaired of conviction and they were discharged, while the sentence of the unfortunates already condemned to be hanged was commuted to transportation.

Aftermath of Emancipation

By JOHN MITCHEL

It is true that Sir Robert Peel and the Duke of Wellington *said* they brought in this measure (a Relief Bill), to avert civil war; but no British statesman ever officially tells the truth, or assigns to any act its real motive. Their real motive was, to buy into the British interests, the landed and educated Catholics; that so the great multitudinous Celtic enemy might be left more absolutely at their mercy.

For, beginning on the very day of Catholic Emancipation, there was a more systematic and determined plan of havoc upon the homes of the poor. First, the "forty-shilling freehold" was abolished. This low franchise for counties had induced landlords to subdivide farms, and to rear up population for the hustings. The franchise at an end, there was no political use for the people; and all encouragements and facilities were furnished by the British Government to get rid of them. Then began the "amelioration" (for benevolence guided all) of clearing off "surplus population," and consolidating the farms. It needed too much of the produce of the island to feed such a mob of Celts; and improved systems of tillage would give more corn and cattle to English markets, more money to Irish landlords.

The code of cheap and easy Ejectment was improved and extended. All these statutes were unknown to the common law of England, and have been invented for the sole sake of the Irish Celt. . . .

To receive some of the exterminated, Poor-houses were erected all over the island, which had the effect of stifling compunction in the ejectors. The Poor-houses were soon filled. . . .

But all these same years, loud and triumphant Agitations were going forward—the "Precursor" Agitation; the Repeal Agitation—

187

and the cheers of imposing demonstrations rent the air. Our poor people were continually assured that they were the finest peasantry in the world—"Alone among the nations." They were told that their grass was greener, their women fairer, their mountains higher, their valleys lower, than those of other lands—that their "moral force" (alas!) had conquered before, and would again— that next year would be the Repeal year; in fine, that Ireland would be the first flower of the earth and the first gem of the sea.

Not that the Irish are a stupid race, or naturally absurd, but the magician bewitched them to their destruction.

All these years, too, a kind of political war of posts was waged between O'Connell and British Ministers . . .

For not one instant did the warfare cease upon farming Celts. In 1843, "Government" issued a notable commission; that is, appointed a few landlords, with Lord Devon at their head, to go through Ireland, collect evidence, and report on the best means (not of destroying the Irish enemy—official documents do not now use so harsh language, but) of ameliorating the relations of landlord and tenant in Ireland. On this commission, O'Connell observed that it was "a jury of butchers trying a sheep for his life" . . .

But the most remarkable sentence occurs in Lord Devon's "Digest of the Evidence," page 399:

"We find that there are at present 326,084 occupiers of land (more than one-third of the total number returned in Ireland), whose holdings vary from seven acres to less than one acre; and are, therefore, inadequate to support the families residing upon them. In the same table, No. 95, page 564, the calculation is put forward, showing that the consolidation of these small holdings up to eight acres, would require the removal of about 192,368 families."

That is, the killing of a million persons. Little did the commissioners hope then, that in four years, British policy, with the famine to aid, would succeed in killing fully two millions, and forcing nearly another million to flee the country. . . .

To this condition had forty years of "moral and peaceful agitation" brought Ireland. The high aspirations, a national Senate and a national flag had sunk to a mere craving for food. And for food Ireland craved in vain. She was to be taught that the Nation

188

which parts with her nationhood, or suffers it to be wrested or swindled from her, thereby loses all. O'Connell died heartbroken in 1847—heartbroken not by a mean vexation at seeing the power departing from him; the man was too great for that; but by the sight of his People sinking every day into death under their inevitable, inexorable doom. . . .

In 1842, or thereabouts, William Makepeace Thackeray came to Dublin, stayed in the Shelbourne Hotel and looked around him. What he saw amused him, especially the local branch of the English Court which still held royal festivities at Dublin Castle.

Hangers-On

By W. M. THACKERAY
(1811–1863)

They love great folks, those honest Emerald Islanders, more intensely than any people I ever heard of, except the Americans. They still cherish the memory of the sacred George IV. They chronicle genteel small beer with never failing assiduity. They go in long trains to a sham Court—simpering in tights and bags, with swords between their legs. O heaven and earth, what joy! Why are the Irish noblemen absentees? If their lordships like respect, where would they get it so well as in their own country?

The Irish noblemen are very likely going through the same delightful routine of duty before their real sovereign—in real tights and bagwigs, as it were, performing their graceful and lofty duties, and celebrating the august service of the throne. These, of course, the truly loyal heart can only respect: and I think a drawing room at St. James's the grandest spectacle that ever feasted the eye or exercised the intellect. The crown, surrounded

189

by its knights and nobles, its priests, its sages, and their respective ladies; illustrious foreigners, men learned in the law, heroes of land and sea, beef-eaters, gold-sticks, gentlemen-at-arms rallying round the throne and defending it with those swords which never knew defeat (and would surely, if tried, secure victory): these are sights and characters which every man must look upon with a thrill of respectful awe, and count amongst the glories of his country. What lady that sees this will not confess that she reads every one of the drawing-room costumes, from Majesty down to Miss Ann Maria Smith; and all the names of the presentations, from Prince Baccabocksky (by the Russian Ambassador) to Ensign Stubbs on his appointment?

We are bound to read these accounts. It is our pride, our duty as Britons. But though one may honour the respect of the aristocracy of the land for the sovereign, yet there is no reason why those who are not of the aristocracy should be aping their betters; and the Dublin Castle business has, I cannot but think, a very high-life-below-stairs look. There is no aristocracy in Dublin. Its magnates are tradesmen—Sir Fiat Haustus, Sir Blacker Dosy, Mr. Serjeant Bluebag, or Mr. Counsellor O'Fee. Brass plates are their titles of honour, and they live by their boluses or their briefs. What call have these worthy people to be dangling and grinning at lord-lieutenants' levees, and playing sham aristocracy before a sham sovereign? Oh, that old humbug of a Castle! It is the greatest sham of all the shams in Ireland.

1846

THE FEARFUL DAYS OF THE FAMINE

*A*lthough Catholic Emancipation had been passed by the English Parliament in 1829, the official Church in Ireland was still Protestant: the landlords, mainly English, used their Irish estates merely for what they could squeeze out of them. Their employees were allowed only as much land as would grow them enough potatoes to support life . . . and Disraeli was one of the few Englishmen to see what all this added up to, and to sympathize. But he got very little support.

Speech in the House of Commons

By DISRAELI
(1804–1881)

A dense population in extraordinary distress inhabit an island where there is an established Church which is not their Church; and a territorial aristocracy, the richest of whom live in a distant capital. Thus they have a starving population, an absentee aristocracy, and an alien Church.

Cecil Woodham-Smith,

an English historian, made her first and deep impression on American readers with her biography of Florence Nightingale. She went on to examine the calamitous leadership of the British generals in the Crimea, and in her blazing narrative THE REASON WHY she told how the Light Brigade was sent to its death. One of the British generals responsible for that decision was the proprietor of vast estates in Ireland, and in tracing his history, Mrs. Woodham-Smith came inevitably to that pitiable disaster, the potato famine. The following is the ATLANTIC MONTHLY condensation of her splendid, compassionate book

The Great Hunger

Ireland's Hunger, England's Fault?

By CECIL WOODHAM-SMITH
(1896–   )

At the beginning of the year 1845 the state of Ireland was, as it had been for nearly seven hundred years, a source of grave anxiety to England. Ireland had first been invaded in 1169; it was now 1845, yet she had been neither assimilated nor subdued. The country had been conquered not once but several times, the land had been confiscated and redistributed over and over again, the population had been brought to the verge of extinction—after Cromwell's conquest and settlement only some half million Irish survived—yet an Irish nation still existed, separate, numerous, and hostile.

The hostility between England and Ireland, which more than six centuries had failed to extinguish, had its roots first of all in race. After the first invasions, the first conquests, the Irish hated the English with the hatred of the defeated and the dispossessed. Nevertheless, eventually the English and the Irish might have fused as the English and the Scots, the English and the Welsh have for practical purposes fused, had it not been that in the sixteenth century racial animosity was disastrously strengthened by religious enmity.

The crucial event was the Reformation. The ideas of liberty which the English cherish and the history of their country's rise to greatness are bound up with Protestantism, while Ireland, alone among the countries of Northern Europe, was scarcely touched by the Reformation. The gulf which resulted could never be bridged. In the political division of Europe which followed the Reformation, England and Ireland were on opposing sides. Henceforward, Irish aspirations could only be fulfilled, Irish faith could only flourish through the defeat of England and the triumph of her enemies.

194

So completely is the history of the one country the reverse of the history of the other that the very names which to an Englishman mean glory, victory, and prosperity to an Irishman spell degradation, misery, and ruin. In Ireland the name of Elizabeth I stands only for the horrors of her Irish conquest; in the defeat of the Armada, Ireland's hopes of independence went down; above all, with the name of William III and the Glorious Revolution of 1688, the very foundation of British liberties, the Catholic Irishman associates only the final subjugation of his country and the degradation and injustice of the penal laws. Freedom for the one meant slavery for the other; victory for the one meant defeat for the other; the good of the one was the evil of the other. Ireland, resentful and hostile, lying only a day's sail, in fine weather, from Britain's coasts, for centuries provided a refuge for enemy agents, a hatching ground for enemy plots; her motto was "England's difficulty is Ireland's opportunity," and in every crisis of England's history she seized the moment of weakness to stab her enemy in the back. It is the explanation, if not the excuse, for the ferocity with which the English have treated Ireland.

In the 1840s, after nearly seven hundred years of English domination, Irish poverty and Irish misery appalled the traveler. Housing conditions were wretched beyond words. The census of 1841 graded houses in Ireland into four classes; the fourth and lowest class consisted of windowless mud cabins of a single room; "nearly half of the families of the rural population," reported the census commissioners, "are living in the lowest state." In parts of the west of Ireland, more than three fifths of the houses were one-room windowless mud cabins, and west of a line drawn from Londonderry to Cork the proportion was two fifths.

Furniture was a luxury; the inhabitants of Tullahobagly, County Donegal, numbering about 9000, had in 1837 only 10 beds, 93 chairs, and 243 stools among them. Pigs slept with their owners, manure heaps choked doors, sometimes even stood inside; the evicted and unemployed put roofs over ditches, burrowed into banks, existing in bog holes.

All this wretchedness and misery could almost without exception be traced to a single source—the system under which land had come to be occupied and owned in Ireland, a system produced by centuries of successive conquests, rebellions, confiscations, and

195

punitive legislation.

In 1843 the British government, recognizing that the land question was at the root of Irish discontent, set up a royal commission "to inquire into the law and practice with regard to the occupation of land in Ireland." This commission, called the Devon Commission after its chairman, the Earl of Devon, visited every part of Ireland, examined 1100 witnesses, printed three huge volumes of evidence, and made its report in February, 1845, a few months before the outbreak of the famine.

The report of the Devon Commission stated that the principal cause of Irish misery was the bad relations between landlord and tenant. Ireland was a conquered country, the Irish peasant a dispossessed man, his landlord an alien conqueror. There was no paternalism such as existed in England, no hereditary loyalty or feudal tie.

With some notable exceptions—whose names survive and are regarded with affection in Ireland today—the successive owners of the soil of Ireland regarded it merely as a source from which to extract as much money as possible, and since a hostile, backward country is neither a safe nor an agreeable place in which to live, from the first conquests the absentee landlord was common in Ireland. Rents were spent in England or on the Continent; in 1842 it was estimated that six million pounds of rents were being remitted out of Ireland, and Kohl, the German traveler, commented on the mansions of absentee landlords, standing "stately, silent, empty." Absentee estates, however, were by no means always the worst managed; and some, in particular the properties of great English territorial magnates—for instance, the estates of the Duke of Devonshire—were models. But too often owners visited property in Ireland only once or twice in a lifetime, sometimes not at all; as Colonel Conolly of Kildare and Donegal told a Select Committee of the House of Lords in 1846, "Where the landlords have never seen their estates, you can hardly suppose that their sympathies are very strong for sufferings they have never witnessed." Meanwhile, almost absolute power was left in the hands of an agent, whose ability was measured by the amount of money he could contrive to extract.

Whether the Irish peasant held under a middleman, a resident, or an absentee landlord, the terms on which he occupied his land

196

were harsh; and two provisions in particular, the two "monster grievances" of Ireland, deprived him of incentive and security.

First, any improvement he made to his holding became, when his lease expired or was terminated, the property of the landlord, without compensation. Second, he very seldom had any security of tenure; the majority of tenants in Ireland were tenants "at will" —that is, the will of the landlord, who could turn them out whenever he chose.

Wretched though their condition might be, the pre-famine Irish peasants were not gloomy. "Their natural condition," wrote Sir Walter Scott during his visit to Ireland in 1825, "is turned towards gaiety and happiness," and the census commissioners noted "the proverbial gaiety and lightheartedness of the peasant people."

Dancing was the universal diversion, and Lord George Hill, who owned property in Donegal, has left an account of moving a cabin with dancing and fiddling. "The custom on such occasions is for the person who has the work to be done to hire a fiddler, upon which engagement all the neighbors joyously assemble and carry in an incredibly short time the stones and timber upon their backs to the new site; men, women and children alternately dancing and working while daylight lasts, at the termination of which they adjourn to some dwelling where they finish the night, often prolonging the dance to dawn of day." Arthur Young, at the end of the eighteenth century, commented on the fine physique of the average Irishman and the good looks of Irish women, and even after the sufferings of the famine, Nassau Senior, the economist, revisiting Ireland, was "struck by the beauty of the population."

The culture of the potato required little attention except at springtime and harvest, and through the long winter nights the people sat within their cabins, fiddling, talking, and telling stories. Firing, in the shape of turf—peat cut from the bog and costing little or nothing—was plentiful. "Few, if any, had any reason to complain of cold," records a manuscript, and poteen, illicit whiskey, was plentiful too. Groups of neighbors gathered for dancing to the fiddle, indoors in the winter, in summer at the crossroads; wakes, with liberal potations of poteen, were social occasions; and crowds gaily traveled immense distances to attend markets, fairs, and above all, races.

Good manners and hospitality were universal among the poorest Irish. "The neighbor or the stranger finds every man's door open, and to walk in without ceremony at meal time and to partake of his bowl of potatoes, is always sure to give pleasure to everyone of the house," wrote Sir John Carr, a Devonshire gentleman who toured Ireland soon after the Union; and twenty years later, Sir Walter Scott found "perpetual kindness in the Irish cabin; butter-milk, potatoes, a stool is offered, or a stone is rolled that your honor may sit down . . . and those that beg everywhere else seem desirous to exercise hospitality in their own houses."

Irish dignity, Irish hospitality, and the easy good manners which still charm the modern traveler have a historical explanation. Three times, at least, the native aristocracy was conquered and dispossessed; many fled from Ireland to exile in France or Spain, but many others remained, to be forced down by poverty and penal legislation to the economic level of the peasantry.

An oppressed and poverty-stricken population in Ireland was already giving signs of future tragedy when a new development made catastrophe inevitable. Between sixty and seventy years before the potato famine, the population of Ireland began and continued to increase at a rate previously unknown in the history of Europe. Why this took place has yet to be fully explained. Demography, the science which deals with the statistics of birth, death, and disease, is a relatively new science, and the waves of population growth which from time to time pass over the world are not yet fully understood. In the case of Ireland, information is lacking; births were not compulsorily registered until 1863, and though the practice of taking a ten-year census began in 1821, the first figures considered reliable are those of 1841.

It is, however, agreed by all authorities that about the year 1780 the population of Ireland began to take an extraordinary upward leap. The increase between 1779 and 1841 has been placed at the almost incredible figure of 172 percent.

During the same period a rapid increase also took place in the population of England and Wales. It is customary to ascribe this to the spread of industrialization, resulting in improved communications and more towns with better opportunities for social intercourse and early marriage; to a more general adoption of

198

vaccination, with a consequent reduction of deaths from smallpox; and in some degree to improved cleanliness and medical care. More adults lived to old age; more babies were born and fewer died.

But this cannot apply to Ireland. Little can have been effected by medical care in a country which in 1841 possessed only thirty-nine infirmaries, apart from hospitals for fever, venereal, ophthalmic, and maternity patients, to serve a population officially calculated at more than eight million, where the only medical aid available to the mass of the people was a limited number of dispensaries. Nor can the growth of towns and the improvement of communications have played much part in the bogs, the mountains, and the lonely cabins of the west; yet Mayo, in Connaught, poorest and most remote of counties, had the largest rural population in Ireland.

Still, certain circumstances favorable to population increase were present in Ireland during this period. First, and most important, there was an abundant supply of incredibly cheap food, easily obtained, in the potato, and the standard of living of the time was such that a diet of potatoes was no great hardship. With the addition of milk or buttermilk, potatoes form a scientifically satisfactory diet, as the physique of the pre-famine Irish proved.

Next, far from acting as a deterrent, the miserably low standards of Irish life encouraged young couples to marry early. No savings were necessary, no outlay was required; a cabin was erected for little or nothing in a few days; the young couple secured a scrap of land, owned a pot, perhaps a stool, not always a bed. Marriages were "daily contracted with the most reckless improvidence. Boys and girls marry literally without habitation or any means of support, trusting, as they say, to Providence as others have done before them." In fact, nothing was to be gained by waiting. Asked why the Irish married so young, the Catholic bishop of Raphoe told the Irish Poor Enquiry of 1835: "They cannot be worse off than they are and . . . they may help each other."

The Irish are fond of children, and family feeling is exceptionally strong. Moreover, in pre-famine Ireland children were a necessity. A Poor Law did not begin to operate until 1838, and then its provisions were limited; thus, a man and woman's insurance against destitution in old age was their children.

There was too, barbarous and half savage though conditions

199

might be, one luxury enjoyed by the Irishman which favored the survival and rearing of children—his cabin was usually well warmed by a turf fire. Ill clothed though he was, sleeping as he did on a mud floor, with his pig in the corner, the Irish peasant did not have to endure cold, nor did his children die of cold. They were warm, they were abundantly fed—as long as the potato did not fail.

By 1841, when a census was taken, the population had reached 8,175,124, and Disraeli declared that Ireland was the most densely populated country in Europe; on arable land, he asserted, the population was denser than that of China.

For this closely packed and rapidly increasing people the only outlet, with the exception of parts of Ulster, was the land. Ireland had never been industrialized; such deposits of coal and iron as she possessed were "unfortunately of more significance to the geologist than the economist," and in 1845 the few industries she did possess were moribund. A remnant of the famous Dublin poplin weavers worked fifteen hours a day for about twelve shillings a week; in the once-prosperous woolen industry, production had fallen about 50 percent in the last twenty years, and three quarters of the frieze, thick woolen cloth worn by the peasantry, was dumped by England. The fisheries of Ireland, too, were undeveloped, and in Galway and Mayo the herring fishermen were too poor to buy salt with which to preserve a catch. Unless an Irish laborer could get hold of a patch of land and grow potatoes on which to feed himself and his children, the family starved.

The consequence was the doom of Ireland. The land was divided and subdivided again and again, and holdings were split into smaller and still smaller fragments, until families were attempting to exist on plots of less than an acre, in some cases half an acre.

Farms had already been divided by middlemen and landlords, but the subdivision which preceded the famine was carried out by the people themselves, frequently against the landlord's will. As the population increased and the demand for a portion of ground grew more and more frantic, land became like gold in Ireland. Parents allowed their children to occupy a portion of their holdings because the alternative was to turn them out to starve; the children, in turn, allowed occupation by their children, and in a comparatively short time three, six, or even ten families were

200

settled on land which could provide food for only one family.

The possession of a piece of land was literally the difference between life and death. "Ejectment," the House of Commons was told in April, 1846, "is tantamount to a sentence of death by slow torture." Turned off the land, evicted families wandered about begging, "miserable and turbulent." Since no employment existed, they crowded the already swarming lanes and slums of the towns, lived in ditches by the roadside until, wasted by disease and hardship, "they die in a little time."

The whole of this structure, the minute subdivisions, the closely packed population existing at the lowest level, the high rents, the frantic competition for land, had been produced by the potato. The potato, provided it did not fail, enabled great quantities of food to be produced at a trifling cost from a small plot of ground. Subdivision could never have taken place without the potato; an acre and a half would provide a family of five or six with food for twelve months, while to grow the equivalent grain required an acreage four to six times as large and some knowledge of tillage as well. Only a spade was needed for the primitive method of potato culture usually practiced in Ireland. Trenches were dug, and beds, called "lazy beds," made; the potato sets were laid on the ground and earthed up from the trenches; when the shoots appeared, they were earthed up again. This method, regarded by the English with contempt, was in fact admirably suited to the moist soil of Ireland. The trenches provided drainage, and crops could be grown in wet ground, while cultivation by the spade enabled potatoes to be grown on mountainsides, where no plow could be used. As the population expanded, potatoes in lazy beds were pushed out into the bog and up the mountain, where no other cultivation would have been possible.

The potato was, moreover, the most universally useful of foods. Pigs, cattle, and fowl could be raised on it, using the tubers which were too small for family use; it was simple to cook; it produced fine children; as a diet, it did not pall. Yet it was the most dangerous of crops. It did not keep, nor could it be stored from one season to another. Thus, every year the nearly two and a half million laborers who had no regular employment more or less starved in the summer, when the old potatoes were finished and the new had not come in. It was for this reason that June, July, and August

201

were called the "meal months"; there was always the danger that potatoes would run out and meal would have to be eaten instead. The laborers would then have to buy it on credit, at exorbitant prices, from the petty dealer and usurer who was the scourge of the Irish village—the dreaded "gombeen-man."

More serious still, if the potato did fail, neither meal nor anything else could replace it. There could be no question of resorting to an equally cheap food—no such food existed; nor could potato cultivation be replaced, except after a long period, by the cultivation of any other food.

In 1844 a report was received that in North America a disease hitherto unknown had attacked the potato crop. The potato of the mid-nineteenth century, not yet even partially immunized against disease by scientific breeding, was singularly liable to failure. The unreliability of the potato was an accepted fact in Ireland, ranking with the vagaries of the weather, and in 1845 the possibility of yet another failure caused no particular alarm.

At the beginning of July of that year, the potato crop promised remarkably well; the weather was then dry and hot. The abrupt change which followed, extraordinary even for the fickle climate of Ireland, brought for upward of three weeks "one continued gloom," with low temperatures and "a succession of most chilling rains and some fog." Nevertheless, at the end of July the crop was still exceptionally heavy, and on July 23 the *Freeman's Journal* reported that "the poor man's property, the potato crop, was never before so large and at the same time so abundant."

The first disquieting news came from an unexpected quarter. At the beginning of August, Sir Robert Peel, the British Prime Minister, received a letter from the Isle of Wight, as famous for its market gardens as anywhere in the south of England, reporting that disease had appeared in the potato crop there. This was the first recorded evidence that the blight which had recently ravaged the potato crop in North America had crossed the Atlantic.

The British government was anxious not only for Ireland but for England. During the previous fifty years potatoes had assumed a dangerous importance in the diet of the English laboring classes. Hard times, the blockade during the Napoleonic Wars, the unemployment and wage cutting which followed the declaration of peace after Waterloo had been gradually forcing the English laborer

202

to eat potatoes in place of bread. A failure would be serious enough for England, but for Ireland it would be disaster, and Ireland loomed in every mind—wretched, rebellious, and utterly dependent on the potato.

It was only a question of time before the blight spread to Ireland, and on September 13, Dr. John Lindley, editor of the *Gardener's Chronicle and Horticultural Gazette*, held up publication of the magazine to make a dramatic announcement. "We stop the Press with very great regret to announce that the potato Murrain has unequivocally declared itself in Ireland. The crops about Dublin are suddenly perishing . . . where will Ireland be in the event of a universal potato rot?"

Nevertheless, through the next few weeks the British government was optimistic. Very likely the failure would be local, as had often happened in the past; and the Home Secretary, who "repeatedly" requested information from Ireland, was receiving many favorable reports. These were explained later by the sporadic nature of the failure of 1845; "the country is like a checker-board," wrote a government official, "black and white next door. Hence the contradictory reports." It was, too, the habitual policy of British governments to discount the veracity of news from Ireland; "there is such a tendency to exaggeration and inaccuracy in Irish reports that delay in acting on them is always desirable," wrote Sir Robert Peel on October 13, 1845.

It has been proved that the organism of the blight fungus is so sensitive to heat and drought that its spread for any considerable distance by air currents is impossible, and the blight fungus almost certainly reached Europe in a diseased tuber carried in a ship from North America. Contemporary scientists attributed blight to the wetness of the summer, and they were very nearly right. Though rain and damp are not the cause of the blight, without them the fungus does not multiply rapidly. Consequently, in a dry summer there is little blight, and the fungus, though present, is more or less dormant. It is when the atmosphere is moist and muggy that spore production reaches its height, and the blight fungus spreads with such rapidity that potato fields seem to be ruined overnight. The soft, warm climate of Ireland, particularly in the west, with its perpetual light rains and mild breezes, provides ideal conditions for the spread of the fungus.

The blight fungus also infects potatoes after digging, a source of despair and bewilderment in 1845. The top and foliage of a plant can be destroyed by blight while the potatoes in the ground beneath may be sound; either the potatoes were too well covered with earth for the blight spore to reach them or, as was frequently the case in Ireland, rain was light and did not wash the spore containers down through the soil. But even so, danger of infection is not over; countless thousands of live spore containers are on the leaves of surrounding plants, and as the potatoes are dug they are showered with spores. If the weather is dry no harm is done, but if it is moist the spore containers find the drop of water they must have to germinate, and within a few hours the fungus is active, growing rapidly through the tubers.

As digging of the potato crop progressed, the news from Ireland grew steadily worse, and the Constabulary Reports of October 15, 1845, were the gloomiest yet forwarded. In Antrim the failure was more serious than at first supposed; Armagh had hardly a sound potato; in the south, Bantry and Clonakilty reported great failure; in Bandon and Kinsale disease was extending, while in the fertile midlands and Kildare blight had appeared. In Wicklow, where the clouds broke on the mountains in rain, potatoes grown between the sea and the mountains were diseased to an alarming extent. In Monaghan, Tyrone, and several other counties it was reported that "potatoes bought a few days ago, seemingly remarkably good, have rotted."

The soundness of the potato when first dug was responsible for bewildering contradictions. Optimists, delighted to witness the digging of what seemed a splendid crop, hastened to send off glowing accounts. In almost every case, hope was short-lived. Within a few days the fine-looking tubers had become a stinking mass of corruption, and growers began to flood the market with potatoes, anxious to get rid of them before the rot set in.

Peel decided to set up a scientific commission in Ireland to investigate what science could do to save the potato. Dr. Lindley agreed to serve with Dr. Lyon Playfair, a chemist of considerable reputation, and they crossed immediately to Dublin. In addition, Peel arranged for the cooperation and assistance of an Irish Catholic scientist of eminence, Professor Robert Kane, knighted in 1846, who was already making an investigation of the potato disease on behalf of the Royal Agricultural Improvement Society for Ireland and had recently published an important book, *The Industrial Resources of Ireland*.

No deliberation was necessary. The briefest possible inquiry was sufficient for the professors to become alarmed, and the scientific commissioners estimated that half the potato crop of Ireland either had been already destroyed or would shortly perish. Thus, to find a method of preventing potatoes sound when dug from rotting was of overwhelming importance. A number of suggestions were now put forward by the commissioners, none of which worked.

Seventy thousand copies of these well-meant suggestions were printed by the government and circulated to local agricultural committees, to newspapers, and to parish priests, who received thirty copies each. This was only a beginning. For between October 26 and November 12 the "untiring industry" of the commissioners produced in rapid succession what the *Times* called "four monster reports," as well as two statements dated from the Royal Dublin Society and addressed to the Lord Lieutenant of Ireland. After having been in Ireland somewhat less than three weeks, the men of science returned to London.

Meanwhile, apart from the appointment of the men of science, the government had taken no steps, and on October 28 a meeting was called by a committee of the Dublin Corporation, under the chairmanship of the lord mayor. Three days later a meeting of citizens was called, which appointed a committee presided over by the Duke of Leinster. On November 3 a deputation of the highest respectability waited on the Lord Lieutenant, Lord Heytesbury, to urge him to adopt measures "to avert calamity." The deputation included the Duke of Leinster, Daniel O'Connell, Lord Cloncurry, the lord mayor of Dublin, Henry Grattan, son of the famous patriot, Sir James Murray, John Augustus O'Neill, and some twenty others.

Their proposals, drawn up by O'Connell, called for the immediate stoppage of the export of corn and provisions and for the prohibition of distilling and brewing from grain; the ports should be thrown open for the free import of food and rice and Indian corn imported from the colonies; relief machinery must be set up in every county, stores of food established, and employ-

205

ment provided on works of public utility. It was proposed that the cost be met by a tax of 10 percent on the rental of resident landlords and from 20 to 50 percent on that of absentees. In addition, a loan of £1,500,000 should be raised on the security of the proceeds of Irish woods and forests.

The Lord Lieutenant received the deputation "very coldly" and read aloud a prepared reply. Reports on the potato crop varied and at times contradicted each other, and it was impossible to form an accurate opinion of the extent of the failure until digging was completed. The proposals submitted by the deputation would at once be placed before the government, but the greater part of them required new legislation, and all must be "maturely weighed." As soon as Lord Heytesbury "had concluded reading, he began bowing the deputation out."

As the news worsened, Sir Robert Peel took a bold step. On November 9 or 10 he ordered, acting on his own responsibility and without waiting for Treasury sanction, £100,000 to be spent on Indian corn, to be purchased in the United States and shipped to Ireland. His purchase of Indian corn proved the decisive factor in relieving the distress of 1845–1846, but the subsequent value to Ireland of Peel's boldness, independence, and strength of mind was unfortunately outweighed by his belief in an economic theory which almost every politician of the day, Whig or Tory, held with religious fervor.

This theory, usually termed laissez-faire (let people do as they think best), insisted that in the economic sphere individuals should be allowed to pursue their own interests and asserted that the government should interfere as little as possible. Not only were the rights of property sacred; private enterprise was revered and respected and given almost complete liberty; and on this theory, which, incidentally, gave the employer and the landlord freedom to exploit their fellowmen, the prosperity of nineteenth-century England had unquestionably been based.

The influence of laissez-faire on the treatment of Ireland during the famine is impossible to exaggerate. Almost without exception the high officials and politicians responsible for Ireland were fervent believers in non-interference by government, and the behavior of the British authorities only becomes explicable when their fanatical belief in private enterprise and their suspicions of

206

any action which might be considered government intervention are borne in mind.

The loss of the potato crop was, therefore, to be made good without government interference, by the operation of private enterprise and private firms using the normal channels of commerce. The government was not to appear in food markets as a buyer; there were to be "no disturbance of the ordinary course of trade" and "no complaints from private traders" on account of government competition.

The flaw in the plan was the undeveloped state of the food and provision trade in a great part of Ireland. Large numbers of people, especially in the west and southwest, hardly purchased food at all; they grew potatoes and lived on them. Shops and organizations for importing foodstuffs and distributing them on the English model were generally found only in more prosperous districts in northeast Ulster, Dublin, some places in eastern Ireland, and the larger towns, like Cork. Where relief would be most needed, the means by which it was to be supplied seldom existed.

Peel's plan, nevertheless, was farseeing and ingenious. He intended to use the Indian corn he had bought as a weapon to keep prices down. It was to be held in reserve, controlled by government, and a supply thrown in whenever prices rose unreasonably. At no time did he contemplate attempting to feed on Indian corn all those who had lost their potatoes; that loss has been estimated by a modern authority at a value in money of £3,500,000, and £100,000 of Indian corn could not conceivably replace it.

Indian corn was purchased because doing so did not interfere with private enterprise. No trade in Indian corn existed; it was virtually unknown as a food in Ireland or any other part of the United Kingdom and was neither imported nor bought and sold. Moreover, it had the immense advantage of being cheap, one of the cheapest foods on which a human being could keep alive.

All expenditure required Treasury sanction—the money to be spent on famine relief, the expenses of the relief commission, the grants for Poor Law, for public works, for medical services; and at the Treasury, standing guard over the British nation's moneybags, was the formidable figure of Charles Edward Trevelyan.

The official title of Trevelyan was assistant secretary, but he was in fact the permanent head of the Treasury, and owing to his abilities and the structure of British administration, which results in a capable permanent official's exercising a high degree of power, he was able to influence policy to a remarkable extent.

Trevelyan was by far the ablest man concerned with Irish relief, and, unaffected by changes of government and policy, he remained a dominant figure throughout the famine years. He had been brought up in what was known as the Clapham Sect, not a religious body but a number of highly cultivated families (including the Wilberforces and the Thorntons of Battersea Rise) who lived around Clapham Common and were distinguished for their philanthropic and evangelical views. Trevelyan, who was of rigid integrity, delighted in reading chapters of the Bible aloud in a "deep sonorous voice."

At the outset of his career, when he was no more than twenty-one, in India he risked his future by publicly denouncing his superior, a very powerful and popular man, for taking bribes. "A perfect storm was raised against the accuser," wrote Macaulay, who was in India at the time and knew Trevelyan well. "He was almost everywhere abused and very generally cut. But, with a firmness and ability scarcely ever seen in a man so young, he brought his proofs forward, and, after an inquiry of some weeks, fully made out his case." His superior was dismissed with ignominy and Trevelyan himself was applauded "in the highest terms," though Lord William Bentinck, Governor-General of India, remarked, "That man is almost always on the right side in every question; and it is well that he is so, for he gives a most confounded deal of trouble when he happens to take the wrong one."

Seven years later Trevelyan married Macaulay's idolized sister, Hannah, in India. At the time of the marriage, Macaulay, who was greatly attached to Trevelyan, wrote: "He has no small talk. His mind is full of schemes of morals and political improvement, and his zeal boils over in his talk. His topics, even in courtship, are steam navigation, the education of the natives, the equalization of the sugar duties, the substitution of the Roman for the Arabic alphabet in Oriental languages." His temper was pronounced "very sweet," his religious feelings ardent, but he was rash and uncompromising in public affairs, and his manner was blunt, almost to roughness, and at times awkward.

At the beginning of the famine, Trevelyan was thirty-eight, at

208

the height of his powers and immensely conscientious, and he had an obsession for work. Though his integrity was absolute and he had a strong sense of justice, he was not the right man to undertake Ireland. He disapproved of the Irish; the cast of his mind, his good qualities were such as to make him impatient with the Irish character. His mind was powerful, his character admirably scrupulous and upright, his devotion to duty praiseworthy, but he had a remarkable insensitiveness. Since he took action only after conscientiously satisfying himself that what he proposed to do was ethical and justified, he went forward impervious to other considerations, sustained, but also blinded, by his conviction of doing right.

When the first relief commission started work in November, 1845, the influence of Trevelyan was limited; his relations with Peel on Ireland were not good. Peel himself laid down the policy for the relief commission, and the instructions for putting it into effect were drawn up by Sir James Graham, the Home Secretary. Within a few months, however, Trevelyan had become director and virtually dictator of Irish relief.

The consequences of a potato failure are not immediate: "The first effect of the disease is not scarcity, but plenty, owing to the people's anxiety to dispose of their potatoes before they become useless." It was not until five or six months after a failure that famine began, after every scrap of food, every partially diseased potato, every fragment that was conceivably edible by human beings had disappeared.

The commissioners, then, had an interval to prepare. They were to "ascertain the extent of the deficiency and watch approaching famine, even in the most remote localities" and to "assist in devising the necessary measures for the employment of the people and their relief."

The relief plan devised by Peel fell into four parts. The first and most important was the organization of local efforts: the relief commissioners were instructed to form committees of local landowners or their agents, magistrates, clergy, and residents of importance. These committees would raise funds, out of which food was to be bought for resale to distressed persons, or in urgent cases given free. Local employment schemes were to be started, and landlords persuaded to give increased employment on their

209

estates. The government pinned its faith on the landlords. "Our main reliance," said Peel, "must be placed on the co-operation of the landed interest with local aid."

The second part of the plan depended on the Irish Board of Works; it was to create extra employment by making new roads, a traditional undertaking for the provision of famine relief.

The third part was concerned with "destitute poor persons affected by fever"; in previous famines the British government had learned that fever always followed scarcity in Ireland. Fever patients might be maintained in a fever hospital, or a house could be hired for their reception, or they could be put in a separate building in the grounds of the local workhouse, but not in the workhouse itself.

Finally, the sale of the government Indian corn would keep down food prices; as soon as they rose unreasonably, a sufficient quantity of the Indian corn was to be thrown on the market to bring them down. Trevelyan conducted "Indian corn experiments" on himself, eating the meal as stirabout (porridge) and in cakes, and he arranged for a halfpenny pamphlet to be prepared, with simple instructions for cooking.

In the long and troubled history of England and Ireland, no issue has provoked so much anger or so embittered relations between the two countries as the indisputable fact that huge quantities of food were exported from Ireland to England throughout the period when the people of Ireland were dying of starvation. "During all the famine years," wrote John Mitchel, the Irish revolutionary, "Ireland was actually producing sufficient food, wool and flax, to feed and clothe not nine but eighteen millions of people"; yet, he asserted, a ship sailing into an Irish port during the famine years with a cargo of grain was "sure to meet six ships sailing out with a similar cargo."

At first sight the inhumanity of exporting food from a country stricken by famine seems impossible to justify or condone. Modern Irish historians, however, have treated the subject with generosity and restraint. They have pointed out that the grain grown in Ireland before the famine was not sufficient to feed the people if they had depended on it alone, that imports must be examined as well as exports; in fact, when the famine was at its worst, four times as much wheat came into Ireland as was exported, and in

210

addition almost 40,000 tons of Indian corn and 50,000 tons of Indian meal.

Suppose, however, the grain and other produce had been kept in the country; it is doubtful if the starving would have benefited substantially. The districts where distress was most severe—Donegal, Mayo, Clare, West Cork—produced little but potatoes. Food from other districts would have had to be brought in and distributed. Grain would have had to be milled, which, as the British government had discovered, was a difficult problem.

Moreover, in the backward areas where famine struck hardest, cooking any food other than the potato had become a lost art. "There is," wrote Trevelyan, "scarcely a woman of peasant class in the West of Ireland whose culinary art exceeds the boiling of a potato. Bread is scarcely ever seen, and an oven is unknown"; and Father Mathew, the celebrated apostle of temperance, whose crusade against drinking had for a time almost suppressed the national vice and whose knowledge of Ireland was unmatched, wrote, "The potato deluge during the past twenty years has swept away all other food from our cottagers and sunk into oblivion their knowledge of cookery." There was no means of distributing homegrown food, no knowledge of how to use it, and in addition, the small Irish farmer was compelled by economic necessity to sell what he grew. He dared not eat it.

Sir Randolph Routh, the chairman of the relief commission, writing to Trevelyan on January 1, 1846, told him that the Irish people did not regard wheat, oats, and barley as food; they were grown to pay the rent, and to pay the rent was the first necessity of life in Ireland. It would be a desperate man who ate up his rent, with the certainty before him of eviction.

Nevertheless, the harsh truth that the poverty of the Irish peasant, the backward state of his country, and the power of his landlord prevented him from benefiting from homegrown food did not mitigate his burning sense of injustice. Forced by economic necessity to sell his produce, he was furiously resentful when food left the market towns under the eyes of the hungry populace, protected by a military escort of overwhelming strength. From Waterford, the Commissariat officer wrote to Trevelyan on April 24, 1846, "The barges leave Clonmel once a week for this place, with the export supplies under convoy which, last Tuesday, consisted of 2

211

guns, 50 cavalry and 80 infantry escorting them on the banks of the Suir as far as Carrick."

It was a sight which the Irish people found impossible to understand and impossible to forget.

In June, 1846, Sir Robert Peel was defeated. The new Whig government, under Lord John Russell, was more to Trevelyan's taste than Peel's administration. As a government servant he had no politics, but in private life he was a Whig, and his relations with Sir Robert Peel had not been happy. On July 6 he wrote in a private letter to Routh, "The members of the new Government began to come today to the Treasury. I think we shall have much reason to be satisfied with our new masters," and he added, on the thirteenth, "Nothing can be more gratifying to our feelings than the manner in which the new Chancellor of the Exchequer has appreciated our exertions."

The new Chancellor of the Exchequer, Charles Wood, who succeeded as Sir Charles Wood, Bart., in December, 1846, and was later created first Viscount Halifax, was congenial to Trevelyan. He had a solid mind and a fixed dislike both of new expenditure and new taxes, and was a firm believer in laissez-faire, preferring to let matters take their course and allow problems to be solved by "natural means." Head of an ancient Yorkshire family, he united love of liberty with reverence for property, a strong sense of public duty, lack of imagination, and stubborn conservatism. Humanitarianism was not among his virtues. Charles Wood remained in office as Chancellor of the Exchequer for six years and came increasingly under Trevelyan's influence. The two men were alike in outlook, conscientiousness, and industry, and Charles Wood brought Trevelyan a further access of power in the administration of Irish relief.

Trevelyan's intention was to restrict Irish relief to a single operation; the Indian corn purchased at the orders of Sir Robert Peel was to be placed in depots, sold to the people—and that was the end. There was to be no replenishment; on July 8 Trevelyan rejected a shipload of Indian corn. "The cargo of the *Sorcière* is not wanted," he wrote to the American agent; "her owners must dispose of it as they think proper."

Trevelyan had an urgent reason for wishing to get Sir Robert Peel's relief scheme for the 1845 failure cleared up and out of the way. He disagreed with it in several important respects, and by

212

July a new and alarming probability had become evident—there were unmistakable signs that the potato was about to fail again.

As early as February 16, 1846, new potatoes had been shown at meetings of the Horticultural Society in London "in which the disease had manifested itself in a manner not to be mistaken," and on February 20, a question had been asked in the House of Commons. In reply it was admitted that the potatoes "exhibited the disease of last autumn," but added that they had been grown from sets of potatoes which were themselves slightly diseased.

Trevelyan and Charles Wood, the Chancellor of the Exchequer, had decided that in the second failure there was to be no government importation of food from abroad and no interference whatsoever with the laws of supply and demand; whatever might be done by starting public works and paying wages, the provision of food for Ireland was to be left entirely to private enterprise and private traders.

The new policy was received by officials in Ireland with dismay, and on August 4 Routh pressed Trevelyan to import food, now and at once. "You cannot answer the cry of want by a quotation from political economy. You ought to have 16,000 tons of Indian corn . . . you ought to have half of the supply which you require in the country before Christmas." How great a quantity would be needed, wrote Routh, would be determined this month, when the main crop began to be dug.

No preparations, however, even if preparations had been made on double the scale urged, could in fact have saved the Irish people from the fate which lay before them. Before the depots could be closed or the public works shut down, almost in a night every potato in Ireland was lost. "On the 27th of last month," wrote Father Mathew to Trevelyan on August 7, "I passed from Cork to Dublin and this doomed plant bloomed in all the luxuriance of an abundant harvest. Returning on the third instant I beheld with sorrow one wide waste of putrefying vegetation. In many places the wretched people were seated on the fences of their decaying gardens, wringing their hands and wailing bitterly the destruction that had left them foodless."

"I shall never forget," wrote Captain Mann, a coast guard officer employed in relief service, "the change in one week in August. On the first occasion, on an official visit of inspection, I had passed

213

over thirty-two miles thickly studded with potato fields in full bloom. The next time the face of the whole country was changed, the stalk remained bright green, but the leaves were all scorched black. It was the work of a night."

Disaster was universal. The failure of 1845 had, to some degree, been partial; the loss, though serious, had been unequally distributed, and the blighted areas "isolated and detached." With the exception of the potatoes, the harvest had been above the average, and though distress was greatly intensified, thanks to the relief scheme the people in many districts had been better off than usual. In the summer of 1846 the situation was very different. The harvest generally was poor, and the people were at the end of their resources. Every rag had already been pawned to buy food, every edible scrap had gone. The people were weakened and despairing.

The gravity of the impending catastrophe was felt by Lord John Russell and his government; reports of the universal failure of the potato were being confirmed by every mail, and new measures for Irish relief had been in course of preparation for some weeks.

The new plans were the work of Trevelyan. He prepared a memorandum, dated on August 1, 1846, in which he detailed last season's relief plans, set out the respects in which they had failed, and outlined a plan to meet the coming crisis. This memorandum formed the basis of the new scheme, and Trevelyan, who possessed the administrative abilities which Lord John Russell's colleagues on the whole lacked, now became virtually dictator of relief for Ireland.

The new relief scheme, briefly, fell under two main heads. First, though public works were again to be undertaken, and on a large scale, the British government would no longer, as last year, bear half their cost. The whole expense was to be paid by the district in which the works were carried out. The cost was to be met by advances from the Treasury, repayable in their entirety in ten years, at 3½ percent interest, and the money for repayment was to be raised by a tax levied on all poor-rate payers in the locality, a momentous and controversial innovation. The expense was designed to "fall entirely on persons possessed of property in the distressed district," who were, after all, responsible for the poor on their estates.

Second, the government would not import or supply any food.

214

There were to be no government depots to sell meal at a low cost or, in urgent cases, to make free issues, as had been done during last season's failure. No orders were to be sent abroad, nor would any purchases be made by government in local markets. It was held that the reason why dealers and import merchants had so signally failed to provide food to replace the potato last season had been the government's purchases. Trade, said Trevelyan, had been "paralysed" on account of these purchases, which interfered with private enterprise and the legitimate profits of private enterprise; and how, he asked, could dealers be expected to invest in the very large stocks necessary to meet this year's total failure of the potato if at any moment government might step in with supplies, sold at low cost, which would deprive dealers of their profit and "make their outlay so much loss"?

This section of the scheme was received with consternation, and Routh, with unaccustomed boldness, wrote from Dublin, "As for the great question of leaving the country to the corn dealers they are a very different class of men from our London, Liverpool and Bristol merchants. I do not believe there is a man among them who would import direct a single cargo from abroad."

Such, very broadly, were the outlines of the scheme devised by Trevelyan for the government to meet the total failure of the potato. In the course of relieving last season's failure, some very painful lessons had been learned. Then the whole laboring population of Ireland, wherever they had the chance, had rushed to throw themselves on the government works; the scheme had, to a large extent, been swamped; there had been confusion and waste; and very large sums of public money had melted away. Yet last year's failure had been only partial; the prospect of relieving a total failure by the same methods was impossible to contemplate. Trevelyan declared that the Exchequer itself would not be equal to the occasion.

Therefore, the first object of the new plans was to "check the exorbitant demands of last season"; they were, in fact, designed not to save Ireland but to protect England. The scheme was to be in force for a year and no longer; writing to Mr. Labouchère, appointed chief secretary for Ireland by the Whigs, Trevelyan spoke of "the year of relief" and laid down, in a Treasury minute, "No advances . . . will in any circumstances be made for carrying on . . . works after the 15th August 1847."

Trevelyan anticipated that there would be what he called a "breathing time" about the second week in August, when the potatoes from the new crop became fit to eat. Last year there had been such a pause while the crop was hurriedly dug and every potato conceivably edible eaten before it rotted. He intended to use this "breathing time" to overhaul the relief organization, so that the departments would be ready "to put our whole machinery in motion at an early date."

Throughout August, 1846, Trevelyan worked very hard indeed. He spoke of being at the Treasury until 3 A.M., "dead beat," and of working weekdays and Sundays alike. An official of the Board of Works summoned over to London was told "to come on Sunday and knock at the private entrance in Downing Street below the Treasury." Every detail of the new relief scheme was controlled by Trevelyan, and all Commissariat and Board of Works, Ireland, letters, as well as all private letters, were by his instructions sent up to him unopened. It was, he wrote, "the most difficult and responsible task that has ever fallen to my lot."

All these exertions were in vain. It was too late for preparation. Disaster was upon Ireland now. No breathing time occurred; the "influx of early potatoes," wrote Routh, on August 13, 1846, "due to the desire to realize something before that something shall be wholly lost . . . failed on account of the rapid progress of the disease," and the notification that the government depots were to close brought frantic protests. Already, in the west, the government meal was all that stood between a swarming population and starvation.

Outside government circles, closing the food depots at the moment of failure appeared inexplicable. The *Times*, no advocate of relief for Ireland, found it impossible to understand why "the authorities cut off supplies with the undisputed fact of an extensive failure of this year's potato crop staring them in the face," and Catholic Archbishop John MacHale, known as "the Lion of St. Jarlath's," told Lord John Russell, "You might as well issue an edict of general starvation as stop the supplies."

But Trevelyan and the British government were not to be shaken in their determination. A quantity of meal, rather under 3000 tons in all, the residue of Sir Robert Peel's scheme, remained in the depots, and permission was given to distribute this to starving dis-

216

tricts, but in the smallest possible quantities, and then only after a relief committee had been formed and a subscription raised to pay for it. No free issues whatever were to be made. Nevertheless, Commissariat officers in Ireland did give food away; a Major Wainwright, for instance, was detected giving a quantity of meal to starving persons in Oughterard, County Galway, early in August and was reprimanded from Whitehall.

Closing the public works was even more difficult. A Treasury minute of July 21, 1846, directing all works to be closed, except in certain unusual cases, had had little effect; on the excuse that works were not finished, or that extraordinary distress existed in the neighborhood, a large number continued. The Chancellor of the Exchequer now ordered that all undertakings must be shut down on August 8, irrespective of whether or not they were completed and of the distress in the district.

Angry demonstrations followed. In Limerick on August 5, on being told their employment was to end, laborers tore up the stretch of road they had just laid; in Cork about August 18 a mob of 400 laborers, declaring they were starving, marched into the town carrying their spades and demanding work; however, they dispersed "quietly" on being addressed by the sub-inspector of police, who added a note to his report that "employment is very much needed."

During a bad year in Ireland the condition of the people invariably took a sharp turn for the worse after October 1; vegetables and gleanings were finished, and in normal years this was the moment at which the people became dependent on the potato—and if the crop was poor, this was when they began to starve. And now there were no potatoes at all.

Trevelyan renounced a basic principle of his scheme: orders for Indian corn were sent to the United States. But on October 14 the American packet brought a discouraging report to Liverpool. Orders for the new crop of Indian corn, to be exported in the spring, were ten times the quantity obtainable; the French government in particular was buying very largely. As for rye, the Prussian government had bought up all available supplies in August and September. Nevertheless, the British government continued to take refuge behind the promise that ample supplies would arrive in December or January.

217

If, however, by a miracle the promised "ample supplies" of Indian corn had arrived in Ireland, the Commissariat would have been quite unable to deal with them. Milling was an insoluble difficulty; either there were no mills or, as in Westport and other places, the mills were occupied by merchants milling grain for their own account and for export, protected by the government's tenderness for private enterprise, while the Indian corn for the starving remained unground. In September an additional misfortune occurred; during a spell of exceptionally hot weather streams all over Ireland went dry, and small country mills were unable to grind.

Eventually the government Indian corn was milled in the Admiralty mills at Deptford, Portsmouth, and Plymouth, the naval mills at Malta, and in hired mills at Rotherhithe and Maldon, Essex, and taken by Admiralty steamer to Ireland.

Trevelyan was then struck by the idea of hand mills; why should not the people grind the Indian corn themselves? he asked. True, the grain of Indian corn was so hard that in the Southern states of America it was milled more than once, but Trevelyan borrowed a hand mill from the museum at India House; a quern, a Celtic hand mill, from the west of Ireland; and another from Wick, in the Shetlands; and "by putting all three into the hands of skilful workmen" hoped "to produce something." A "manufactory of handmills" was actually established by Captain Mann at Kilkee, County Clare, early in November; each hand mill cost the impossibly large sum, for the Irish destitute, of fifteen shillings, but a number were bought out of charitable funds and distributed free.

Yet there was a simpler solution: why should not the people eat Indian corn unground? On October 9 a memorandum was sent out to relief committees informing them that "Indian corn in its unground state affords an equally wholesome and nutritious food" as when ground into meal. It could be used in two ways: the grain could be crushed between two good-sized stones and then boiled in water, with a little grease or fat, "if at hand." Or it could be used without crushing, simply by soaking it all night in warm water, changing this, in the morning, for clear, cold water, bringing to the boil, and boiling the corn for an hour and a half; it could then be eaten with milk, with salt, or plain. Boiling without crushing was the method particularly recommended. "Ten pounds of the corn so prepared is ample food for a laboring man for seven days.

218

. . . Corn so used," continued the memorandum, blandly, "will be considerably cheaper to the Committee and the people than meal, and will be well adapted to meet the deficiency of mill power. . . ."

Unground Indian corn is not only hard but sharp and irritating—it even pierces the intestines—and is all but impossible to digest. Boiling for an hour and a half did not soften the flint-hard grain, and Indian corn in this state eaten by half-starving people produced agonizing pains, especially in children.

Autumn was now passing into winter. The nettles and black-berries, the edible roots and cabbage leaves on which hundreds of people had been eking out an existence disappeared; flocks of wretched beings, resembling human scarecrows, had combed the blighted potato fields over and over again until not a fragment of a potato that was conceivably edible remained. Children began to die. In Skibbereen workhouse, more than 50 percent of the children admitted after October 1, 1846, died; the deaths, said the workhouse physician, were due to "diarrhœa acting on an exhausted constitution." This was probably bacillary dysentery.

At this moment of suffering, unprecedented weather added greatly to the misery of the people. The climate of Ireland is famous for its mildness; years pass without a fall of snow; in the gardens of the south and west semitropical plants flourish, and tubers of the genus *Dahlia* can be left to winter in the ground without damage from frost. In 1846, at the end of October, it became cold, and in November snow began to fall. Six inches of snow and drifts were reported at the early date of November 12 from Tyrone.

The winter of 1846–1847 was "the most severe in living memory," and the longest. Frost was continuous; icy gales blew "perfect hurricanes of snow, hail and sleet," with a force unknown since the famous "great wind" of 1839; roads were impassable, and transport was brought to a standstill. In the autumn and winter of 1846–1847 the wind came from the northeast; it had blown across Russia, and it was icy. The whole continent of Europe that winter was gripped by bitter cold, and in England, by the middle of December, the Thames was a mass of floating ice.

To the Irish people the abnormal severity of the winter brought disaster. One of the compensations of the nineteenth-century Irish peasant's life was warmth. The climate was normally mild, and the

219

possession of a supply of peat almost universal; a turf fire burned in the Irish cabin night and day, and in normal times did not go out perhaps for a century. Since potatoes do not require cultivation during the winter, the Irish peasant was not forced to go out in bad weather; he spent the cold, wet days indoors, and though he was dressed in rags and his children were naked except for a single garment, they endured little hardship.

Now he had to go out in his rags to labor on the public works, be drenched with rain and driving snow and cut by icy gales; and more often than not, he was already starving. Laborers began to "faint with exhaustion," and a Board of Works engineer told Trevelyan that "as an engineer he was ashamed of allotting so little task-work for a day's wages, while as a man he was ashamed of requiring so much." After the end of November, Routh's reports contained a rapidly increasing number of cases of deaths on the works from starvation aggravated by exposure to cold, snow, and drenching rain.

The people became bewildered. They had taken in very little of what was happening; at this period Irish was spoken in rural districts and English barely understood, while in the west English was not understood at all. No attempt was made to explain the catastrophe to the people; on the contrary, government officials and relief committee members treated the destitute with impatience and contempt; the wretched, ragged crowds provoked irritation, heightened by the traditional English distrust and dislike of the native Irish.

Trevelyan had reached the conclusion that everything that could and should be done for Ireland had been done, and that any further step could only be taken at the expense of the rest of the United Kingdom. "I deeply regret the primary and appalling evil of the insufficiency of the supplies of food in this country," he wrote on December 22, "but the stores we are able to procure for the western division of Ireland are insufficient even for that purpose, and how can we undertake more?" In a private letter to Routh he wrote, "If we were to purchase for Irish use faster than we are now doing, we should commit a crying injustice to the rest of the country."

The outcome of this policy was such a tragedy as overtook the district of Skibbereen. Starvation in Skibbereen had been reported as early as September, and on December 3 two Protestant clergymen from the district, Mr. Caulfield and Mr. Townsend, crossed to London and saw Trevelyan at the Treasury. They told him the government relief scheme was failing in Skibbereen. The sole employment in Skibbereen was on the public works, but only eightpence a day was paid, which was not sufficient to feed a family; sixty to seventy persons who would otherwise die of hunger were fed daily with soup at Mr. Caulfield's house. The two clergymen implored the government to send food. No food was sent.

On December 15 Mr. Nicholas Cummins, the well-known magistrate of Cork, had paid a visit to Skibbereen and the surrounding district and had been horrified by what he saw. He appears to have written to the authorities, but without result, because on December 22 he addressed a letter to the Duke of Wellington, who was an Irishman, and also sent a copy to the *Times*. It was published on December 24, 1846.

"My Lord Duke," wrote Mr. Cummins.

Without apology or preface, I presume so far to trespass on your Grace as to state to you, and by the use of your illustrious name, to present to the British public the following statement of what I have myself seen within the last three days. Having for many years been intimately connected with the western portion of the County of Cork, and possessing some small property there, I thought it right personally to investigate the truth of several lamentable accounts which had reached me, of the appalling state of misery to which that part of the country was reduced. I accordingly went on the 15th instant to Skibbereen, and to give the instance of one townland which I visited, as an example of the state of the entire coast district, I shall state simply what I saw. . . . Being aware that I should have to witness scenes of frightful hunger, I provided myself with as much bread as five men could carry, and on reaching the spot I was surprised to find the wretched hamlet apparently deserted. I entered some of the hovels to ascertain the cause, and the scenes which presented themselves were such as no tongue or pen can convey the slightest idea of. In the first, six famished and ghastly skeletons, to all appearances dead, were huddled in a corner on some filthy straw, their sole covering what seemed a ragged horse-cloth, their wretched legs hanging about, naked above the knees. I approached with horror, and found by a low moaning they were alive —they were in fever, four children, a woman and what had once been a man. It is impossible to go through the detail. Suffice it to say, that in a few minutes I was surrounded by at least 200 such phantoms, such frightful spectres as no words can describe, either from famine or from fever. Their demoniac yells are still ringing in my ears, and their horrible images are fixed upon by brain. My heart sickens at the recital, but I must go on.

In another case, decency would forbid what follows, but it must be told. My clothes were nearly torn off in my endeavour to escape from the throng of pestilence around, when my neckcloth was seized from behind by a grip which compelled me to turn, I found myself grasped by a woman with an infant just born in her arms and the remains of a filthy sack across her loins—the sole covering of herself and baby. The same morning the police opened a house on the adjoining lands, which was observed shut for many days, and two frozen corpses were found, lying upon the mud floor, half devoured by rats.

A mother, herself in a fever, was seen the same day to drag out the corpse of her child, a girl about twelve, perfectly naked, and leave it half covered with stones. In another house, within 500 yards of the cavalry station at Skibbereen, the dispensary doctor found seven wretches lying unable to move, under the same cloak. One had been dead many hours, but the others were unable to move either themselves or the corpse.

Routh blamed the landlords. The proprietors of the Skibbereen district, he told Trevelyan, "draw an annual income of £50,000." There were twelve landowners, of whom the largest was Lord Carbery, who, Routh declared, drew £15,000 in rents; next was Sir William Rixon Beecher, on whose estate the town of Skibbereen stood; Sir William, alleged Routh, drew £10,000, while the Reverend Stephen Townsend, a Protestant clergyman, drew £8000. "Ought such destitution to prevail with such resources?" Routh inquired, but suggested no action, and officially the appeals for Skibbereen were answered by a Treasury minute written on behalf of the Lords of the Treasury by Trevelyan on January 8, 1847. "It is their Lordships' desire," ran the minute, "that effectual relief should be given to the inhabitants of the district in the neighbourhood of Skibbereen ... the local Relief Committees should be stimulated to the utmost possible exertion; soup kitchens should be established under the management of these Committees at such distances as will render them accessible to all the destitute inhabit-

222

ants and . . . liberal donations should be made by Government in aid of funds raised by local subscriptions." These counsels of perfection closed the discussion.

As if starvation were not enough, a new terror assailed the Irish people. The government had been warned in the autumn of 1846 that after famine "there will follow, as a natural consequence, as in former years, typhus fever or some other malignant pestilence"; and fever, on a gigantic scale, was now beginning to ravage Ireland.

The Irish people spoke of "famine fever," but in fact two separate diseases were present, typhus and relapsing fever, both conveyed by the common louse and both already familiar in Ireland.

Typhus is a horrifying disease and was regarded by the Irish people with terror. Rickettsia attack the small blood vessels of the body, especially those of the skin and brain, and the patient becomes all but unrecognizable; the circulation of his blood is impeded, his face swells, and he turns the dark congested hue which has given typhus its Irish name of "black fever."

The organisms of relapsing fever enter the human bloodstream through the skin, like Rickettsia, and once infection has taken place the progress of the disease is rapid; within a few hours high fever and vomiting begin, continuing for several days. A crisis, with profuse sweating, follows, succeeded by extreme exhaustion. One crisis, however, does not indicate the end of the attack: six to seven days later there is a relapse; microscopic examination shows the organisms to be swarming in the blood once more; high fever and vomiting are again followed by a crisis; and should the patient survive, the pattern may be repeated three or four times before the attack finally comes to an end.

Never had conditions been so fatally favorable to the rapid spread of lice as in the famine winter of 1846–1847. The people were filthy. They had sold every stitch that would fetch the fraction of a penny, and they were wearing the same rags day after day, and night and day. Their bedding had been sold, and they slept covered with rags and old coats; to heat water to wash themselves or their clothes was out of the question; they were eating their food half or wholly raw, because they had no money to buy fuel; indeed, after months of starvation, even the strength to fetch water had disappeared.

223

The abnormal severity of the winter drove the people to huddle together for warmth; a fire or even a light in a cabin attracted neighbors and passersby; the traditional hospitality of the Irish poor provided a welcome, and all lay down to sleep in the warmth, side by side, on the cabin floor.

Hosts of beggars and homeless paupers tramped the roads, drifting from place to place without a fixed destination, filthy, starving, and louse-infested, often with fever actually on them. "Whole families were to be seen lying in fever by the roadside"; the contemporary name for the epidemic was "road fever." Yet the poor Irish, however distressed themselves, never refused admission to the poorest and most abject mendicant. The Irishman, wrote the Central Board of Health, "thinks himself accursed if he refuses admission to a begging stranger."

The total of those who died during the fever epidemic and of famine diseases will never be known, but probably about ten times more died of disease than of starvation. Among the upper classes, the percentage of those who caught fever and died was high; in Cavan upper-class mortality was estimated at 66 percent; around Ballinrobe 70 percent who took the fever perished; and in Sligo, Roscommon, Newry, Tuam, Leitrim, Tyrone, Lowtherstown, and almost every district in Ireland mortality among the upper classes was reported to be proportionately much higher than among the poor. The reason probably was that the constant occurrence of fever cases in their midst had brought the poor Irish some degree of immunity. No legal register of deaths existed at the period, and though the government asked repeatedly for estimates of the number of deaths, they were told an estimate was impossible. Too many had died for funeral services to be said over the bodies, and corpses had been buried at night, leaving no trace.

But horrors taking place in Ireland were only one aspect of the fever epidemic. As the terrible months of the autumn and winter of 1846–1847 went by and to starvation was added pestilence, the minds of the Irish people turned in an unprecedented direction. Before the potato failure, to leave Ireland had been regarded as the most terrible of all fates, and transportation was the most dreaded of sentences. But now the people, terrified and desperate, began to flee a land which seemed accursed. In a great mass movement they made their way, by tens of thousands, out of Ireland, across the

224

ocean to America or across the sea to Britain. Yet they did not leave fever behind; fever went with them, and the path to a new life became a path of horror.

The famine emigration, the exodus from Ireland in which hundreds of thousands of Irish fled from their country because to remain was death, is historically the most important event of the famine.

It was the famine emigrants, leaving their country with hatred in their hearts for the British and the British government, who built up communities across the ocean, above all in the United States, where the name of Britain was accursed. Their descendants continued to be Britain's powerful and bitter enemies, exacting vengeance for the sufferings their forbears endured. It is estimated that about a million and a quarter emigrants from Ireland crossed the Atlantic to North America during the years of the potato blight, and there was an even larger emigration across the Irish Channel to Great Britain, to Liverpool, Glasgow, and the ports of south Wales.

The Irish famine emigration is unlike most other emigrations because it was of a less civilized and less skilled people into a more civilized and more skilled community. Other emigrations have been of the independent and the sturdy in search of wider horizons, and such emigrants usually brought with them knowledge and technical accomplishment which the inhabitants of the country in which they settled did not possess. The Irish, from their abysmal poverty, brought nothing, and this poverty had forced them to become habituated to standards of living which the populations among whom they came considered unfit for human beings. Cellar dwellings, whether in English towns or the cities of North America, were almost invariably occupied by the Irish. Poverty, ignorance, and bewilderment brought them there, but it must not be forgotten that cellar dwellings resembled the dark, mud-floored cabins in which over half the population of Ireland had been accustomed to live under British rule.

The vast majority of emigrants to British North America landed at Quebec and went up the St. Lawrence to Montreal, a distance of 180 miles. But there was very little desire on the part of Irish emigrants to settle in British North America; with an almost frantic longing they wished to go to the United States. In 1847 the United States, with its nearly 23 million inhabitants and its rapidly develop-

225

ing territories, was immeasurably in advance of Canada.

Material advantages were not the only magnet which drew the Irish emigrant away from Canada to the United States. The native Irishman had become convinced that no justice or opportunity could exist for him under the Union Jack, and he shrank from the British North American colonies.

To offset the attractions of the United States, the British government consistently made the passage to British North America cheaper than to United States ports, and in addition transported poor emigrants who declared their intention of settling in Canada free, in barges, up the St. Lawrence into the interior. The urgent need of the British North American colonies for population was not, however, the British government's only reason for encouraging Irish emigration. The fear of an enormous poverty-stricken Irish migration into Britain was always present, and eighteen years before the famine, in 1827, a parliamentary committee had asserted that the choice was whether the Irish were to be enabled to emigrate to the North American colonies by fares' being kept down or "to deluge Great Britain with poverty and wretchedness and gradually but certainly to equalize the state of the English and Irish peasantry."

Cheap passages did not result in emigrants' settling in British North America. Advantage was taken of the low fare to cross the Atlantic to Quebec in a British ship, and often the emigrant, by alleging that his intention was to settle in Canada, procured free transport up the St. Lawrence before making his entry into the United States by the simple method of walking across the border.

In Canada in the spring of 1847, intelligent officials and citizens apprehensively awaited the immigration which would fall on them as soon as the St. Lawrence was clear of ice. The reports reaching Quebec of the frightful state of Ireland indicated a very large Irish immigration, destitute and in bad health. The idea, however, that fever, known to be raging in Ireland, constituted a danger crossed no one's mind. What was called "ship fever" was a well-known disease, recognized as being typhus but considered to arise from overcrowding and dirt in the confined space of a ship.

Regulations at Quebec required that all ships with passengers coming up the St. Lawrence should stop at the quarantine station on Grosse Isle, thirty miles down the river, for medical inspection;

226

those vessels which had sickness on board were then detained, and the sick taken to the quarantine hospital. Grosse Isle, a beautiful island lying in the middle of the majestic St. Lawrence, had been selected as the site for a quarantine station in 1832, at the time of a cholera epidemic; it is small, and its peculiar charm lies in the number of trees and shrubs which grow down to the water's edge and are mirrored in the St. Lawrence, so that the island seems to float. The brief coastline is diversified by a number of tiny rocky bays; in the interior large trees grow from green turf, and there is a remarkable variety of wild flowers. Near the river the quarantine buildings, which still exist, are low and white and do not detract from the beauty of the landscape; on rising ground above them a small white church nestles in green trees. "A fairy scene," exclaimed an emigrant as he approached the island. In this island paradise an appalling tragedy was to take place.

On February 19, 1847, Dr. Douglas, the medical officer in charge of the quarantine station at Grosse Isle, asked for £3000 to make preparations for the coming immigration, pointing out that during the previous year the number admitted to the quarantine hospital had been twice as large as usual and that reports from Ireland indicated that the state of the immigrants this year would be worse. Far from getting £3000, Dr. Douglas was assigned just under £300. He was allowed one small steamer, the *St. George,* to ply between Grosse Isle and Quebec and given permission to hire a sailing vessel, provided one could be found for not more than £50 for the season.

The citizens of Quebec, however, were so uneasy that at the beginning of March, 1847, they sent a petition to the secretary of state for the colonies, Earl Grey, in which they pointed out that the number of Irish immigrants was annually rising, that the present distress in Ireland must mean a further large increase, that they viewed with alarm the probable fate of poor Irish immigrants in the rigorous winter climate of Canada, and that there was also the possibility of such immigrants' bringing disease. They begged the Canadian government to take action.

There was one man who might have been able to convince the Canadian government that a catastrophe was approaching, Alexander Carlisle Buchanan. He was the chief emigration officer, he was esteemed in official circles, his reports were studied, his opinion

227

carried weight. Nevertheless, Buchanan, though he anticipated a very considerable increase in sickness, "did not make any official representation to Government" because, as he wrote, "it was a subject that did not come within the control of my department." The government, therefore, received no official warning that the emigration from Ireland was likely to present any problem, beyond being unusually large.

The opening of the St. Lawrence was late in 1847; "the merry month of May started with ice an inch thick," reported the Quebec *Gazette*, and the first vessel, the *Syria*, did not arrive until May 17. Less than a week later, the catastrophe had taken place and was beyond control. The *Syria* had 84 cases of fever on board, out of a total of 241 passengers; nine persons had died on the voyage, and one was to die on landing at Grosse Isle. All its passengers were Irish, had crossed to Liverpool to embark, and had spent one night at least in the cheap lodginghouses of Liverpool. In Dr. Douglas' opinion, 20 or 24 more were certain to sicken, bringing the total for the *Syria* to more than 100, and the quarantine hospital, built for 150 cases, could not possibly accommodate more than 200.

Dr. Douglas now told the Canadian government that he had "reliable information" that 10,600 emigrants at least had left Britain for Quebec since April 10. "Judging from the specimens just arrived," large numbers would have to go to the hospital; and he asked permission to build a new shed, to cost about £150, to be used as a hospital. On May 20, he received authority to erect the shed, provided the cost was kept down to £135.

Four days after the *Syria*, on May 21 eight ships arrived with a total of 430 fever cases. Two hundred and five were taken into the hospital, which became dangerously overcrowded, and the rest had to be left on board ship. "I have not a bed to lay them on or a place to put them," wrote Dr. Douglas. "I never contemplated the possibility of every vessel arriving with fever as they do now." Three days later, seventeen more vessels arrived, all with fever; a shed normally used to accommodate passengers detained for quarantine was turned into a hospital and instantly filled. There were now 695 persons in hospital and 164 on board ship waiting to be taken off; and Dr. Douglas wrote that he had received a message that twelve more vessels had anchored, "all sickly."

On May 26 thirty vessels, with 10,000 emigrants on board, were

228

waiting at Grosse Isle. On May 31 forty vessels were waiting, extending in a line two miles down the St. Lawrence; about 1100 cases of fever were on Grosse Isle in sheds, tents, and laid in rows in the little church; an equal number were on board the ships, waiting to be taken off; and a further 45,000 emigrants at least were expected.

By July, more than 2500 sick were on Grosse Isle, and conditions were appalling. "Medical men," wrote Dr. Douglas, were "disgusted with the disagreeable nature of their duties in treating such filthy cases." Many doctors died; Dr. Benson of Dublin, who had experience in fever hospitals in Ireland, arrived on May 21 and volunteered his services, but caught typhus and died six days later. Each of the medical officers was ill at some time, and three other doctors died of typhus in addition to Dr. Benson. At one period, twelve out of a medical staff of fourteen were ill; of the two other doctors, one left because he was afraid of catching typhus and one was summoned to a dying parent, leaving Dr. Douglas virtually single-handed. Patients on the ships were often left for four or five days without any medical attention; under the Passenger Act of 1842 ships were not compelled to carry a doctor, and only one doctor besides Dr. Benson happened to have been a passenger.

Nurses, too, were unobtainable, and the sick suffered tortures from lack of attention. A Catholic priest, Father Moylan, gave water to sick persons in a tent who had had nothing to drink for eighteen hours; another, Father McQuirk, was given carte blanche by Dr. Douglas to hire nurses, as many as possible, from among the healthy passengers. He offered high wages and told the women, speaking as their priest, that it was their duty to volunteer, but not one came forward. The fear of fever among the Irish, said Dr. Douglas, was so great that "the nearest relatives abandon each other whenever they can." The only persons who could be induced to take charge of the sick were abandoned and callous creatures, of both sexes, who robbed the dead.

The state of the emigrants as they landed was frightful. Very many of them had passed the voyage in a state of starvation. The official weekly issue of seven pounds of provisions was intended to guard against absolute destitution, but "it never could have been expected to be enough to sustain an adult through the voyage," reported the Senate Committee of the United States on Sickness and Mortality in Emigrant Ships. Passage brokers at Liverpool made a practice of displaying a loaf of bread in their offices to the starving Irish "to delude the poor into the belief that they will be fed at sea."

On the voyage, water often ran short, casks leaked; dishonest provisioning merchants bought cheap casks which had previously been used for wine, vinegar, or chemicals that made the water they contained undrinkable. When a government inquiry was held into the disaster at Grosse Isle, Alexander Carlisle Buchanan testified that during the summer of 1847 "the provisions of the Passenger Act appear to have been very generally observed by the masters of Emigrant vessels," and he was no doubt correct. But the Passenger Act of 1842 reduced requirements to such a bare minimum that very little had to go wrong for the emigrant to suffer severely, even if he were fortunate enough not to fall a victim to typhus.

By the middle of the summer of 1847, imposing a quarantine for fever had been abandoned as hopeless. The line of ships waiting for inspection was now several miles long; to make quarantine effective, 20,000 to 25,000 contacts should be isolated for whom there was no room on the small island. Therefore, to carry out the quarantine regulations was, wrote Dr. Douglas, "physically impossible," and at the end of May passengers on ships with fever were allowed to stay after the fever cases had been removed and to perform their quarantine on board, the period to be fifteen days instead of ten. Dr. Douglas believed that a simple washing down and airing would make the holds healthy. "After ablutions with water," he wrote, "by opening stern ports and bow ports . . . a complete current of air can pass through the hold, in fact a bird can fly through it." So the passengers remained in the holds, with disastrous consequences.

So great was the number of sick that "a fatal delay of several days" occurred before fever cases were taken away; meanwhile, sick and healthy were cooped up together, and fresh infection took place. The *Agnes*, for instance, which arrived with 427 passengers, had only 150 alive after a quarantine of fifteen days.

In a wooded hollow, one of the most beautiful of the miniature valleys of Grosse Isle, once the site of the emigrant cemetery, a four-sided monument commemorates those who died. On the first side the inscription runs:

230

> In this secluded spot lie the mortal remains of
> 5,294 persons, who, flying from pestilence and
> famine in Ireland in the year 1847, found in
> America but a grave.

A second side bears the names of Dr. Benson of Dublin and of three other doctors who died while attending the sick; the third, the names of two doctors who died on Grosse Isle during the cholera epidemic of 1832–1834; and the fourth records that the monument was erected by Dr. Douglas and eighteen medical assistants who were on duty during the epidemic of 1847.

Over 100,000 emigrants left the United Kingdom for British North America in 1847. By the end of that year, it is estimated, 20,000 had died in Canada—5300, at the lowest estimate, on Grosse Isle, and 14,706 in Quebec, Montreal, Kingston, and Toronto. A further 1120 died in the province of New Brunswick, and 25,000 persons at least had been in Canadian hospitals. Crossing the Atlantic exacted a fearful toll, and 15,000 emigrants perished during the voyage, the majority from typhus. "If crosses and tombs could be erected on the water," wrote one of the commissioners for emigration in the United States, "the whole route of the emigrant vessels from Europe to America would long since have assumed the appearance of a crowded cemetery."

The flow of emigrants, "practically all of them Irish," from British North America across the border into the United States provoked angry resentment. United States officials at river and lake ports and captains of United States ferryboats turned back poor Irish emigrants; steamboats plying at St. John's and on Lake Champlain refused them as passengers; the United States authorities at Ogdensburg sent them back; and the official in charge of the ferry at Lowiston was sent to prison for landing Irish emigrants on the United States shore. Nevertheless, thousands of poor Irish did cross the border, and those who went from Canada were able-bodied men who left their wives and young children, their parents and aged relatives behind them, to be maintained by the British government and the generosity of the inhabitants of British North America. If the men established themselves in the United States, their families joined them; if not, the families remained a permanent charge on British charity.

The poor Irish emigrant was excluded and feared and, by a section of the populace, persecuted as well; but the generosity and the sympathy of the citizens of the United States for nations in distress were already strong, and when the tragedy taking place in Ireland became known, shiploads of food and thousands of dollars began to pour across the Atlantic.

The first organizers of the United States aid for Ireland on a large scale were the Quakers, the Society of Friends; and, headed by Jacob Harvey, a prominent citizen of New York, an Irishman, and a Friend, they became the main channel for the transmission of relief.

Family feeling is stronger in Ireland than anywhere else in Europe, and sending money home was already a characteristic of the Irish emigrant. "I am proud to say," wrote Jacob Harvey, "that the Irish in America have always remitted more money, ten times over, than all the foreigners put together!" He estimated that the total amount sent home by Irish emigrants in America during 1847 amounted to a million dollars, or £200,000 at the then prevailing rate of about five dollars to the pound sterling.

The response of the citizens of the United States to the appeal for starving Ireland was "on a scale unparalleled in history." A great public meeting was held in Washington on February 9, 1847, under the chairmanship of the vice president of the United States, at which it was recommended that meetings should be held in every city, town, and village so that a large national contribution might be raised and "forwarded with all practicable dispatch to the scene of suffering." Meetings all over the country, from Albany to New Orleans, followed; on several occasions, Nicholas Cummins' letter describing the state of Skibbereen was read, and large sums were collected. New York, for instance, sent more than $30,000, and Philadelphia, in spite of the anti-Irish riots of 1844, more than $20,000, with an additional sum of $3800 which had been raised in 1846. Mayors and chief collectors of customs at the ports of New York, Boston, Philadelphia, and Baltimore, with members of the Senate, volunteered to receive local contributions and forward them to Ireland, placing them "in such hands for distribution as they, in their discretion, may think advisable." The contributions were entrusted to the Friends, who acted, among other bodies, as agents for money collected for Ireland by Tam-

232

many, the central organization of the Democratic Party of the United States. The Catholic churches in New England sent $19,000, and the Catholic church in Brooklyn $13,000. Other contributions included $20,000 sent by Bishop Fitzpatrick of Boston to Archbishop Crolly of Armagh on March 1, 1847, and a further $4000 later; the historian of the Catholic diocese of Boston estimates that a total of $150,000 was subscribed in the diocese for Irish relief.

"Donation parties" for Ireland were held undenominationally; concerts and tea parties were organized; and young ladies in select New York boarding schools devoted their recreation time to making "useful and beautiful articles" which were sold for Ireland.

A high proportion of contributions were in kind, not in cash, encouraged by an announcement made early in February that the British government would pay the freight on all donations of food, and that on United States roads and canals no tolls on provisions for Ireland would be charged. In many states, South Carolina for instance, railroads volunteered to carry packages marked "Ireland" free. The amount of freight paid by the British government on the donations of food consigned to the Society of Friends amounted to the considerable sum of £33,017 5s. 7d. Cities and towns in the United States chartered vessels to go to Ireland. Newark, New Jersey, sent the brig *Overmann* at the end of March to the Committee of the Society of Friends in Cork to distribute "without distinction of religious sect or location," and the Irish Relief Committee of Philadelphia sent the bark *John Walsh* to Londonderry, the brig *St. George* to Cork, and the brig *Lydia Ann* to Limerick, to be disposed of at the discretion of the Committee of the Society of Friends.

On July 29, 1847, the treasurer of the New York Irish Relief Committee wrote to the Society of Friends in Dublin, "I think there is now an appearance of an end being brought to this glorious demonstration of a nation's sympathy for poor suffering Ireland." Transport of food across the United States in winter was not possible, because the canals, which were then the main arteries of communication, froze; and in the autumn of 1847 the collection of subscriptions for Ireland ceased. Generosity had been astonishing; Cincinnati, for example, had expected to raise $6000

233

but had sent $30,000, and New York contributed to the value of more than $200,000. About £16,000 in cash was forwarded to the Central Relief Committee of the Friends in Dublin, and the food consigned to their committees in Dublin and Cork amounted to nearly ten thousand tons. In addition, large quantities of clothing were dispatched, on which no value was put by the donors in the United States.

To arrive at any accurate total is impossible; while the Society of Friends formed the main channel, large sums in donations and from collections in Catholic churches were also forwarded to Catholic bishops in Ireland. A modern United States authority estimates the total value of gifts at a million dollars, a sum worth many times its value today. This was in addition to money remitted by Irish emigrants themselves.

But while American generosity to Ireland during the famine has rightly become a tradition, it should not be overlooked that money was subscribed in England. Queen Victoria personally gave £2000. The British Association for the Relief of Extreme Distress expended about £391,700 in Ireland, and the Society of Friends raised £42,906; other societies in England subscribed £70,916. The final total, not including money raised in Ireland, was more than £505,000, amounting at the rate of exchange at the time to over $2,500,000.

The famine had brought about a change in the attitude of the British government toward Ireland. It was impossible any longer to deny that something was dangerously wrong with the state of Ireland, and while there was little to choose between the rebellious people and the irresponsible extravagant landlords—as Lord John Russell remarked, "a plague on both your houses"—England, for her own safety, could not abandon Ireland entirely. Therefore, though direct responsibility for Irish relief was to cease, Lord John wished to lay a "ground work" for "permanent improvement," and on July 17 he wrote, "What we must chiefly look for is advance of money for good profitable works, be they drainage, harbours, railroads, reclamation of waste lands, or what not. In short we must give very little for relief and much for permanent improvement—that is my programme for next year." The government had about a million pounds in hand already earmarked for

234

Ireland, which it proposed to devote to works of permanent improvement.

A substantial financial concession was also given to Irish property owners when, on July 8, Sir Charles Wood announced that half the money advanced by the British government to finance public works and soup kitchens would be forgiven, a sum of £4,500,000. It seemed that a ray of hope for Ireland was becoming visible, especially as, during the summer of 1847, the position of Lord John Russell's government was strengthened by victory in a general election. But with the ill luck which dogged Ireland at this moment, Great Britain was overtaken by a serious financial crisis, one of the most serious the country had ever experienced, and the Treasury found itself dangerously short of money.

"The falling off in the Revenue," wrote Lord John on September 10, "still above one million sterling in two months, damages all my views of being able to help Ireland out of the savings of the loan." Once again urgent domestic affairs in Great Britain pushed Ireland into the background. "I have been so worried about the state of trade in the city," Lord John told the Earl of Clarendon, the Lord Lieutenant of Ireland, "that I have little time to write or think on other matters," and he warned him, "I fear you have a most troublesome winter ahead of you . . . and here we have no money."

Charles Wood, the Chancellor of the Exchequer, flatly refused financial help for Ireland. "I have no money," he told Clarendon. He would refrain from pressing Ireland for repayments due on money already advanced, but no fresh money would be forthcoming. "The more bent I am on throwing present expenditure on them, the more lenient I am disposed to be as to what is expended already," he wrote. "I have the most perfect understanding on this subject with Trevelyan."

From this point onward, good intentions on the part of the British government became increasingly difficult to discern. Making every allowance for the depleted state of the Treasury, and bearing in mind the large sums already expended on Irish relief, sums representing many times their value today, it is still hardly possible to explain, or to condone, the British government's determination to throw the Irish destitute on the local poor rate, the

235

able-bodied men being sent to the workhouse to discourage applications.

The Irish Poor Law Extension Act of 1847 guaranteed that all the expense of relief was to be borne by the already hard-pressed landlords. The property of Ireland was to maintain the poverty of Ireland. Relief operations under the Soup Kitchen Act, by which England had helped to finance the issue of more than three million rations daily, had been rapidly brought to an end. By August 15, Commissariat depots had been closed, the meal and grain being sold not cheaply but at current market prices, and remainders not being given away but picked up by government steamer.

If the new Poor Law was to be effective, the workhouses must be cleared and filled with ablebodied men who were destitute; but to clear the workhouses proved impossible. The Poor Law guardians were unwilling to turn the helpless out; at Galway, for instance, they indignantly refused, while at Tralee, the immense distressed district which contained two estates under the Court of Chancery, the workhouse inmates had no clothes to put on and no shelter to which to return, for landlords customarily took advantage of destitute persons' being forced to enter the workhouse to pull their cabins down.

The Treasury had no intention of acting, nor any doubt what should be done—taxes must be collected, force must be used. "Arrest, remand, do anything you can," wrote Charles Wood to Clarendon on November 22; "send horse, foot and dragoons, all the world will applaud you, and I should not be at all squeamish as to what I did, to the verge of the law, and a little beyond."

By the middle of December, 1847, the destitute, half naked, and starving were besieging the workhouses. From Tralee on December 15, Mr. Dobree of the Commissariat reported that the able-bodied were "coming up in masses to be refused," 700 to 800 at a time. The workhouse, which held 1400, was full; "the labouring class have no visible means of existence." Ballina workhouse on December 11 had 500 more inmates than it had been built to contain; Kilrush on December 14 had 500 to 600 too many; Galway on December 19 had 500, of whom 200 were fever cases; Erris was "out of control," with three quarters of the population urgently requiring relief.

The sufferings of the people began to approach the horrors of

236

the winter of 1846–1847; the country, generally speaking, was ruined, pauperism was spreading, there was no employment, and though the yield of the potato crop was superb, the quantity planted was inadequate—only 20 percent of that of previous years, because of the failure to provide seed potatoes. Dead bodies were found lying by roadsides and in fields; men who had tramped many miles to a workhouse only to be refused admittance died at the gates; a man turned away from Tipperary workhouse died after lying outside the gates for twelve hours.

The spring of 1848 was cold in Ireland; throughout February there were falls of snow, and the country people believed that snow would prevent the reappearance of blight. In 1847 the potato crop had proved superb, and now potatoes were planted all over Ireland in what Lord Clarendon described as a "frenzy of confidence."

Severe sacrifices were made to obtain seed potatoes: clothes, bedsteads, tables, and chairs were sold, and a Poor Law inspector reported that small occupiers, "already reduced to a state of all but pauperism, are straining every nerve to plant potatoes as largely as possible as a last desperate venture." Potatoes were "stuck in everywhere they could be planted and everyone's hopes were raised at the idea of a return to the old system." Landlords looked forward to rents' being paid, the people to having enough to eat. Reports coming in to the Board of Works in Dublin estimated the amount of land put down to potatoes, compared with the previous year, as twice as much in some districts, in others three, four, five, and even ten times as much. Almost no green crops—cabbages, beans, carrots, kale—had been sown; the resident magistrate at Ballinasloe reported that the "small farmers have abandoned attempts at any other kind of crop and have staked all they possessed or could borrow" on potatoes.

Through May and until halfway through June, the weather was favorable. But from the middle of June, 1848, the terrible story of 1846 was repeated, blow after blow. The weather changed and became continually wet; by the middle of July the catastrophe had begun. "We were all in the greatest spirits at the approach of plenty," wrote Father John O'Sullivan, parish priest of Kenmare, on July 16, "but blight has made its appearance. On the morning of the 13th, to the astonishment of everyone, the potato

237

fields that had, on the previous evening, presented an appearance that was calculated to gladden the hearts of the most indifferent, appeared blasted, withered, blackened and, as it were, sprinkled with vitriol, and the whole country has in consequence been thrown into dismay and confusion."

For the Irish people, "the famine" will always mean these years of concentrated disaster in which blight first appeared and in rapid succession the partial failure of 1845 was followed by the total failure of 1846 and the second total failure of 1848. The history of what then occurred is deeply engraved in the memory of the Irish race; all hope of assimilation with England was then lost, and bitterness without parallel took possession of the Irish mind.

The treatment of the Irish people by the British government during the great potato famine has been described as genocide, race murder. The British government has been accused, and not only by the Irish, of wishing to exterminate the Irish people, as Cromwell wished to "extirpate" them and as Hitler wished to exterminate the Jews. The 1840s, however, must not be judged by the standards of today, and whatever parsimony and callousness the British government displayed toward Ireland were paralleled seven years later by the treatment of her own soldiers which brought about the destruction of the British Army in the Crimea.

The conduct of the British government during the famine is divided into two periods. During the first, from the date of the partial famine in 1845 until the transfer to the Poor Law in the summer of 1847, the government behaved with considerable generosity. An elaborate relief organization was set up, public works were started on a scale never attempted before, and what was for the time a very large sum of money indeed, more than eight million pounds, was advanced. Not enough was done, considering the size of the catastrophe, but it is doubtful if any government in Europe at that date would have done more.

But during the second period, after the transfer to the Poor Law in the summer of 1847, the behavior of the British government is difficult to defend. Lord John Russell and his advisers, in particular Sir Charles Wood and Trevelyan, were aware of the state of the Irish Poor Law. They knew that most of the distressed areas were bankrupt, that the worst had never been anything

238

else, that in those districts where poverty, destitution, and starvation were greatest the workhouses were badly equipped or not equipped at all, dirty, understaffed, and disorganized. They knew that in the most distressed areas, taxes for the relief of the poor in normal times had been virtually uncollectable, while in others they had to be collected with the aid of police, troops, and sometimes ships of war, and even then were only partially gathered. Yet, with these facts before them, the government threw the hordes of wretched destitute on their local poor rates, refusing assistance when the second total failure of the potato occurred in 1848. Since Britain was passing through a financial crisis, the justification of the government's actions was expediency, but it is difficult to reconcile expediency with duty and moral principles.

The most serious charge against the British government, however, is not the transfer to the Poor Law. Neither during the famine nor for decades afterwards were any measures of reconstruction or agricultural improvement attempted, and this neglect condemned Ireland to decline. A devastating new disease had attacked the potato; nothing to equal the total destruction of 1846 had been seen before; yet no serious effort was made to teach the people to grow any other crop, and when Lord Clarendon tried to effect improvement by means of "agricultural instructors," his scheme was ridiculed, Charles Wood writing contemptuously of Clarendon's "hobby." The Irish small tenant was inevitably driven back on the potato: he was penniless, starving, ignorant; the only crop he knew how to cultivate was the potato; generally speaking, the only tool he owned and could use was a spade. He had no choice. Yet when the potato failed totally again in 1848, the government exploded in fury. "In 1847," Lord John wrote, angrily, "eight millions were advanced to enable the Irish to supply the loss of the potato crop and to cast about them for some less precarious food. . . . The result is that they have placed more dependence on the potato than ever and have again been deceived. How can such people be assisted?"

As nothing was done to improve agriculture, so nothing was done to improve the system under which land was occupied in Ireland. Tenants at will remained tenants at will; twenty years after the famine, Isaac Butt was still writing, "The vast majority of the occupiers of land in Ireland are at this moment liable to be

239

turned out at the pleasure of their landlords"; and improvements carried out by the tenant continued to become the property of the landlord.

These misfortunes were not part of a plan to destroy the Irish nation; they fell on the people because the government of Lord John Russell was afflicted with an extraordinary inability to foresee consequences. It has been frequently declared that the parsimony of the British government during the famine was the main cause of the sufferings of the people, and parsimony was certainly carried to remarkable lengths; but obtuseness, shortsightedness, and ignorance probably contributed more.

To take only a few instances, it did not occur to Lord John Russell and his advisers that, by forcing the famine-stricken applicant for relief to give up every possession, they were creating fresh armies of paupers, even though Lord Clarendon had inquired if it were wise to compel a man to become a pauper, when he was not one already, in order to be saved from starvation. It was not, apparently, anticipated that refusing to assist the famine-stricken small tenants with seed would result in holdings' being left unsown, nor that, unless some means of subsistence were provided, men with families who had lost their winter food must crowd on the public works.

Even the self-evident truth that Ireland is not England was not realized by the government in Whitehall; the desolate, starving west was assumed to be served by snug grocers and prosperous merchants and to be a field for private enterprise; bankrupt squireens living in jerry-built mansions with rain dripping through the roof became county gentry, and plans for sea transport of corn were made as if the perilous harbors of the west coast were English ports.

Much of this obtuseness sprang from the fanatical faith of mid-nineteenth-century British politicians in the economic doctrine of laissez-faire—no interference by government, no meddling with the operation of natural causes. The government was perpetually nervous of being too good to Ireland and of corrupting the Irish people by kindness and so stifling the virtues of self-reliance and industry. In addition, hearts were hardened by the antagonism then felt by the English toward the Irish, an antagonism rooted far back in religious and political history; and at the period of the

240

famine, irritation had been added as well. The discreditable state of Ireland, the subject of adverse comment throughout the civilized world, her perpetual misfortunes, the determined hostility of most of her population, even their character provoked intense irritation in England. It is impossible to read the letters of British statesmen of the period—Charles Wood and Trevelyan, for instance—without astonishment at the influence exerted by antagonism and irritation on government policy in Ireland during the famine.

It is not characteristic of the English to behave as they have behaved in Ireland; as a nation, the English have proved themselves to be capable of generosity, tolerance, and magnanimity—but not where Ireland is concerned. As Sydney Smith, the celebrated writer and wit, wrote: "The moment the very name of Ireland is mentioned, the English seem to bid adieu to common feeling, common prudence and common sense, and to act with the barbarity of tyrants and the fatuity of idiots."

How many people died in the famine will never precisely be known. It is almost certain that, owing to geographical difficulties and the unwillingness of the people to be registered, the census of 1841 gave a total smaller than the population in fact was. Officers engaged in relief work put the population as much as 25 percent higher; landlords distributing relief were horrified when providing, as they imagined, for 60 persons to find more than 400 "start from the ground."

In 1841 the population of Ireland was given as 8,175,124; in 1851, after the famine, it had dropped to 6,552,385, and the census commissioners calculated that, at the normal rate of increase, the total should have been 9,018,799, so that a loss of at least 2,500,000 persons had taken place. Between 1846 and 1851, nearly a million persons emigrated, and it therefore appears that, roughly, about a million and a half perished during the famine, of hunger, diseases brought on by hunger, and fever. Between 1848 and 1864, however, thirteen million pounds was sent home by emigrants in America to bring relatives out of Ireland, and it is part of the famine tragedy that, because no adequate measures of reconstruction were undertaken, a steady drain of the best and most enterprising left Ireland, to enrich other countries.

241

Time brought retribution. By the outbreak of World War II Ireland was independent, and she would not fight on England's side. Liberty and England did not appear to the Irish to be synonymous, and the Free State remained neutral. Many thousands of Free State Irishmen volunteered, but the famous regiments of southern Ireland had ceased to exist, and the "inexhaustible nursery of the finest soldiers" was no longer at England's service.

There was also a more direct payment. Along the west coast of Ireland, in Mayo especially, on remote Clare Island, and in the dunes above the Six Mile Strand are a number of graves of petty officers and able seamen of the British Navy and Merchant Service, representatives of many hundreds who were drowned off the coast of Ireland because the Irish harbors were not open to British ships. From these innocents, in all probability ignorant of the past, who had never heard of failures of the potato, evictions, fever, and starvation, was exacted part of the price for the famine.

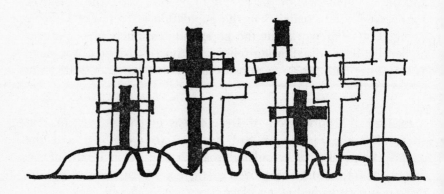

The Passing of the Gael

By ETHNA CARBERY
(1866–1902)

They are going, going, going from the valleys and the hills,
They are leaving far behind them heathery moor and mountain rills,
All the wealth of hawthorn hedges where the brown thrush sways
    and thrills.

They are going, shy-eyed cailins, and lads so straight and tall,
From the purple peaks of Kerry, from the crags of wild Imaal,
From the greening plains of Mayo, and the glens of Donegal.

They are leaving pleasant places, shores with snowy sands out-
    spread;
Blue and lonely lakes a-stirring when the wind stirs overhead;
Tender living hearts that love them, and the graves of kindred
    dead.

They shall carry to the distant land a teardrop in the eye
And some shall go uncomforted—their days an endless sigh
For Kathaleen Ni Houlihan's sad face, until they die.

Oh, Kathaleen Ni Houlihan, your road's a thorny way,
And 'tis a faithful soul would walk the flints with you for aye,
Would walk the sharp and cruel flints until his locks grew gray.

So some must wander to the East, and some must wander West;
Some seek the white wastes of the North, and some a Southern
    nest;
Yet never shall they sleep so sweet as on your mother breast.

Within the city streets, hot, hurried, full of care,
A sudden dream shall bring them a whiff of Irish air—
A cool air, faintly scented, blown soft from otherwhere.

Oh, the cabins, long deserted!—Olden memories awake—
Oh, the pleasant, pleasant places!—Hush! the blackbird in the brake!
Oh, the dear and kindly voices!—Now their hearts are fain to ache.

They may win a golden store—sure the whins were golden too;
And no foreign skies hold beauty like the rainy skies they knew;
Nor any night wind cool the brow as did the foggy dew.

.   .   .

They are going, going, going, and we cannot bid them stay;
Their fields are now the stranger's, where the stranger's cattle
stray.
Oh! Kathaleen Ni Houlihan, your way's a thorny way!

Emigration

MARY COLUM *wrote from America, in* 1928:

I remember still with emotion the emigration of the young
people of the neighborhood to America. In those days the farmer's
children were raised for export. There were times of the year—
in spring or fall—when there would be a sort of group emigration;
that is, a dozen or so would start off together once or twice a week
for a few weeks to take the train to the boat at Queenstown or
Derry. Generally each group was bound for the same town in
America where they had friends or relatives who had paid their
passage money beforehand or sent them their tickets. The night
before their departure there would be a farewell gathering called
an American wake in one of the houses of the emigrating boys or
girls. There would be singing and dancing interlarded with tears
and lamentations until the early hours of the morning, when, without sleep, the young people started for the train, the mothers
sometimes keening as at a funeral or a wake for the dead, for the
parting would often be forever and the parents might never see
again the boy or girl who was crossing the ocean. There was, I
remember, a steep hill on the road near our house, and when the
emigrating party reached the bottom of it, it was their habit to
descend from the sidecars and carts to ease the horses, and they
would climb the height on foot. As they reached the top from
which they could see the whole countryside, they would turn
and weepingly bid farewell to the green fields, the little white
houses, the sea, and the rambling roads they knew so well. The
hill was called the Hill of Weeping in Gaelic, because of all those

who had wept their farewells from the top of it. The bulk of the departing boys and girls were untrained and ill-educated, and so had to take unskilled jobs in their new country. But some of those who emigrated with education or some money became successful businessmen and lawyers, sometimes famous lawyers. However, I have known educated Irishmen and women in all sorts of work in America, a cousin of a peer a doorman, the son of a baronet a bartender, and others elevator men and waiters. In fact the educated Irishman often did not fit into American life at all.

From *Life and the Dream*

The Exile of Erin

There came to the beach a poor exile of Erin
The dew on his thin robe was heavy and chill
For his country he sigh'd when at twilight repairing
To wander alone by the wind-beaten hill.

Oh, why do you weep for the exile of Erin
Who sighed for his far-distant county of Cork?
For he turned his sad eyes to the skyscrapers soaring
And before the sun rose he was Mayor of New York.

Going into Exile

By LIAM O'FLAHERTY
(1897–   )

Patrick Feeney's cabin was crowded with people. In the large kitchen men, women, and children lined the walls, three deep in places, sitting on forms, chairs, stools, and on one another's knees. On the cement floor three couples were dancing a jig and raising a quantity of dust, which was, however, soon sucked up the chimney by the huge turf fire that blazed on the hearth. The only clear space in the kitchen was the corner to the left of the fireplace, where Pat Mullaney sat on yellow chair, with his right ankle resting on his left knee, a spotted red handkerchief on his head that reeked with perspiration, and his red face contorting as he played a tattered old accordion. One door was shut and the tins hanging on it gleamed in the firelight. The opposite door was open and over the heads of the small boys that crowded in it and outside it, peering in at the dancing couples in the kitchen, a starry June night was visible and, beneath the sky, shadowy great crags and misty, whitish fields lay motionless, still, and sombre. There was a deep, calm silence outside the cabin and within the cabin, in spite of the music and dancing in the kitchen and the singing in the little room to the left, where Patrick Feeney's eldest son Michael sat on the bed with three other young men, there was a haunting melancholy in the air.

The people were dancing, laughing and singing with a certain forced and boisterous gaiety that failed to hide from them the real cause of their being there, dancing, singing, and laughing. For the dance was on account of Patrick Feeney's two children, Mary and Michael, who were going to the United States on the following morning.

Feeney himself, a black-bearded, red-faced, middle-aged peasant, with white ivory buttons on his blue frieze shirt and his hands stuck in his leather waist belt, wandered restlessly about the kitchen, urging the people to sing and dance, while his mind was in agony all the time, thinking that on the following day he would lose his two eldest children, never to see them again perhaps. He kept talking to everybody about amusing things, shouted at the dancers, and behaved in a boisterous and abandoned manner. But every now and then he had to leave the kitchen, under the pretence of going to the pigsty to look at a young pig that was supposed to be ill. He would stand, however, upright against his gable and look gloomily at some star or other, while his mind struggled with vague and peculiar ideas that wandered about in it. He could make nothing at all of his thoughts, but a lump always came up his throat, and he shivered, although the night was warm.

Then he would sigh and say with a contraction of his neck, "Oh, it's a queer world this and no doubt about it. So it is." Then he would go back to the cabin again and begin to urge on the dance, laughing, shouting, and stamping on the floor.

Towards dawn, when the floor was crowded with couples, arranged in fours, stamping on the floor and going to and fro, dancing the "Walls of Limerick," Feeney was going out to the

246

gable when his son Michael followed him out. The two of them walked side by side about the yard over the grey sea pebbles that had been strewn there the previous day. They walked in silence and yawned without need, pretending to be taking the air. But each of them was very excited. Michael was taller than his father and not so thickly built, but the shabby blue serge suit that he had bought for going to America was too narrow for his broad shoulders and the coat was too wide around the waist. He moved clumsily in it and his hands appeared altogether too bony and big and red, and he didn't know what to do with them. During his twenty-one years of life he had never worn anything other than the homespun clothes of Inverara, and the shop-made clothes appeared as strange to him and as uncomfortable as a dress suit worn by a man working in a sewer. His face was flushed a bright red and his blue eyes shone with excitement. Now and again he wiped the perspiration from his forehead with the lining of his grey tweed cap.

At last Patrick Feeney reached his usual position at the gable end. He halted, balanced himself on his heels with his hands in his waist belt, coughed, and said, "It's going to be a warm day." The son came up beside him, folded his arms, and leaned his right shoulder against the gable.

"It was kind of Uncle Ned to lend the money for the dance, father," he said, "I'd hate to think that we'd have to go without something or other, just the same as everybody else has. I'll send you that money the very first money I earn, father . . . even before I pay Aunt Mary for my passage money. I should have all that money paid off in four months, and then I'll have some more money to send you by Christmas!"

And Michael felt very strong and manly recounting what he was going to do when he got to Boston, Massachusetts. He told himself that with his great strength he would earn a great deal of money. Conscious of his youth and his strength and lusting for adventurous life, for the moment he forgot the ache in his heart that the thought of leaving his father inspired in him.

The father was silent for some time. He was looking at the sky with his lower lip hanging, thinking of nothing. At last he sighed as a memory struck him.

"What is it?" said the son. "Don't weaken, for God's sake. You will only make it hard for me."

"Fooh!" said the father suddenly with pretended gruffness. "Who is weakening? I'm afraid that your new clothes make you impudent." Then he was silent for a moment and continued in a low voice:

"I was thinking of that potato field you sowed alone last spring the time I had the influenza. I never set eyes on the man that could do it better. It's a cruel world that takes you away from the land that God made you for."

"Oh, what are you talking about, father?" said Michael irritably. "Sure what did anybody ever get out of the land but poverty and hard work and potatoes and salt?"

"Ah yes," said the father with a sigh, "but it's your own, the land, and over there"—he waved his hand at the western sky—"you'll be giving your sweat to some other man's land, or what's equal to it."

"Indeed," muttered Michael, looking at the ground with a melancholy expression in his eyes, "it's poor encouragement you are giving me."

They stood in silence fully five minutes. Each hungered to embrace the other, to cry, to beat the air, to scream with excess of sorrow. But they stood silent and sombre, like nature about them, hugging their woe. Then they went back to the cabin. Michael went into the little room to the left of the kitchen, to the three young men who fished in the same curragh with him and were his bosom friends. The father walked into the large bedroom to the right of the kitchen.

The large bedroom was also crowded with people. A large table was laid for tea in the centre of the room and about a dozen young men were sitting at it, drinking tea and eating buttered raisin cake. Mrs. Feeney was bustling about the table, serving the food and urging them to eat. She was assisted by her two younger daughters and by another woman, a relative of her own. Her eldest daughter Mary, who was going to the United States that day, was sitting on the edge of the bed with several other young women. The bed was a large four-poster bed with a deal canopy over it, painted red, and the young women were huddled together on it. So that there must have been about a dozen of them there. They were Mary Feeney's particular friends, and they stayed with

248

her in that uncomfortable position just to show how much they liked her. It was a custom.

Mary herself sat on the edge of the bed with her legs dangling. She was a pretty, dark-haired girl of nineteen with dimpled, plump, red cheeks and ruminative brown eyes that seemed to cause little wrinkles to come and go in her little low forehead. Her nose was soft and small and rounded. Her mouth was small and the lips were red and open. Beneath her white blouse that was frilled at the neck and her navy blue skirt that outlined her limbs as she sat on the edge of the bed, her body was plump, soft, well-moulded, and in some manner exuded a feeling of freshness and innocence. So that she seemed to have been born to be fondled and admired in luxurious surroundings instead of having been born a peasant's daughter, who had to go to the United States that day to work as a servant or maybe in a factory.

And as she sat on the edge of the bed crushing her little handkerchief between her palms, she kept thinking feverishly of the United States, at one moment with fear and loathing, at the next with desire and longing. Unlike her brother she did not think of the work she was going to do or the money that she was going to earn. Other things troubled her, things of which she was half ashamed, half afraid, thoughts of love and of foreign men and of clothes and of houses where there were more than three rooms and where people ate meat every day. She was fond of life, and several young men among the local gentry had admired her in Inverara. But . . .

She happened to look up and she caught her father's eyes as he stood silently by the window with his hands stuck in his waist belt. His eyes rested on hers for a moment and then he dropped them without smiling, and with his lips compressed he walked down into the kitchen. She shuddered slightly. She was a little afraid of her father, although she knew that he loved her very much and he was very kind to her. But the winter before he had whipped her with a dried willow rod, when he caught her one evening behind Tim Hernon's cabin after nightfall, with Tim Hernon's son Bartly's arms around her waist and he kissing her. Ever since, she always shivered slightly when her father touched her or spoke to her.

"Oho!" said an old peasant who sat at the table with a saucer full of tea in his hand and his grey flannel shirt open at his thin, hairy, wrinkled neck. "Oho! indeed, but it's a disgrace to the island of Inverara to let such a beautiful woman as your daughter go away, Mrs. Feeney. If I were a young man, I'll be flayed alive if I'd let her go."

There was a laugh and some of the women on the bed said, "Bad cess to you, Patsy Coyne, if you haven't too much impudence, it's a caution." But the laugh soon died. The young men setting at the table felt embarrassed and kept looking at one another sheepishly, as if each tried to find out if the others were in love with Mary Feeney.

"Oh, well, God is good," said Mrs. Feeney, as she wiped her lips with the tip of her bright, clean, check apron. "What will be must be, and sure there is hope from the sea, but there is no hope from the grave. It is sad and the poor have to suffer, but . . ." Mrs. Feeney stopped suddenly, aware that all these platitudes meant nothing whatsoever. Like her husband she was unable to think intelligibly about her two children going away. Whenever the reality of their going away, maybe for ever, three thousand miles into a vast unknown world, came before her mind, it seemed that a thin bar of some hard metal thrust itself forward from her brain and rested behind the wall of her forehead. So that almost immediately she became stupidly conscious of the pain caused by the imaginary bar of metal and she forgot the dread prospect of her children going away. But her mind grappled with the things about her busily and efficiently, with the preparation of food, with the entertaining of her guests, with the numerous little things that have to be done in a house where there is a party and which only a woman can do properly. These little things, in a manner, saved her, for the moment at least, from bursting into tears whenever she looked at her daughter and whenever she thought of her son, whom she loved most of all her children, because perhaps she nearly died giving birth to him and he had been very delicate until he was twelve years old. So she laughed down in her breast a funny laugh she had that made her heave, where her check apron rose out from the waistband in a deep curve. "A person begins to talk," she said with a shrug of her shoulders sideways, "and then a person says foolish things."

"That's true," said the old peasant, noisily pouring more tea from his cup to his saucer.

250

But Mary knew by her mother laughing that way that she was very near being hysterical. She always laughed that way before she had one of her fits of hysterics. And Mary's heart stopped beating suddenly and then began again at an awful rate as her eyes became acutely conscious of her mother's body, the rotund, short body with the wonderful mass of fair hair growing grey at the temples and the fair face with the soft liquid brown eyes, that grew hard and piercing for a moment as they looked at a thing and then grew soft and liquid again, and the thin-lipped small mouth with the beautiful white teeth and the deep perpendicular grooves in the upper lip and the tremor that always came in the corner of the mouth, with love, when she looked at her children. Mary became acutely conscious of all these little points, as well as of the little black spot that was on her left breast below the nipple and the swelling that came now and again in her legs and caused her to have hysterics and would one day cause her death. And she was stricken with horror at the thought of leaving her mother and at the selfishness of her thoughts. She had never been prone to thinking of anything important, but now, somehow for a moment, she had a glimpse of her mother's life that made her shiver and hate herself as a cruel, heartless, lazy, selfish wretch. Her mother's life loomed up before her eyes, a life of continual misery and suffering, hard work, birth pangs, sickness, and again hard work and hunger and anxiety. It loomed up and then it fled again, a little mist came before her eyes and she jumped down from the bed, with a jaunty twirl of her head that was her habit when she set her body in motion.

"Sit down for a while, mother," she whispered, toying with one of the black ivory buttons on her mother's brown bodice. "I'll look after the table."

"No, no," murmured the mother with a shake of her whole body, "I'm not a bit tired. Sit down, my treasure. You have a long way to travel today."

And Mary sighed and went back to the bed again.

At last somebody said: "It's broad daylight." And immediately everybody looked out and said, "So it is, and may God be praised." The change from the starry night to the grey, sharp dawn was hard to notice until it had arrived. People looked out and saw the morning light sneaking over the crags silently, along the ground, pushing the mist banks upwards. The stars were growing dim. A long way off invisible sparrows were chirping in their ivied perch in some distant hill or other. Another day had arrived and even as the people looked at it, yawned and began to search for their hats, caps, and shawls preparing to go home, the day grew and spread its light and made things move and give voice. Cocks crew, blackbirds carolled, a dog let loose from a cabin by an early riser chased madly after an imaginary robber, barking as if his tail were on fire. The people said good-bye and began to stream forth from Feeney's cabin. They were going to their homes to see to the morning's work before going to Kilmurrage to see the emigrants off on the steamer to the mainland. Soon the cabin was empty except for the family.

All the family gathered into the kitchen and stood about for some minutes talking sleepily of the dance and of the people who had been present. Mrs. Feeney tried to persuade everybody to go to bed, but everybody refused. It was four o'clock and Michael and Mary would have to set out for Kilmurrage at nine. So tea was made and they all sat about for an hour drinking it and eating raisin cake and talking. They only talked of the dance and of the people who had been present.

There were eight of them there, the father and mother and six children. The youngest child was Thomas, a thin boy of twelve, whose lungs made a singing sound every time he breathed. The next was Bridget, a girl of fourteen, with dancing eyes and a habit of shaking her short golden curls every now and then for no apparent reason. Then there were the twins, Julia and Margaret, quiet, rather stupid, flat-faced girls of sixteen. Both their upper front teeth protruded slightly and they were both great workers and very obedient to their mother. They were all sitting at the table, having just finished a third large pot of tea, when suddenly the mother hastily gulped down the remainder of the tea in her cup, dropped the cup with a clatter to her saucer, and sobbed once through her nose.

"Now mother," said Michael sternly, "what's the good of this work?"

"No, you are right, my pulse," she replied quietly. "Only I was just thinking how nice it is to sit here surrounded by all my children, all my little birds in my nest, and then two of them going to fly away made me sad." And she laughed, pretending to treat it as a foolish joke.

"Oh, that be damned for a story," said the father, wiping his mouth on his sleeve; "there's work to be done. You Julia, go and get the horse. Margaret, you milk the cow and see that you give enough milk to the calf this morning." And he ordered everybody about as if it were an ordinary day of work.

But Michael and Mary had nothing to do and they sat about miserably conscious that they had cut adrift from the routine of their home life. They no longer had any place in it. In a few hours they would be homeless wanderers. Now that they were cut adrift from it, the poverty and sordidness of their home life appeared to them under the aspect of comfort and plenty.

So the morning passed until breakfast time at seven o'clock. The morning's work was finished and the family gathered together again. The meal passed in a dead silence. Drowsy after the sleepless night and conscious that the parting would come in a few hours, nobody wanted to talk. Everybody had an egg for breakfast in honor of the occasion. Mrs. Feeney, after her usual habit, tried to give her egg first to Michael, then to Mary, and as each refused it, she ate a little herself and gave the remainder to little Thomas who had a singing in his chest. Then the breakfast was cleared away. The father went to put the creels on the mare so as to take the luggage into Kilmurrage. Michael and Mary got the luggage ready and began to get dressed. The mother and the other children tidied up the house. People from the village began to come into the kitchen as was customary, in order to accompany the emigrants from their home to Kilmurrage.

At last everything was ready. Mrs. Feeney had exhausted all excuses for moving about, engaged on trivial tasks. She had to go into the big bedroom where Mary was putting on her new hat. The mother sat on a chair by the window, her face contorting on account of the flood of tears she was keeping back. Michael moved about the room uneasily, his two hands knotting a big red handkerchief behind his back. Mary twisted about in front of the mirror that hung over the black wooden mantelpiece. She was spending a long time with the hat. It was the first one she had ever worn, but it fitted her beautifully, and it was in excellent taste. It was given to her by the schoolmistress, who was very fond of her, and she herself had taken it in a little. She had an instinct for beauty in dress and deportment.

But the mother, looking at how well her daughter wore the cheap navy blue costume and the white frilled blouse, and the little round black hat with a fat, fluffy, glossy curl covering each ear, and the black silk stockings with blue clocks in them, and the little black shoes that had laces of three colours in them, got suddenly enraged with . . . She didn't know with what she got enraged. But for the moment she hated her daughter's beauty, and she remembered all the anguish of giving birth to her and nursing her and toiling for her, for no other purpose than to lose her now and let her go away, maybe to be ravished wantonly because of her beauty and her love of gaiety. A cloud of mad jealousy and hatred against this impersonal beauty that she saw in her daughter almost suffocated the mother, and she stretched out her hands in front of her unconsciously and then just as suddenly her anger vanished like a puff of smoke, and she burst into wild tears, wailing, "My children, oh, my children, far over the sea you will be carried from me, your mother." And she began to rock herself and she threw her apron over her head.

Immediately the cabin was full of the sound of bitter wailing. A dismal cry rose from the women gathered in the kitchen. "Far over the sea they will be carried," began woman after woman, and they all rocked themselves and hid their heads in their aprons. Michael's mongrel dog began to howl on the hearth. Little Thomas sat down on the hearth beside the dog and, putting his arms around him, he began to cry, although he didn't know exactly why he was crying, but he felt melancholy on account of the dog howling and so many people being about.

In the bedroom the son and daughter, on their knees, clung to their mother, who held their heads between her hands and rained kisses on both heads ravenously. After the first wave of tears she had stopped weeping. The tears still ran down her cheeks, but her eyes gleamed and they were dry. There was a fierce look in them as she searched all over the heads of her two children with them, with her brows contracted, searching with a fierce terror-stricken expression, as if by the intensity of her stare she hoped to keep a living photograph of them before her mind. With her quivering lips she made a queer sound like "im-m-m-m" and she

254

kept kissing. Her right hand clutched at Mary's left shoulder and with her left she fondled the back of Michael's neck. The two children were sobbing freely. They must have stayed that way a quarter of an hour.

Then the father came into the room, dressed in his best clothes. He wore a new frieze waistcoat, with a grey and black front and a white back. He held his soft black felt hat in one hand and in the other hand he had a bottle of holy water. He coughed and said in a weak gentle voice that was strange to him, as he touched his son, "Come now, it is time."

Mary and Michael got to their feet. The father sprinkled them with holy water and they crossed themselves. Then, without looking at their mother, who lay in the chair with her hands clasped on her lap, looking at the ground in a silent tearless stupor, they left the room. Each hurriedly kissed little Thomas, who was not going to Kilmurrage, and then, hand in hand, they left the house. As Michael was going out the door he picked a piece of loose whitewash from the wall and put it in his pocket. The people filed out after them, down the yard and on to the road, like a funeral procession. The mother was left in the house with little Thomas and two old peasant women from the village. Nobody spoke in the cabin for a long time.

Then the mother rose and came into the kitchen. She looked at the two women, at her little son, and at the hearth, as if she were looking for something she had lost. Then she threw her hands into the air and ran out into the yard.

"Come back," she screamed, "come back to me."

She looked wildly down the road with dilated nostrils, her bosom heaving. But there was nobody in sight. Nobody replied. There was a crooked stretch of limestone road surrounded by grey crags that were scorched by the sun. The road ended in a hill and then dropped out of sight. The hot June day was silent. Listening foolishly for an answering cry, the mother imagined she could hear the crags simmering under the hot rays of the sun. It was something in her head that was singing.

The two old women led her back into the kitchen.
"There is nothing that time will not cure," said one.
"Yes. Time and patience," said the other.

The Irish Emigrant

By LADY DUFFERIN
(1807–1867)

I'm sitting on the stile, Mary,
    Where we sat side by side,
On a bright May morning, long ago,
    When first you were my bride.
The corn was springing fresh and green,
    And the lark sang loud and high,
And the red was on your lip, Mary,
    And the love-light in your eye.
The place is little changed, Mary,
    The day is bright as then,
The lark's loud song is in my ear,
    And the corn is green again;
But I miss the soft clasp of your hand,
    And the breath warm on my cheek,
And I still keep listening for the words
    You nevermore may speak,
You nevermore may speak.

'Tis but a step down yonder lane,
    The little church stands near—
The church where we were wed, Mary—
    I see the spire from here;
But the graveyard lies between, Mary,
    My step might break your rest,
Where you, my darling, lie asleep
    With your baby on your breast.

I'm very lonely now, Mary,
    The poor make no new friends;
But, oh, they love the better still
    The few our Father sends.
And you were all I had, Mary,
    My blessing and my pride;
There's nothing left to care for now
    Since my poor Mary died.

Yours was the good, brave heart, Mary,
  That still kept hoping on,
When trust in God had left my soul,
  And half my strength was gone.
There was comfort ever on your lip,
  And the kind look on your brow;
I bless you, Mary, for that same,
  Though you can't hear me now.

I'm bidding you a long farewell,
  My Mary, kind and true!
But I'll not forget you, darling,
  In the land I'm going to.
They say there's bread and work for all,
  And the sun shines always there;
But I'll not forget old Ireland
  Were it fifty times as fair.

Home Sickness

By GEORGE MOORE
(1852-1933)

He told the doctor he was due in the bar-room at eight o'clock
in the morning; the bar-room was in a slum in the Bowery; and he
had only been able to keep himself in health by getting up at
five o'clock and going for long walks in Central Park.

"A sea voyage is what you want," said the doctor. "Why not
go to Ireland for two or three months? You will come back a
new man."

"I'd like to see Ireland again."

And he began to wonder how the people at home were getting
on. The doctor was right. He thanked him, and three weeks afterwards he landed in Cork.

As he sat in the railway carriage he recalled his native village—
he could see it and its lake, and then the fields one by one, and
the roads. He could see a large piece of rocky land—some three
or four hundred acres of headland stretching out into the winding

257

lake. Upon this headland the peasantry had been given permission to build their cabins by former owners of the Georgian house standing on the pleasant green hill. The present owners considered the village a disgrace, but the villagers paid high rents for their plots of ground, and all the manual labour that the Big House required came from the village: the gardeners, the stable helpers, the house and the kitchen maids.

Bryden had been thirteen years in America, and when the train stopped at his station, he looked round to see if there were any changes in it. It was just the same blue limestone station house as it was thirteen years ago. The platform and the sheds were the same, and there were five miles of road from the station to Duncannon. The sea voyage had done him good, but five miles were too far for him today; the last time he had walked the road, he had walked it in an hour and a half, carrying a heavy bundle on a stick.

He was sorry he did not feel strong enough for the walk, the evening was fine, and he would meet many people coming home from the fair, some of whom he had known in his youth, and they would tell him where he could get a clean lodging. But the carman would be able to tell him that; he called the car that was waiting at the station, and soon he was answering questions about America. But he wanted to hear of those who were living in the old country, and after hearing the stories of many people he had forgotten, he heard that Mike Scully, who had been away in a situation for many years as a coachman in the King's County, had come back and built a fine house with a concrete floor. Now there was a good loft in Mike Scully's house, and Mike would be pleased to take in a lodger.

Bryden remembered that Mike had been in a situation at the Big House; he had intended to be a jockey, but had suddenly shot up into a fine tall man, and had had to become a coachman instead. Bryden tried to recall the face, but he could only remember a straight nose, and a somewhat dusky complexion. Mike was one of the heroes of his childhood, and now his youth floated before him, and he caught glimpses of himself, something that was more than phantom and less than a reality. Suddenly his reverie was broken: the carman pointed with his whip, and Bryden saw a tall, finely built, middle-aged man coming through the gates, and the

258

driver said, "There's Mike Scully."

Mike had forgotten Bryden even more completely than Bryden had forgotten him, and many aunts and uncles were mentioned before he began to understand.

"You've grown into a fine man, James," he said, looking at Bryden's great width of chest. "But you are thin in the cheeks, and you're very sallow in the cheeks too."

"I haven't been very well lately—that is one of the reasons I have come back; but I want to see you all again."

Bryden paid the carman, wished him "God-speed," and he and Mike divided the luggage between them, Mike carrying the bag and Bryden the bundle, and they walked round the lake, for the townland was at the back of the demesne; and while they walked, James proposed to pay Mike ten shillings a week for his board and lodging.

He remembered the woods thick and well-forested; now they were windworn, the drains were choked, and the bridge leading across the lake inlet was falling away. Their way led between long fields where herds of cattle were grazing; the road was broken— Bryden wondered how the villagers drove their carts over it, and Mike told him that the landlord could not keep it in repair, and he would not allow it to be kept in repair out of the rates, for then it would be a public road, and he did not think there should be a public road through his property.

At the end of many fields they came to the village, and it looked a desolate place, even on this fine evening, and Bryden remarked that the county did not seem to be as much lived in as it used to be. It was at once strange and familiar to see the chickens in the kitchen; and, wishing to re-knit himself to the old habits, he begged of Mrs. Scully not to drive them out, saying he did not mind them. Mike told his wife that Bryden was born in Duncannon, and when she heard Bryden's name she gave him her hand, after wiping it in her apron, saying he was heartily welcome, only she was afraid he would not care to sleep in a loft.

"Why wouldn't I sleep in aloft, a dry loft! You're thinking a good deal of America over here," said he, "but I reckon it isn't all you think it. Here you work when you like and sit down when you like; but when you have had a touch of blood poisoning as I had, and when you have seen young people walking with a stick, you

259

think that there is something to be said for old Ireland."

"Now won't you be taking a sup of milk? You'll be wanting a drink after travelling," said Mrs. Scully.

And when he had drunk the milk, Mike asked him if he would like to go inside or if he would like to go for a walk.

"Maybe it is sitting down you would like to be."

And they went into the cabin, and started to talk about the wages a man could get in America, and the long hours of work.

And after Bryden had told Mike everything about America that he thought of interest, he asked Mike about Ireland. But Mike did not seem to be able to tell him much that was of interest. They were all very poor—poorer, perhaps, than when he left them.

"I don't think anyone except myself has a five pound note to his name."

Bryden hoped he felt sufficiently sorry for Mike. But after all Mike's life and prospects mattered little to him. He had come back in search of health: and he felt better already; the milk had done him good, and the bacon and cabbage in the pot sent forth a savoury odour. The Scullys were very kind, they pressed him to make a good meal; a few weeks of country air and food, they said, would give him back the health he had lost in the Bowery; and when Bryden said he was longing for a smoke, Mike said there was no better sign than that. During his long illness he had never wanted to smoke, and he was a confirmed smoker.

It was comfortable to sit by the mild peat fire watching the smoke of their pipes drifting up the chimney, and all Bryden wanted was to be let alone; he did not want to hear of anyone's misfortunes, but about nine o'clock a number of villagers came in, and their appearance was depressing. Bryden remembered one or two of them—he used to know them very well when he was a boy; their talk was as depressing as their appearance, and he could feel no interest whatever in them. He was not moved when he heard that Higgins the stonemason was dead; he was not affected when he heard that Mary Kelly, who used to go to do the laundry at the Big House, had married; he was only interested when he heard she had gone to America. No, he had not met her there; America is a big place. Then one of the peasants asked him if he remembered Patsy Carabine, who used to do the gardening at the Big House. Yes, he remembered Patsy well. Patsy was in the poorhouse. He

260

had not been able to do any work on account of his arm; his house had fallen in; he had given up his holding and gone into the poorhouse. All this was very sad, and to avoid hearing any further unpleasantness, Bryden began to tell them about America. And they sat round listening to him; but all the talking was on his side; he wearied of it; and looking round the group he recognized a ragged hunchback with grey hair; twenty years ago he was a young hunchback, and, turning to him, Bryden asked him if he was doing well with his five acres.

"Ah, not much. This has been a bad season. The potatoes failed; they were watery—there is no diet in them."

These peasants were all agreed that they could make nothing out of their farms. Their regret was that they had not gone to America when they were young; and after striving to take an interest in the fact that O'Connor had lost a mare and foal worth forty pounds Bryden began to wish himself back in the slum. When they left the house he wondered if every evening would be like the present one. Mike piled fresh sods on the fire, and he hoped it would show enough light in the loft for Bryden to undress himself by.

The cackling of some geese in the road kept him awake, and the loneliness of the country seemed to penetrate to his bones, and to freeze the marrow in them. There was a bat in the loft—a dog howled in the distance—and then he drew the clothes over his head. Never had he been so unhappy, and the sound of Mike breathing by his wife's side in the kitchen added to his nervous terror. Then he dozed a little; and lying on his back he dreamed he was awake, and the men he had seen sitting round the fireside that evening seemed to him like spectres come out of some unknown region of morass and reedy tarn. He stretched out his hands for his clothes, determined to fly from this house, but remembering the lonely road that led to the station he fell back on his pillow. The geese still cackled, but he was too tired to be kept awake any longer. He seemed to have been asleep only a few minutes when he heard Mike calling him. Mike had come half-way up the ladder and was telling him that breakfast was ready.

"What kind of breakfast will he give me?" Bryden asked himself as he pulled on his clothes. There were tea and hot griddle cakes for breakfast, and there were fresh eggs; there was sunlight in the kitchen, and he liked to hear Mike tell of the work he was going to

261

do in the fields. Mike rented a farm of about fifteen acres, at least ten of it was grass; he grew an acre of potatoes and some corn, and some turnips for his sheep. He had a nice bit of meadow, and he took down his scythe, and as he put the whetstone in his belt Bryden noticed a second scythe, and he asked Mike if he should go down with him and help him to finish the field.

"You haven't done any mowing this many a year; I don't think you'd be of much help. You'd better go for a walk by the lake, but you may come in the afternoon if you like and help to turn the grass over."

Bryden was afraid he would find the lake shore very lonely but the magic of returning health is sufficient distraction for the convalescent, and the morning passed agreeably. The weather was still and sunny. He could hear the ducks in the reeds. The days dreamed themselves away, and it became his habit to go to the lake every morning. One morning he met the landlord, and they walked together, talking of the country, of what it had been, and the ruin it was slipping into. James Bryden told him that ill health had brought him back to Ireland; and the landlord lent him his boat, and Bryden rowed about the islands, and resting upon his oars he looked at the old castles, and remembered the prehistoric raiders that the landlord had told him about. He came across the stones to which the lake dwellers had tied their boats, and these signs of ancient Ireland were pleasing to Bryden in his present mood.

As well as the great lake there was a smaller lake in the bog where the villagers cut their turf. This lake was famous for its pike, and the landlord allowed Bryden to fish there, and one evening when he was looking for a frog with which to bait his line he met Margaret Dirken driving home the cows for the milking. Margaret was the herdsman's daughter, and she lived in a cottage near the Big House; but she came up to the village whenever there was a dance, and Bryden had found himself opposite to her in the reels. But until this evening he had had little opportunity of speaking to her, and he was glad to speak to someone, for the evening was lonely, and they stood talking together.

"You're getting your health again," she said. "You'll soon be leaving us."

"I'm in no hurry."

"You're grand people over there; I hear a man is paid four dollars

262

a day for his work."

"And how much," said James, "has he to pay for his food and for his clothes?"

Her cheeks were bright and her teeth small, white, and beautifully even; and a woman's soul looked at Bryden out of her soft Irish eyes. He was troubled and turned aside, and catching sight of a frog looking at him out of a tuft of grass he said "I have been looking for a frog to put upon my pike line."

The frog jumped right and left, and nearly escaped in some bushes, but he caught it and returned with it in his hand.

"It is just the kind of frog a pike will like," he said. "Look at its great white belly and its bright yellow back."

And without more ado he pushed the wire to which the hook was fastened through the frog's fresh body, and dragging it through the mouth he passed the hooks through the hind legs and tied the line to the end of the wire.

"I think," said Margaret, "I must be looking after my cows; it's time I got them home."

"Won't you come down to the lake while I set my line."

She thought for a moment and said, "No, I'll see you from here."

He went down to the reedy tarn, and at his approach several snipe got up, and they flew above his head uttering sharp cries. His fishing rod was a long hazel stick, and he threw the frog as far as he could into the lake. In doing this he roused some wild ducks; a mallard and two ducks got up, and they flew toward the larger lake. Margaret watched them; they flew in a line with an old castle; and they had not disappeared from view when Bryden came toward her, and he and she drove the cows home together that evening.

They had not met very often when she said, "James, you had better not come here so often calling to me."

"Don't you wish me to come?"

"Yes, I wish you to come well enough, but keeping company is not the custom of the country, and I don't want to be talked about."

"Are you afraid the priest would speak against us from the altar?"

"He has spoken against keeping company, but it is not so much what the priest says, for there is no harm in talking."

"But if you are going to be married there is no harm in walking

263

out together."

"Well, not so much, but marriages are made differently in these parts; there is not much courting here."

And the next day it was known in the village that James was going to marry Margaret Dirken.

His desire to excel the boys in dancing had caused a stir of gaiety in the parish, and for some time past there had been dancing in every house where there was a floor fit to dance upon; and if the cottager had no money to pay for a barrel of beer, James Bryden, who had money, sent him a barrel, so that Margaret might get her dance. She told him that they sometimes crossed over into another parish where the priest was not so averse to dancing, and James wondered. And next morning at Mass he wondered at their simple fervour. Some of them held their hands above their head as they prayed, and all this was very new and very old to James Bryden. But the obedience of these people to their priest surprised him. When he was a lad they had not been so obedient, or he had forgotten their obedience; and he listened in mixed anger and wonderment to the priest, who was scolding his parishioners, speaking to them by name, saying that he had heard there was dancing going on in their homes. Worse than that, he said he had seen boys and girls loitering about the roads, and the talk that went on was of one kind—love. He said that newspapers containing love stories were finding their way into the people's houses, stories about love, in which there was nothing elevating or ennobling. The people listened, accepting the priest's opinion without question. And their submission was pathetic. It was the submission of a primitive people clinging to religious authority, and Bryden contrasted the weakness and incompetence of the people about him with the modern restlessness and cold energy of the people he had left behind him.

One evening, as they were dancing, a knock came to the door, and the piper stopped playing, and the dancers whispered, "Someone has told on us; it is the priest."

And the awe-stricken villagers crowded round the cottage fire, afraid to open the door. But the priest said that if they did not open the door he would put his shoulder to it and force it open. Bryden went towards the door, saying he would allow no one to threaten him, priest or no priest, but Margaret caught his arm and told him that if he said anything to the priest, the priest would

264

speak against them from the altar, and they would be shunned by the neighbours. It was Mike Scully who went to the door and let the priest in, and he came in saying they were dancing their souls into hell.

"I've heard of your goings on," he said, "of your beer drinking and dancing. I will not have it in my parish. If you want that sort of thing you had better go to America."

"If that is intended for me, sir, I will go back tomorrow. Margaret can follow."

"It isn't the dancing, it's the drinking I'm opposed to," said the priest, turning to Bryden.

"Well, no one has drunk too much, sir," said Bryden.

"But you'll sit here drinking all night," and the priest's eyes went toward the corner where the women had gathered, and Bryden felt that the priest looked on the women as more dangerous than the porter. "It's after midnight," he said, taking out his watch.

By Bryden's watch it was only half-past eleven, and while they were arguing about the time Mrs. Scully offered Bryden's umbrella to the priest, for in his hurry to stop the dancing the priest had gone out without his; and, as if to show Bryden that he bore him no ill will, the priest accepted the loan of the umbrella, for he was thinking of the big marriage fee that Bryden would pay him.

"I shall be badly off for the umbrella tomorrow," Bryden said, as soon as the priest was out of the house. He was going with his father-in-law to a fair. His father-in-law was learning him how to buy and sell cattle. And his father-in-law was saying that the country was mending, and that a man might become rich in Ireland if he only had a little capital. Bryden had the capital, and Margaret had an uncle on the other side of the lake who would leave her all he had, that would be fifty pounds, and never in the village of Duncannon had a young couple begun life with so much prospect of success as would James Bryden and Margaret Dirken.

Some time after Christmas was spoken of as the best time for the marriage; James Bryden said that he would not be able to get his money out of America before the spring. The delay seemed to vex him, and he seemed anxious to be married, until one day he received a letter from America, from a man who had served in the bar with him. This friend wrote to ask Bryden if he were coming back. The letter was no more than a passing wish to see Bryden again. Yet Bryden stood looking at it, and everyone wondered what could be in the letter. It seemed momentous, and they hardly believed him when he said it was from a friend who wanted to know if his health were better. He tried to forget the letter, and he looked at the worn fields, divided by walls of loose stones, and a great longing came upon him.

The smell of the Bowery slum had come across the Atlantic, and had found him out in this western headland; and one night he awoke from a dream in which he was hurling some drunken customer through the open doors into the darkness. He had seen his friend in his white duck jacket throwing drink from glass into glass amid the din of voices and strange accents; he had heard the clang of money as it was swept into the till, and his sense sickened for the bar-room. But how should he tell Margaret Dirken that he could not marry her? She had built her life upon this marriage. He could not tell her that he would not marry her . . . yet he must go. He felt as if he were being hunted; the thought that he must tell Margaret that he could not marry her hunted him day after day as a weasel hunts a rabbit. Again and again he went to meet her with the intention of telling her he did not love her, that their lives were not for one another, that it had all been a mistake, and that happily he had found out it was a mistake soon enough. But Margaret, as if she guessed what he was about to speak of, threw her arms about him and begged him to say he loved her, and that they would be married at once. He agreed that he loved her, and that they would be married at once. But he had not left her many minutes before the feeling came upon him that he could not marry her—that he must go away. The smell of the bar-room hunted him down. Was it for the sake of the money that he might make there that he wished to go back? No, it was not the money. What then? His eyes fell on the bleak country, on the little fields divided by bleak walls; he remembered the pathetic ignorance of the people, and it was these things that he could not endure. It was the priest who came to forbid the dancing. Yes, it was the priest. As he stood looking at the line of the hills the bar-room seemed by him. He heard the politicians, and the excitement of politics was in his blood again. He must go away from this place—he must get back to the bar-room. Looking up, he saw the scanty orchard, and he hated the spare road that led to the village, and he hated the little hill at the

266

top of which the village began, and he hated more than all other places the house where he was to live with Margaret Dirken—if he married her. He could see it from where he stood—by the edge of the lake, with twenty acres of pasture land about it, for the landlord had given up part of his demesne land to them.

He caught sight of Margaret, and he called her to come through the stile.

"I have just had a letter from America."

"About the money?" she said.

"Yes, about the money. But I shall have to go over there."

He stood looking at her, seeking for words; and she guessed from his embarrassment that he would say to her that he must go to America before they were married.

"Do you mean, James, you will have to go at once?"

"Yes," he said, "at once. But I shall come back in time to be married in August. It will only mean delaying our marriage a month."

They walked on a little way talking, and every step he took James felt that he was a step nearer the Bowery slum. And when they came to the gate Bryden said, "I must hasten or I shall miss the train."

"But," she said, "you are not going now—you are not going today?"

"Yes, this morning. It is seven miles. I shall have to hurry not to miss the train."

And then she asked him if he would ever come back.

"Yes," he said, "I am coming back."

"If you are coming back, James, why not let me go with you?"

"You could not walk fast enough. We should miss the train."

"One moment, James. Don't make me suffer; tell me the truth. You are not coming back. Your clothes—where shall I send them?"

He hurried away, hoping he would come back. He tried to think that he liked the country he was leaving, that it would be better to have a farmhouse and live there with Margaret Dirken than to serve drinks behind a counter in the Bowery. He did not think he was telling her a lie when he said he was coming back. Her offer to forward his clothes touched his heart, and at the end of the road he stood and asked himself if he should go back to her. He would miss the train if he waited another minute, and he ran

267

on. And he would have missed the train if he had not met a car. Once he was on the car he felt himself safe—the country was already behind him. The train and the boat at Cork were mere formulae; he was already in America.

The moment he landed he felt the thrill of home that he had not found in his native village, and he wondered how it was that the smell of the bar seemed more natural than the smell of the fields, and the roar of crowds more welcome than the silence of the lake's edge. He offered up a thanksgiving for his escape, and entered into negotiations for the purchase of the bar-room.

. . .

He took a wife, she bore him sons and daughters, the bar-room prospered, property came and went; he grew old, his wife died, he retired from business, and reached the age when a man begins to feel there are not many years in front of him, and that all he has had to do in life has been done. His children married, lonesomeness began to creep about him in the evening and when he looked into the firelight, a vague, tender reverie floated up, and Margaret's soft eyes and name vivified the dusk. His wife and children passed out of mind, and it seemed to him that a memory was the only real thing he possessed, and the desire to see Margaret again grew intense. But she was an old woman, she had married, maybe she was dead. Well, he would like to be buried in the village where he was born.

There is an unchanging, silent life within every man that none knows but himself, and his unchanging, silent life was his memory of Margaret Dirken. The bar-room was forgotten and all that concerned it and the things he saw most clearly were the green hillside and the bog lake and the rushes about it, and the greater lake in the distance, and behind it the blue line of wandering hills.

268

The Trial of John Mitchel 1848

By JOHN MITCHEL

Clubs were formed expressly for arming; rifles were eagerly purchased; and the blacksmiths' forges poured forth pike-heads. Sedition, treason, were openly preached and enforced; and the United Irishman was established specifically as an Organ of Revolution. The Viceroy, Lord Clarendon, became alarmed: he concentrated eight thousand troops in Dublin; he covered the land with detectives; and informers were the chief frequenters of the Castle. . . .

. . . a Bill was brought in by Sir George Grey, and made into an Act by large majorities, providing that anyone who should levy war against the Queen, or endeavour to deprive her of her title, or by open and advised speaking, printing, or publishing, incite others to the same, should be "deemed guilty of felony" and transported. . . . the case grew pressing. All the country was fast becoming aroused; and many thousands of pikes were in the hands of the peasantry. The soldiers of several regiments, being Irish, were well known to be very willing to fraternise with the people, upon a first success and the police, in such an event would have been a green-coated Irish army upon the moment.

Birch and Clarendon would not even wait to get their enemy fairly into the new felony. They caused three to be arrested in the meantime (O'Brien, Meagher, and the present writer), on a charge of sedition; but on bringing the two former to trial, it was found that the juries (special juries in the Court of Queen's Bench) had not been closely enough packed; and the prosecutions failed. In my case, though there were two indictments, one for a speech, and one for an article, and two juries had actually been struck, "Government" felt that a failure would be at least dangerous, so the Viceroy suddenly caused my arrest on a charge of "treason-felony" under his new Act and determined to, not try, but pretend to try me, at the next Commissioners in Green Street—at any rate to clear Ireland of me and so get rid of one obstacle at least to the fulfillment of British policy.

Here, then, this narrative leaves the general affairs of the country and shrinks to the dimensions of a single prosecution. From the day that I entered my dungeon (the 23rd of May, 1848), I knew but by hearsay how the British Government fulfilled the designs and administered the dispensations of Providence in Ireland—how the Famine was successfully exploited; how the Poor rates doubled and trebled, and were diligently laid out in useless works; how the Orange Lodges were supplied with arms from the Castle; how the mere Celtic peasantry were carefully deprived of all weapons; how the landlords were gradually broken and impoverished by the pressure of rates, until the beneficent "Encumbered Estates Bill" had to come in and solve their difficulties—a great stroke of British policy, whereby it was hoped (now that the tenantry were cleared to the proper point) to clear out the landlords, too, and replace them with English and Scottish purchasers. In short, how the last conquest was consummated, let other pens than mine describe. . . .

Two or three days after my pretended trial—as I find in the papers—the same Lord John Russell, being questioned again by Mr. Keogh on the exclusion of Catholics on all the three trials, declared that in the case of Mr. O'Brien and Mr. Meagher, jurors had not been set aside for political or religious opinions; but, said his Lordship, "I have no explanation to offer with respect to what has taken place on the trial of Mr. Mitchel."

In short, the cause of "civilization" and of British Law and Order, required that I should be removed to a great distance from Ireland, and that my office and printing materials should become the property of Her Majesty. Though the noble old Robert Holmes, who advocated the prisoner's cause that day, had had the tongue of men and of angels, he could have made no impression there. A verdict of "guilty," and a sentence of fourteen years' transportation had been ordered by the Castle: and it was done.

From *The Jail Journal*

The Emigrant's Letter*

By PERCY FRENCH

Dear Danny,
I'm takin' the pen in me hand
To tell you we're just out o' sight o' the land;
In the grand Allan liner we're sailin' in style,
But we're sailin' away from the Emerald Isle;
And a long sort o' sigh seemed to rise from us all
As the waves hid the last bit of ould Donegal.
Och! it's well to be you that is takin' yer tay
Where they're cuttin' the corn in Creeshla the day.

I spoke to the captain—he won't turn her round,
And if I swum back I'd be apt to be drowned,
So here I must stay—oh! I've no cause to fret,
For their dinner was what you might call a banquet
But though it is "sumpchus," I'd swop the whole lot
For the ould wooden spoon and the stirabout pot;
And sweet Katty Farrell a-wettin' the tay
Where they're cuttin' the corn in Cresshla the day!

If Katey is courted by Patsey or Mick,
Put a word in for me with a lump of a stick,
Don't kill Patsey outright, he has no sort of a chance
But Mickey's a rogue you might murther at wance
For Katey might think as the longer she waits
A boy in the hand is worth two in the States:
And she'll promise to honour, to love and obey
Some robber that's roamin' round Creeshla the day.

Good-bye to you Dan, there's no more to be said,
And I think the salt wather's got into me head,
For it dreeps from me eyes when I call to me mind,
The friends and the colleen I'm leavin' behind;
Oh, Danny, she'll wait; whin I bid her good-bye,
There was just the laste taste of a tear in her eye,
And a break in her voice whin she said "you might stay,
But plaze God you'll come back to ould Creeshla some day."

* By kind permission of Messrs. Keith Prowse Music Publishing Co. Ltd.

Gustave de Beaumont, in his book, "L'Irlande Sociale, Politique et Religieuse" published in 1839 said that "If by Union we understand the concord and sympathy of two nations, we must confess that this term is quite unsuited to the so-called United Kingdom," and he went on to predict further trouble.

The Whiteboys

By GUSTAVE DE BEAUMONT

. . . Some day or other a voice will be raised amongst these poor farmers, which proclaims:

"The earth alone supplies us with food, let us cling to it closely, and not quit it. The landlord or agent bids us depart—let us stay. The courts of justice order it—still let us stay—an armed force is sent to compel us—let us resist it. Let us oppose all our forces to an unjust force, and in order that the injustice should not reach us, let us enact the most terrible penalties against those by whom it is committed. Be it enacted:

"That whoever shall attempt, directly or indirectly, to deprive us of our farms, shall be punished with death. That the landlord, middleman, or agent, who shall eject a tenant from his estate, shall be punished with death. That the landlord who demands a higher rent than that which we have fixed, shall be punished with death. That he who bids a higher rent for a farm, takes the place of an ejected tenant, purchases by auction or otherwise goods that have been distrained, shall be punished with death. . . ."

These are, doubtless, dreadful laws—they are those of the Whiteboys, an atrocious code, worthy of a semicivilized people, which has no light to guide its efforts, and finding no sympathy anywhere, looks to its inner instinct for safety and protection.

The famine led those who survived to gather what strength was left and fight for their own land. Smoldering resentment against landlords who lived abroad and were only interested in grinding the last penny out of their tenants inevitably led towards further rebellion.

272

1879

THE FIGHT AGAINST
THE LANDLORDS

After THE BOOK OF KELLS.

As THE TIMES *(London) of May 30, 1850, says:*

"Two classes in Ireland stand arrayed in deadly hostility to each other; the proprietors of the land on the one side, the holders and tillers of it on the other. Sympathies for the misery of each other seem entirely to have left the breasts of both parties. The law, indeed, looks with different eyes upon the acts of the two bands carrying on this deadly fray."

GEORGE BERNARD SHAW *in his play "Back to Methuselah," set in the year 3000* A.D., *gives the following dialogue:*

"I am speaking the plainest English. Are you the *landlord?*"
"There is a tradition in this part of the country of an animal with a name like that. It used to be hunted and shot in the barbarous ages. It is quite extinct now."

A̶rthur Griffith, who subsequently became the first President of the Executive Council of the Irish Free State in 1922 (an office corresponding to that of Prime Minister in Great Britain), wrote in the preface to John Mitchel's "Jail Journal" the following passages.

Parnell

By ARTHUR GRIFFITH
(1872–1922)

Thirty years later, Mitchel's policy, interpreted and applied in a stronger generation by the man whose career Mitchel's writings molded—Charles Stewart Parnell—brought the stoutest bulwark of English power in Ireland to the ground. When Parnell bade the farmers of Ireland "Keep a firm grip on their holdings," he crystallized into a phrase the policy Mitchel urged unsuccessfully in 1848. Mitchel's generation failed him, his sacrifice seemed vain—but, sixty years after, we can look back to the Ireland of slavish resignation—the land of carcases and ruins—the Finis Hiberniae of the

274

cheering auditors to a British Minister and the leaderwriters of the English press, and, seeing out of that degradation and misery and ruin new forces grow to encounter and defeat English policy in Ireland, realize that the haughty spirit of a great Irishman though baffled in its own generation may set the feet of our country in the way of triumph in the next. Fifty years passed ere the voice of Swift in the "Drapier's Letters" spoke winningly to England through the cannon of the Volunteers. Thirty years after Mitchel was borne a shackled prisoner from a cowed country, two strong fortresses of England's power in Ireland perished in the fires of resistance to oppression he had rekindled in an abject land.

Now came the fight for the land, which the Irish decided to win back at all costs from their English so-called landlords. Some were in favor of open rebellion, but others, with Charles Stewart Parnell as their leader, were in favor of firm but legal measures. In October 1879, Parnell and Davitt founded the Land League.

Fair Rent, Fixed Tenure, Free Sale

By R. BARRY O'BRIEN
(1874–1918)

This was the doctrine which Parnell and the Leaguers preached from the hilltops, and which the masses of the people willingly obeyed.

On September 19, 1880, Parnell attended a mass meeting at Ennis. There, in a speech which rang throughout the land, he struck the keynote of the agitation; he laid down the lines on which the league should work. Slowly, calmly, deliberately, without a quiver of passion, a note of rhetoric, or an exclamation of anger, but in a tone that penetrated his audience like the touch of cold steel, he proclaimed war against all who should resist the mandates of the League.

"Depend upon it that the measure of the Land Bill next session will be the measure of your activity and energy this winter. It will be the measure of your determination not to pay unjust rates; it will be the measure of your determination to keep a firm grip on your homesteads. It will be the measure of your determination not to bid for farms from which others have been evicted, and to use the strong force of public opinion to deter any unjust men amongst yourselves—and there are many such—from bidding for such farms. Now what are you to do to a tenant who bids for a farm from which his neighbour has been evicted?"

Here there was much excitement, and cries of "Kill him!" "Shoot him!" Parnell waited, with his hands clasped behind his back, looking quietly out upon the crowd until the tumult subsided, and then softly resumed, "Now I think I heard somebody say 'Shoot him!'—(A voice: "Yes, quite right")—but I wish to point out to you a very much better way—a more Christian and a more charitable way, which will give the lost sinner an opportunity of repenting."

Here there were inquiring glances, and a lull, and a silence, which was scarcely broken until Parnell finished the next sentence—a long sentence, but every word of which was heard, as the voice of the speaker hardened and his face wore an expression of remorseless determination. "When a man takes a farm from which another has been evicted, you must show him on the roadside when you meet him, you must show him in the streets of the town—(A voice: "Shun him!")—you must show him at the shop counter, you must show him in the fair and in the marketplace, and even in the house of worship, by leaving him severely alone, by putting him into a moral Coventry, by isolating him from his kind as if he was a leper of old—you must show him your detestation of the crime he has committed, and you may depend upon it that there will be no man so full of avarice, so lost to shame, as to dare the public opinion of all right-thinking men and to transgress your unwritten code of laws."

The closing sentence was received with a shout of applause; the doctrine of boycotting, as it afterwards came to be called, was accepted with popular enthusiasm.

Three days afterwards the peasants of Connaught showed how ready they were to practise as Parnell had preached. Captain Boycott, the agent of Lord Erne, had been offered by the tenants on the estate what they conceived to be a just rent. He refused to take it, and the tenants refused to give more; whereupon ejectment

276

processes were issued against them.

On September 22, the process server went forth to serve the ejectments. He was met by a number of peasants, who forced him to abandon the work and retreat precipitately to the agent's house. Next day the peasants visited the house and adjoining farm, and ordered the servants in Captain Boycott's employ to depart—a mandate which was promptly obeyed; the result being that the unfortunate gentleman was left without farm labourers or stablemen, while his crops remained ungathered and unsaved. Nor did the peasants stop here. They forbade the local shopkeepers to serve him, told the blacksmith and laundress not to work for him, threatened the postboy who carried his letters, and upon one occasion stopped and "cautioned" the bearer of a telegram.

Captain Boycott was "left severely alone, put into moral Coventry." As days wore on it became a matter of pressing importance to him to have his crops saved, but no one in the neighbourhood could be got to do the work. In these circumstances an opportunity, gladly seized, for "demonstrating in force" was given to the Ulster Orangemen. One hundred of them offered to "invade" Connaught to save Captain Boycott's crops. The Captain informed the authorities of Dublin Castle that fifty men would be quite sufficient for agricultural purposes; and being himself a man of peace, he did not feel at all disposed to see a hundred Orangemen marching in battle array over his farm, shouting "to hell with the Pope," and drinking the memory of the glorious, pious, and immortal William at his expense. Fifty Orangemen were accordingly despatched to Connaught under the protection of a large force of military and police (with two field pieces) to save Captain Boycott's crops. The work done the Orangemen, accompanied by Captain Boycott, departed in peace, and the Connaught peasants were left masters of the situation.

From *The Life and Times of Charles Stewart Parnell*

Boycott

(1832–1897)

BOYCOTT . . . The word was first used in Ireland, and was derived from the name of Captain Charles Cunningham Boycott (1832–97), agent for the estates of the Earl of Erne in County Mayo. For refusing in 1880 to receive rents at figures fixed by the tenants, Captain Boycott's life was threatened, his servants were compelled to leave him, his fences torn down, his letters intercepted and his food supplies interfered with. It took a force of 900 soldiers to protect the Ulster Orangemen who succeeded finally in getting in his crops. Boycotting was an essential part of the Irish Nationalist "Plan of Campaign," and was dealt with under the Crimes act of 1887. The term soon came into common use, and was speedily adopted into many foreign languages.

From *The Encyclopaedia Britannica*

During a lecture tour in America, John Redmond made the following speech in The Broadway Theatre, New York, on November 29th, 1896:

Parnell in the House of Commons

By JOHN REDMOND
(1856–1918)

When I entered Parliament, fifteen years ago, the British public was in the very midst of one of the most desperate of the Irish crises. An Irish leader had arisen who had taken a new way of obtaining redress for Ireland. Mr. Parnell found that the British Parliament insisted upon turning a deaf ear to Ireland's claim for justice. He resolved to adopt the simple yet masterly device of preventing Parliament doing any work at all until it consented to listen. In this policy he was successful. He was the first man, who, as Wendell Philips afterward said of him in Boston, made John Bull listen to the vioce of Ireland. . . .

278

He was in a small minority . . . they talked by the hour upon every subject that arose, until the astonished Legislature suddenly woke up to the fact that by the action of this handful of young Irishmen the entire legislative machine had been brought to a standstill. Then there burst over the heads of Mr. Parnell and his friends a perfect storm of abuse, hatred, and passion. Their rising to address the House was invariably the signal for an outburst of howls of execration and Mr. Parnell in particular often stood for half an hour at a time before he could utter a word. But he proved himself perfectly insensible to such methods. He cared neither for the praise nor the abuse of this British Parliament. His object was to injure it so long as it refused to listen to the just claims of his country. If the House groaned, he smiled and paused until the groans were over. If the House was turbulent, he remained calm. He spoke always reasonably, always at great length. By degrees he came to be feared almost as much as hated. Again and again, he and Mr. Biggar were expelled from the House. The next day they invariably returned and calmly resumed their tactics. On one famous occasion Mr. Biggar spoke for four hours. At first, Members indulged in the usual interruptions, and seeing that Mr. Biggar rather welcomed them as affording him a pleasant rest, they adopted another plan to discourage him and left the House in a body, some half-dozen only of their number remaining. Looking in an hour later, they found him still on his legs reading long extracts from Blue Books to empty benches. An hour later he was still talking. After three hours the Speaker attempted to cut him short. There is a rule of the House that every Member must make himself audible to the chair, and Mr. Biggar's voice had grown weak and husky. "The Hon. Member is not making himself audible to the chair," said Mr. Speaker Brand. "That is because I am too far away from you sir," said Mr. Biggar, who immediately gathered together his books and papers, and picking up his glass of water walked solemnly up the floor of the House and took up a position within a yard of the chair. "As you have not heard me, Mr. Speaker," said he, "perhaps I had better begin all over again."

Parliament thus lay absolutely at the mercy of this new policy, and Liberals and Tories alike threw all considerations of Party aside, and devoted themselves to the task of devising some new rules to rescue the House of Commons from destruction. . . .

While these events had been occurring in Parliament, the Land League movement had sprung into life in Ireland, and almost the first work which the New House of Commons under Gladstone, was asked to undertake was the passage of a Coercion Act, suspending the Constitution and abolishing Trial by Jury. All England was ablaze with excitement. Mr. Parnell and his Party were engaged in a life and death struggle in the House of Commons to prevent the passage of the measure. . . .

I shall never forget the appearance the Chamber presented. The floor was littered with paper. A few disheveled and weary Irishmen on one side of the house, about a hundred infuriated Englishmen upon the other; some of them still in evening dress, and wearing what once were the white shirts of the night before last. Mr. Parnell was upon his legs with pale cheeks and drawn face, his hands clenched behind his back, facing without flinching a continuous roar of interruption. It was now about eight o'clock. Half of Mr. Parnell's followers were out of the Chamber snatching a few moments' sleep in the library or smokeroom. Those who remained had each a specified period of time allotted to him to speak, and they were wearily waiting their turn. . . .

It was the Englishmen—the members of the first assembly of gentlemen in Europe as they love to style it—who howled and roared and almost foamed at the mouth with rage, at the calm and pale-faced young man, who stood patiently facing them and endeavouring from time to time to make himself heard. The galleries were filled with strangers every whit as excited as the Members, and even then the ladies' gallery contained its dozen or so of eager spectators. No one knew what was going to happen. There was no power under the Rules of the House to stop the debate, it had resolved itself into a question of physical endurance, and it seemed as if the Irishmen, battling for the liberties of their country were capable of resisting until the impotence of the House of Commons had covered it with the contempt and ridicule of Europe.

At last the end came suddenly and unexpectedly. . . .

The correspondent of a great English newspaper thus described the scene:

"Amid breathless silence the Speaker began to read from a paper which trembled like an aspen leaf in his hand. . . . Never since Cromwell entered the House, at the head of his men-at-arms, had

280

regular parliamentary procedure been subject to this swift and arbitrary cutting off by the mandate of a single man. But the Speaker got through his task with dignity, being strengthened by the burst of enthusiastic cheers which greeted him."

The Irish Members endeavoured to protest by speech against this proceeding, and failing in the attempt, they rose in their seats and left the Chamber in a body, shouting "Privilege," a cry not heard in that place since Charles I attempted to invade the liberty of Parliament. So ended the first battle over this Coercion Bill, the net result being that England found, in order to suspend the Constitution in Ireland, she was obliged to destroy the most cherished tradition and the most precious possession of her Parliament—*the freedom of speech of its members.*

*F*anny Parnell was the sister and champion of her brother Charles. She died before his downfall, which would have been a great sorrow to her, for her sense of justice was as acute as the irony displayed in this poem.

Keep the Law

By FANNY PARNELL
(1849–1882)

Keep the law, oh, keep it well—keep it as your rulers do!
Be not righteous overmuch—when they break it so can you!
As they rend their pledge and bond, rend you, too, their legal
thongs;
When they crush your chartered rights, tread you down your
chartered wrongs.
Help them on, and help them aye, help them as true brethren
should, boys;
All that's right and good for them, sure for you is right and good,
boys.
Hold the rent and hold the crops, boys. Pass the word from town
to town,
Pull away the props, boys, so you'll pull coercion down.

A Remarkable Man

By WILLIAM E. GLADSTONE
(1809–1898)

Prime Minister of England,
and in some respects friendly towards Ireland.

Parnell was the most remarkable man I ever met. I do not say the ablest man; I say the most remarkable and the most interesting. He was an intellectual phenomenon. He was unlike anyone I had ever met. He did things and he said things unlike other men. His ascendancy over his party was extraordinary. There has never been anything like it in my experience in the House of Commons. He succeeded in surrounding himself with very clever men, with men exactly suited for his purpose. They have changed since, I don't know why. Everything seems to have changed. But in his time he had a most efficient party, an extraordinary party. I do not say extraordinary as an Opposition, but extraordinary as a Government. The absolute obedience, the strict discipline, the military discipline, in which he held them was unlike anything I have ever seen. They were always there, they were always ready, they were always united, they never shirked the combat, and Parnell was supreme all the time. . . . Oh, Parnell was a most remarkable man and most interesting. I don't think he treated me well at the end, but my interest in him has never abated, and I feel an intense interest in his memory now. . . . Poor fellow! poor fellow! It was a terrible tragedy. I do believe firmly that if these divorce proceedings had not taken place there would be a Parliament in Ireland today.

The Fall of the Leader

By JOHN J. HORGAN
(1881–   )

In December, 1889, Captain O'Shea instituted proceedings for divorce against his wife, citing Parnell as correspondent. The trial took place in November, 1890. There was no defence. "I would rather appear to be dishonourable than be dishonourable," Parnell said to his colleagues a few weeks later during the historic meetings in Committee Room 15. The meaning of these apparently enigmatic words has now at last been made clear. O'Shea was in truth a dispossessed but not a deceived husband. . . . Parnell refused to plead the obvious and conclusive defence of O'Shea's collusion for the good reason that it would have been successful, and so have prevented him from marrying Mrs. O'Shea. O'Shea must have been sure that this would happen when he launched the proceedings. There can be little doubt now that he was the chosen tool of others; and all the available indications suggest that his friend, that malicious, ambitious and unscrupulous politician, Joseph Chamberlain, hungry for power and office, was foremost in the initiation and planning of the blow. . . .

The Irish Catholic Hierarchy, three weeks after the divorce court verdict, now added their condemnation. . . .

At fierce meetings in Committee Room 15 the Irish Party fought the matter out whilst the Irish people, breathless with anxiety, waited without. Parnell sought vainly to ride the whirlwind. . . .

On 6th December, 1890, the Irish Party, that fine weapon of tempered steel which Parnell had forged and used with such matchless skill, broke in two, forty-five members declaring themselves against Parnell, twenty-two supporting him.

Looking back through the veil of time, which has softened bitterness and eliminated hatred, one can realize that there were serious faults and mistakes made on both sides. The truth is that the Irish members, without any choice on their part, were faced with one of the most heart-rending problems ever presented to a body of patriotic politicians. These, for the most part, humble, self-educated men, nearly all Catholics, confronted by the immoral and apparently disgraceful conduct of their cherished leader . . . broke under the strain. . . .

. . . Deserted even by some of his friends, rushing backwards and forwards between Dublin and Brighton, his frail physical strength finally gave way. He took seriously ill with rheumatic fever and died at Brighton on 6th October, 1891. The political assassins who had persuaded O'Shea to strike had succeeded beyond their wildest hopes. They had wrecked Gladstone's plans, disrupted the Irish people and killed Parnell.

All Ireland stood aghast at the tragic news. The life of the country seemed to have ceased with his. . . . Even his political enemies stood dismayed at this frightful climax to their campaign against him. He had died, as he had promised, fighting to the end. . . .

A Discussion

By JAMES JOYCE
(1882–1941)

He was for Ireland and Parnell, and so was his father, and so was Dante too; for one night at the band on the esplanade, she had hit a gentleman on the head with her umbrella because he had taken off his hat when the band played *God Save The Queen* at the end.

Mr. Dedalus gave a snort of contempt.

"Ah, John," he said. "It is true for them. We are an unfortunate priestridden race and always were and always will be till the end of the chapter."

Uncle Charles shook his head, saying, "A bad business! A bad business!"

Mr. Dedalus repeated, "A priestridden Godforsaken race!"

He pointed to the portrait of his grandfather on the wall to his right.

"Do you see that old chap up there, John?" he said. "He was a good Irishman when there was no money in the job. He was condemned to death as a whiteboy. But he had a saying about our clerical friends, that he would never let one of them put his two feet under his mahogany."

Dante broke in angrily, "If we are a priestridden race, we ought to be proud of it! They are the apple of God's eye. *TOUCH*

284

THEM NOT, says Christ, *FOR THEY ARE THE APPLE OF MY EYE.*"

"And can we not love our country then?" asked Mr. Casey. "Are we not to follow the man that was born to lead us?"

"A traitor to his country!" replied Dante. "A traitor, an adulterer! The priests were right to abandon him. The priests were always the true friends of Ireland."

"Were they, faith!" said Mr. Casey.

He threw his fist on the table and, frowning angrily, protruded one finger after another.

"Didn't the bishops of Ireland betray us in the time of the union when Bishop Lanigan presented an address of loyalty to the Marquess Cornwallis? Didn't the bishops and priests sell the aspirations of their country in 1829 in return for Catholic emancipation? Didn't they denounce the fenian movement from the pulpit and in the confession box? And didn't they dishonor the ashes of Terence Bellew MacManus?"

His face was glowing with anger and Stephen felt the glow rise to his own cheek as the spoken words thrilled him. Mr. Dedalus uttered a guffaw of coarse scorn.

"O, by God," he cried. "I forgot little old Paul Cullen. Another apple of God's eye!"

Dante bent across the table and cried to Mr. Casey, "Right! Right! They were always right! God and morality and religion come first."

Mrs. Dedalus, seeing her excitement, said to her, "Mrs. Riordan, don't excite yourself answering them."

"God and religion before everything!" Dante cried. "God and religion before the world!"

Mr. Casey raised his clenched fist and brought it down on the table with a crash.

"Very well, then," he shouted hoarsely, "if it comes to that, no God for Ireland!"

"John! John!" cried Mr. Dedalus, seizing his guest by the coat sleeve.

Dante stared across the table, her cheeks shaking. Mr. Casey struggled up from his chair and bent across the table towards her, scraping the air from before his eyes with one hand as though he were tearing aside a cobweb.

"No God for Ireland!" he cried. "We have had too much God in Ireland. Away with God!"

"Blasphemer! Devil!" screamed Dante, starting to her feet and almost spitting in his face.

Uncle Charles and Mr. Dedalus pulled Mr. Casey back into his chair again, talking to him from both sides reasonably. He stared before him out of his dark flaming eyes, repeating, "Away with God, I say!"

Dante shoved her chair violently aside and left the table, upsetting her napkinring which rolled slowly along the carpet and came to rest against the foot of an easy chair. Mrs. Dedalus rose quickly and followed her towards the door. At the door Dante turned round violently and shouted down the room, her cheeks flushed and quivering with rage, "Devil out of hell! We won! We crushed him to death! Fiend!"

The door slammed behind her.

Mr. Casey, freeing his arms from his holders, suddenly bowed his head on his hands with a sob of pain.

"Poor Parnell!" he cried loudly. "My dead king!"

He sobbed loudly and bitterly.

Stephen raising his terror stricken face, saw that his father's eyes were full of tears.

From *A Portrait of an Artist as a Young Man*

Bright Hopes

By LADY WILDE
Mother of Oscar Wilde
(1826–1896)

Bitter was the past; let it rest, a new aeon
    Preaches a new Gospel to man not in vain,
Earth through all the kingdoms echoes back the paean
    Chanted once by Angels on the star-lit plain.

Brotherhood of Nations, disdaining ancient quarrel,
    Brotherhood of Peoples, flushed with a nobler rage,
Palm branch and Olive let us mingle with the Laurel
    In the radiant future of the coming age!

From *The Dawn*

286

The Men From Over the Bog

By LORD DUNSANY
(1878–1957)

And another memory I have of that day, that is almost as clear to my mind as the memory of my father and myself before the fire in the library; and that is the picture of a long man in a frayed black coat that came below his knees, galloping down the street of a village in which all the houses were thatched, and all had low white walls shining in sunlight. I should not call it a memory, because I never saw it, but I pictured the scene so clearly when I was young, when the man came up to High Gaut, and said, "I galloped all the way from Lisronagh to tell you that the geese are in on the bog," that the picture is still here among my memories. And a keen joy stamped the picture clear on my mind, for shooting was the greatest adventure I then had known, and a pheasant the largest bird I had ever shot; and that gray traveller the goose, with his wariness, his rarity and romance, was a greater prize to me then than any the world could offer me now. And my father would not let me go to Lisronagh, because I had not done my holiday task. It was a book of Dickens, and everyone else in my division at Eton would do it in the train going down from Paddington. I see now that fifty minutes in a crowded railway carriage may not be enough in which to read one of Dickens' novels; but the feeling that my father did not understand is deeper and older and stronger. Yes, it is with me yet.

So in the evening we were sitting before the fire in the library, and it was late, and he had sent for the glass of milk that he always drank with whiskey before going to bed. There were only us: my mother had died years ago. We were alone in the large house but for the cook and the kitchen maid and the one housemaid: the butler lived half a mile away, and had long gone to bed. And there was a boy, living over the stables, who did odd work in the house by day. We were not talking much. Perhaps I was sore about not having been allowed to go to Lisronagh; I don't remember now. Of course I had had ample warning about the holiday task; my father had often told me to do it and I had not started it yet: partly laziness; chiefly, I suppose; and partly that feeling that my father did not understand the attitude of the world to a holiday task: my world, I mean. I obeyed my father as much as most boys do; but there was one curious thing over which he seemed to exert all his personal force, all that was left to him as he grew old, and even more, as though he called up hidden reserves of power; and that was that one day in that room he might say to me "Look at the picture," and if ever he did I was to go immediately to a little Dutch picture at the end of the room and watch it; I forget for how long, but I was to watch it minutely. And, if ever he said those words, I was never to think that he did not mean them, or that it was a joke, or that there was time to spare. He told me this often. Why? He never told me why.

Well, there we were sitting, and the house was all shut up; my father always went round every shutter himself to see they were properly fastened, and I used to think it rather unnecessary, for we knew everybody all round us; but once when I said something of this to my father he had replied, "You never know who might come over the bog." And certainly on the other side of the bog there were hills of which we knew nothing. Yet the idea that, even over there, could be anyone with enmity for my father, seemed, I remember, absurd to me: for one thing he did not seem active enough to have his share of such enmities; but that was a boy's idea, forgetting he had been younger.

We were talking, when at all, about Lisronagh, for I wanted quietly to find out what day I might go; when the housemaid brought in the milk, a tumbler of plain milk which he used to mix with the whiskey himself, after tasting the milk to see that it was not sour. The housemaid left the room, and he put his hand to the tumbler that stood on a table beside him. I can see him now more clearly than I can picture faces seen yesterday; tall and thin, with fine profile, with the firelight in his graying beard. And I was talking of Lisronagh. I thought he would have let me go next day, till he said definitely, "Not this week." I remember the words because they fell on my ears with such a sense of disaster, yearning as I was to get to Lisronagh before the geese had gone, and because they were the last words, but four, that I ever heard him say. He lifted the glass of milk to his lips and then put it down again, and turned to me and said, "Look at the picture." And he said it with

288

none of the authority I had expected, if ever I really expected he would say those words at all, with less authority by far than that with which he forbade me to go to Lisronagh, but as though he were very tired.

I did as I had been taught. I went without thinking he did not mean it, or that there was time to spare: I went to the little Dutch picture and gazed at the tiny figures, skating past churches and windmills over gray ice. The picture was near the door, the only door in the room, which was shut, until it was opened from outside, and four tall men came in. Then I looked round, and my father was gone.

I saw at once that the men were from the other side of the bog; they were dark and strange and like none of our men. They peered round the room, then one of them looked at me fixedly and said, "There is no one we have a greater respect for than your father, but it is a pity he mixed himself up with politics the way he did; and it's the way it is we want to speak to him, and no one could be sorrier than myself that I have to say it."

Then I knew they had come to shoot my father.

So I said, "He is up in his room, but I'll go and fetch him."

"You will not, sir," said the same man. "But we will come with you."

So they looked amongst all the curtains in the library, and behind a sofa that there was, and found nothing, and then I walked slowly up the stairs, and they came with me. So slowly I went that one of them shouted, "Come *on*, now." And at that I started forward and ran up a few steps, and fell at the top of a flight. I got up slowly, and then limped a little. All this gained time.

When we came to the door of my father's room I knocked, but they shoved in past me. The room was in darkness and I got a match for them and lit a candle: they looked round the room carefully, and we gained time there.

I said, "He must be in his study." And then I added, "Perhaps he is in another bedroom. Shall we go there first?"

But the man who had spoken before said, "You will go to the study." So I did as he told me and we all went downstairs. All the time I was calculating how far my father could have got. How he had got out of the library I had no idea; there was only one door and all the shutters were shut; but gone he had. And even if he went by some narrow passage, and difficult steps in the dark, I calculated that with our various trifling delays, that all add up, he had gone by now as far as we had, and that that should have just taken him clear of the house. He would make of course for the stables: that was a hundred yards. And then he would have to get in, and saddle his horse and get out again, and past the gate by the house, before one could think him safe.

When we entered the study I think they saw at a glance that my father was not there, and never had been. It was not only that the fire was unlighted, but the look and feel of the room told you at once that it never was used by anyone. And indeed, except for meals, we never used any room at all but the library. And they all looked at me in a rather nasty way.

"If you don't show us where he is, we'll burn the house," said one of them that had not spoken before.

"You will not," I said, looking straight at him.

And his face fell at that, and I saw the eyes of all of them turn downwards. For they knew, whoever they were or wherever they came from, that we kept a piece of the true Cross at High Gaut, and had done for ages, ever since it had been granted to us for the help my family gave in a war of one of the popes. I saw they were thinking of it, and did not have to remind them that if a man burned that, the flames might not be so easily quenched. They would flicker about his soul all through eternity.

But you do not always know, when you invoke powers like that, whom in the end they will benefit. The leader turned to me and told me to get the cross. It was a crystal cross and part of the crystal was hollow, and in the hollow the piece of the true Cross was. I knew what they wanted it for: they were going to swear me on it. And I grew suddenly afraid of the cross, and afraid of the men.

I had to get it: it was in that very room; in a little golden box on a marble table. It was never locked up; there was no need for that. I went across the room to get it, and they all drew their pistols as I went. They took them out of their pockets in which I knew they had them, but they had not shown them before. Now they were getting annoyed because they had not found my father, and I saw that they were not going to let me escape from swearing to them on the Cross. They were long, single-barrelled pistols, old even then; nothing like the automatics they use nowadays.

290

When I came back with the relic I saw that they had me covered. I came up to them and lifted it in my hand, and they all dropped on their knees. "Do you swear," said the leader, kneeling before me, but still covering me with the long black pistol, "to the best of your knowledge and your belief that your father is still in this house?"

And while he spoke I heard the clip, clop, clip clop, of my father's horse coming out of the stables. But it was only coming at a walk. That was of course so as to make less noise, and then there was a gate that he would have to open, but somehow I had thought he would gallop. Almost at once he got on to the grass, and they had not heard him, but he had to come right past the house. I could still hear every step of the horse, but I suppose it is easier to hear what you are listening for, if you are listening as I was; while they were all watching me and the cross that I held and waiting for me to speak, and they never heard the horse coming by on the grass. But they would have if I hadn't spoken just when I did. He wasn't safe till he'd opened the gate another fifty yards on. "I swear," I said, "to the best of my knowledge and my belief," speaking slowly, spinning it out as long as I could, to drown the noise of the hooves, "that my father is in this house."

I suppose one puts one's soul in danger oftener than one thinks, and in less good causes. The risk frightened me when I took it. If it wasn't the true Cross, and (God help me) I've sometimes doubted it, then no harm was done. If it was, could it be on the side of these four men and against my father? But I was not easy about what I'd done for a single moment, till I went to Father McGillicud and told him all. "And would you murder your father," he said, "and with the true Cross in your hand?" Then I knew that I'd done right.

When I had sworn I put the relic down, and they all rose from their knees, and as they rose I heard the hoofbeats stop. My father was opening the gate.

That is the scene that remains with me today, so far away from Ireland, as clear as any picture that one could hang on the wall; the old room in my home, and the four men kneeling before me with their pistols. It takes a wealth of experience in many peaceful years to make a man forget having looked from the wrong end along firearms; and the first time he probably never forgets; but it is their earnest, devout faces that I see in my memory as vividly as their weapons.

When I put the relic down they began to search the house. My father must still have been fumbling with the gate, for I did not hear as yet the sound I was waiting for. It was one of those gates that you had to dismount to open. I went with them from room to room; and suddenly, in the first room that we came to, I heard my father's horse. It was trotting now. I began talking hurriedly, and still they seemed not to hear the horse. There was the lodge still ahead of him, and the lodge gates, but I felt he was almost safe now. I never knew how these men had come, whether on horse or driving or on foot, and did not know what means of pursuit they might have; but I felt he was nearly safe, though I wished he would gallop. We went from room to room, and they searched thoroughly, paying no attention to my suggestions that I made to drown the sound of the trotting hooves, growing fainter and fainter; but, in the hugeness and the stillness of the night, they were clearly audible all the way to the lodge. Sometimes the four tall men stopped suddenly and listened, to hear if my father was moving about the house before them, but they never heard the hooves. Large deserted rooms that we never used we passed through, with a feeling of emptiness and damp about them, and so little suggesting the presence of either my father or any living man that one of them said to me, "Was there ever a ghost here?" And partly because of the look and feel of the room, with only one candle burning, and partly because of the habit I had picked up from the people all round me of rather avoiding a straight answer, I said, "I wouldn't trust it." I think that hurried them on, which is what I should most have avoided; but, as they came to the last room, I heard, all of a sudden, ring out in the heart of the night the sound of a horse galloping. It was my father, clear of the lodge, on the high road. It must have been half a mile away, but the sound of a horse at night galloping is a sound that they could not have missed. They all stood still at once. "It's himself," said one. They looked at me, but gave up any notion of my complicity; then they turned to their own plans and began to hurry towards the hall door. I started making conversation with them about shooting. One of them listened to me, and soon I was telling him of the geese on Lisronagh bog. It was a safer topic than some that they might have started, if left to themselves. To

292

look at him you would have said that he was the worst of the four, and yet he told me little things about shooting that are pure gold to a boy; and, when he saw how keen I was on the geese, he said to me just as they all went out through the door, "And a goose takes a long time to get his pace up. Don't aim so much in front of a goose as you do at other birds."

And then when they'd all gone he opened the door again and put his head inside, and said, word for word as I write it, "And if it ever comes to it, and God knows the world's full of trouble, aim a foot in front of a man walking, at a hundred yards."

An age is the reversal of an age:
When strangers murdered Emmet, Fitzgerald, Tone,
We lived like men that watch a painted stage.
What matter for the scene, the scene once gone:
It had not touched our lives. But popular rage,
Hysterica passio dragged this quarry down.
None shared our guilt; nor did we play a part
Upon a painted stage when we devoured his heart.

W. B. Yeats

A Gaelic Song

By ETHNA CARBERY

A murmurous tangle of voices,
    Laughter to left and right,
We waited the curtain's rising,
    In a glare of electric light;
When down through the din came, slowly,
    Softly, then clear and strong,
The mournful minor cadence
    Of a sweet old Gaelic song.

Like the trill of a lark new-risen,
    It trembled upon the air,
And wondering eyes were lifted
    To seek for the singer there;
Some dreamed of the thrush at noontide,
    Some fancied a linnet's wail,
While the notes went sobbing, sighing,
    O'er the heartstrings of the Gael.

. . .

A river twined through its shallows,
    Cool waves crept up on a strand,
Or fierce, like a mighty army,
    Swept wide on a conquered land;
The Dead left cairn and barrow,
    And passed in noble train,
With sheltering shield, and slender spear—
    Ere the curtain rose again.

. . .

It was the soul of Eire
    Awakening in speech she knew,
When the clans held the glens and the mountains,
    And the hearts of her chiefs were true:
She hath stirred at last in her sleeping,
    She is folding her dreams away,
The hour of her destiny neareth—
    And it may be today—today!

1916

EASTER WEEK
AND THE TROUBLES

On Easter Monday, 1916, the Irish once and for all rose up in rebellion against the English. They proclaimed Ireland to be a republic. The following can be read today beneath the statue of Cuchulainn, who is symbolic of Irish heroism:

Easter 1916
Proclamation of the Irish Republic

Poblacht na h Eireann
The Provisional Government of
The Irish Republic
to
The People of Ireland

IRISHMEN AND IRISHWOMEN:

IN THE NAME OF GOD and of the dead generations from which she receives her old tradition of nationhood, Ireland, through us, summons her children to her flag and strikes for her freedom.

HAVING ORGANISED and trained her manhood through her secret revolutionary organisation, the Irish Republican Brotherhood, and through her open miltary organisations, the Irish Volunteers and the Irish Citizen Army, having patiently perfected her discipline, having resolutely waited for the right moment to reveal itself, she now seizes that moment, and, supported by her exiled children in America and by gallant allies in Europe, but relying in the first on her own strength, she strikes in full confidence of victory.

WE declare the right of the people of Ireland to the ownership of Ireland, and to the unfettered control of Irish destinies, to be sovereign and indefeasible. The long usurpation of that right by a foreign people and government has not extinguished the right, nor can it ever be extinguished except by the destruction of the Irish people. In every generation the Irish have asserted their right to National freedom and sovereignty; six times during the past three hundred years they have asserted it in arms. Standing on that fundamental right and again asserting it in arms in the face of the world, we hereby proclaim the Irish Republic as a Sovereign Independent State, and we pledge our lives and the lives of our comrades-in-arms to the cause of its freedom, of its welfare, and of its exaltation among the nations.

296

THE Irish Republic is entitled to, and hereby claims, the allegiance of every Irishman and Irishwoman. The Republic guarantees religious and civil liberty, equal rights and equal opportunities to all its citizens, and declares its resolve to pursue the happiness and prosperity of the whole nation and of all its parts, cherishing all the children of the nation equally, and oblivious of the differences carefully fostered by an alien government, which have divided a minority from the majority in the past.

UNTIL OUR ARMS have brought the opportune moment for the establishment of a permanent National Government, representative of the whole people of Ireland and elected by the suffrages of all her men and women, the Provisional Government, hereby constituted, will administer the civil and military affairs of the Republic in trust for the people.

WE place the cause of the Irish Republic under the protection of the Most High God, Whose blessing we invoke upon our arms, and we pray that no one who serves that cause will dishonor it by cowardice, inhumanity, or rapine. In this supreme hour the Irish nation must, by its valour and discipline and by the readiness of its children to sacrifice themselves for the common good, prove itself worthy of the august destiny to which it is called.

Signed on Behalf of the Provisional Government,

THOMAS J. CLARKE,
SEAN MACDIARMADA,
THOMAS MACDONAGH,
P. H. PEARSE,
EAMONN CEANNT,
JAMES CONNOLLY,
JOSEPH PLUNKETT.

POBLACHT NA H EIREANN.
THE PROVISIONAL GOVERNMENT
OF THE
IRISH REPUBLIC
TO THE PEOPLE OF IRELAND.

IRISHMEN AND IRISHWOMEN: In the name of God and of the dead generations from which she receives her old tradition of nationhood, Ireland, through us, summons her children to her flag and strikes for her freedom.

Having organised and trained her manhood through her secret revolutionary organisation, the Irish Republican Brotherhood, and through her open military organisations, the Irish Volunteers and the Irish Citizen Army, having patiently perfected her disciplne, having resolutely waited for the right moment to reveal itself, she now seizes that moment, and, supported by her exiled children in America and by gallant allies in Europe, but relying in the first on her own strength, she strikes in full confidence of victory.

We declare the right of the people of Ireland to the ownership of Ireland, and to the unfettered control of Irish destinies, to be sovereign and indefeasible. The long usurpation of that right by a foreign people and government has not extinguished the right, nor can it ever be extinguished except by the destruction of the Irish people. In every generation the Irish people have asserted their right to national freedom and sovereignty; six times during the past three hundred years they have asserted it in arms. Standing on that fundamental right and again asserting it in arms in the face of the world, we hereby proclaim the Irish Republic as a Sovereign Independent State, and we pledge our lives and the lives of our comrades-in-arms to the cause of its freedom, of its welfare, and of its exaltation among the nations.

The Irish Republic is entitled to, and hereby claims, the allegiance of every Irishman and Irishwoman. The Republic guarantees religious and civil liberty, equal rights and equal opportunities to all its citizens, and declares its resolve to pursue the happiness and prosperity of the whole nation and of all its parts, cherishing all the children of the nation equally, and oblivious of the differences carefully fostered by an alien government, which have divided a minority from the majority in the past.

Until our arms have brought the opportune moment for the establishment of a permanent National Government, representative of the whole people of Ireland and elected by the suffrages of all her men and women, the Provisional Government, hereby constituted, will administer the civil and military affairs of the Republic in trust for the people.

We place the cause of the Irish Republic under the protection of the Most High God, Whose blessing we invoke upon our arms, and we pray that no one who serves that cause will dishonor it by cowardice, inhumanity, or rapine. In this supreme hour the Irish nation must, by its valour and discipline and by the readiness of its children to sacrifice themselves for the common good, prove itself worthy of the august destiny to which it is called.

Signed on Behalf of the Provisional Government,
THOMAS J. CLARKE.
SEAN Mac DIARMADA.   THOMAS MacDONAGH.
P. H. PEARSE.   EAMONN CEANNT.
JAMES CONNOLLY.   JOSEPH PLUNKETT.

O*verwhelmed and completely surrounded, the leaders who had signed the Declaration of Independence gave themselves up to certain execution rather than see their fellow countrymen slaughtered. The leader, Padraic Pearse, made this statement before his execution on May 2nd, 1916.*

Kilmainham Prison

By PADRAIC PEARSE
(1879–1916)

The following is the substance of what I said when asked today by the President of the Court-Martial at Richmond Barracks whether I had anything to say in my defence:

I desire, in the first place, to repeat what I have already said in letters to General Maxwell and Brigadier General Lowe. My object in agreeing to an unconditional surrender was to prevent the further slaughter of the civil population of Dublin and to save the lives of our gallant fellows, who, having made for six days a stand unparalleled in military history, were now surrounded, and in the case of those under the immediate command of H.Q., without food. I fully understand now, as then, that my own life is forfeit to British law, and I shall die very cheerfully if I can think that the British Government, as it has already shown itself strong, will now show itself magnanimous enough to accept my single life in forfeiture and to give a general amnesty to the brave men and boys who have fought at my bidding.

In the second place, I wish it to be understood that any admissions I make here are to be taken as involving myself alone. They do not involve and must not be used against anyone who acted with me, not even those who may have set their names to documents with me. (The Court assented to this.)

I admit that I was Commandant-General Commanding-in-Chief of the forces of the Irish Republic which have been acting against you for the past week, and that I was President of the Provisional Government. I stand over all my acts and words done or spoken, in these capacities. When I was a child of ten I went on my bare knees by my bedside one night and promised God that I should devote my life to an effort to free my country. I have kept the promise. I have helped to organize, to arm, to train, and to discipline my fellow-countrymen to the sole end that, when the time came, they might fight for Irish freedom. The time, as it seemed to me, did come, and we went into the fight. I am glad we did, we seem to have lost, but we have not lost. To refuse to fight would have been to lose, to fight is to win; we have kept faith with the past, and handed on a tradition to the future. I repudiate the assertion of the prosecutor that I sought to aid and abet England's enemy. Germany is no more to me than England is. I asked and accepted German aid in the shape of arms and an expeditionary force, we neither asked for nor accepted German gold, nor had any traffic with Germany but what I state. My object was to win Irish freedom. We struck the first blow ourselves, but I should have been glad of an ally's aid.

I assume that I am speaking to Englishmen who value their freedom and who profess to be fighting for the freedom of Belgium and Serbia; believe that we too love freedom and desire it. To us it is more desirable than anything in the world. If you strike us down now we shall rise again and renew the fight, you cannot conquer Ireland, you cannot extinguish the Irish passion for freedom; if our deed has not been sufficient to win freedom then our children will win it by a better deed.

The Irish "Troubles" 1916-1923

By EDGAR HOLT
(1900–   )

In all, 14 men were shot for their part in the Easter Rising in Dublin, and one—Thomas Kent—for killing an R.I.C. head constable in resisting arrest at Fermoy, county Cork, on Easter Tuesday. All the signatories of the proclamation were executed—Pearse, MacDonagh and Clarke on May 3, Plunkett on May 4, Ceannt on May 8 and Connolly and MacDermott on May 12. Connolly's execution seemed particularly gruesome, because one of his wounds had gangrened and he had to be carefully nursed until he was well enough to be put into a chair to face the firing party. The other seven who were shot were Edward Daly, commandant at the Four

299

Courts; Sean Heuston, who had held the Mendicity Institution; John MacBride and Michael O'Hanrahan, MacDonagh's chief lieutenants at Jacob's factory; Michael Mullin, commandant at St. Stephen's Green; Con Colbert, one of Ceannt's senior officers; and William Pearse, who was not in the insurgents' inner councils and was apparently executed for the crime of being Padriac's brother. Many other death sentences were passed, but were commuted to terms of penal servitude either for life or for ten years. Among those whose sentences were commuted to life imprisonment were William T. Cosgrave, Constance Markievicz, Eamon de Valera, Thomas Ashe and Robert Brennan. The courts-martial went on after the executions had ceased, and the last, which began on May 22, was on Eoin MacNeill, who, though he had taken no part in the rising, had to face eight charges of attempting to cause disaffection among the civil population of Ireland and four of acting in a way likely to prejudice recruiting. He, too, was sentenced to penal servitude for life.

Of the Dublin commandants only de Valera escaped execution. This was largely due to the curious point of his nationality. He was not a British subject, for his father was Spanish, and British nationality could not descend to him through his Irish mother; yet he was not legally an American. To acquire permanent American citizenship he would have had to register with a U.S. consulate at 18 and take the Oath of Allegiance at 21, and he had done neither of these things. Technically he was a stateless person, yet the fact of his American birth remained, and appeals for mercy were made on his behalf both by Redmond and by the U.S. consulate in Dublin. The appeals were readily heard by Asquith, who was equally anxious not to affront American feelings and to call a halt to the apparently endless stream of executions; and on May 11, the day before the last executions took place, it was announced that the sentence of death passed on de Valera had been commuted to life imprisonment.

An additional complaint against Maxwell's policy was that the courts-martial were held privately, and no record of their proceedings was ever published, apart from the bare statement of their findings; but in spite of this secrecy, some of the dead men's last words became known later. At their last meeting Connolly gave his daughter Nora a statement in which he had written: "Believing that

300

the British Government has no right in Ireland, never had any right in Ireland and never can have any right in Ireland, the presence in any one generation of Irishmen of even a respectable minority ready to die to affirm that truth makes that Government for ever a usurpation and a crime against human progress." Tom MacDonagh's "Last and inspiring speech" was soon to be sold as a broadsheet in the streets of Dublin: it had the gallant ring to be expected in the words of a lively poet and critic unexpectedly turned into a man of action. "It will be said," MacDonagh proudly told his judges, "that our movement was doomed to failure. It has proved so. Yet it might have been otherwise. There is always a chance of success for brave men who challenge fortune." Of Pearse's speech there is no record, but in his last hours in prison he wrote one of the loveliest of all his poems, "The Wayfarer," in which he poignantly recalled the beauty of the world to which he was soon to say good-bye:

> The beauty of the world hath made me sad,
> This beauty that will pass;
> Sometimes my heart hath shaken with great joy
> To see a leaping squirrel in a tree,
> Or a red ladybird upon a stalk,
> Or little rabbits in a field at evening,
> Lit by a slanting sun,
> Or some green hill where shadows drifted by,
> Some quiet hill where mountainy man hath sown
> And soon would reap; near to the gate of Heaven;
> Or children with bare feet upon the sands
> Of some ebbed sea, or playing on the streets
> Of little towns in Connacht,
> Things young and happy.
> And then my heart hath told me:
> These will pass,
> Will pass and change, will die and be no more,
> Things bright and green, things young and happy;
> And I have gone upon my way
> Sorrowful.*

* *The Wayfarer*, by Padraic Pearse. *Written the night before his execution.*

Plunkett, too, used his last moments of life to write a poem, which began touchingly:

> Life that's sweet, so sweet, crumbles at my feet.
> I would not retreat from a course so meet.

It was written to his bride of a few hours, Grace Gifford, whose sister was the wife of Tom MacDonagh, though their family was strongly Unionist. Plunkett and Grace Gifford would have been married on Easter Sunday if there had not been a hitch over the church arrangements. Their wedding took place in the prison chapel at 11:30 on the night before Plunkett's execution.

In the weeks which followed the Rising, 3,149 men and 77 women were arrested in Ireland by the British authorities, though some were soon released. The majority were sent to England, where, in addition to some 160 who had been convicted by courts-martial, 1,862 men and five women were interned without trial. Prisoners who had been sentenced to penal servitude were sent to English prisons and a few of the internees who were thought to be particularly influential, such as Arthur Griffith, were also detained in gaol; but most of the internees were eventually collected in a big camp at Frongoch, in Wales.

It was as these prisoners and internees were marched to the quays that the change in Dublin's feelings began to make itself evident. Pearse's belief that Ireland needed a blood sacrifice to arouse her national spirit was proved correct; the great architects of the insurrection did more for Ireland by their deaths than they had been able to do by their lives. The Irish had not, indeed, become Sinn Feiners. Those who believed in Redmond and Home Rule before the Rising had not lost their faith; the wives of the many Irish soldiers serving in the British Army still formed a solid anti-revolutionary bloc. But many Irishmen and Irishwomen had now shed the hostility to the insurgents they had felt during Easter Week. Internees were no longer hissed or jeered at; instead friends rushed out to shake hands with them and half-bottles of whiskey were thrust into their pockets. "God save you," cried the watching crowds. "God have pity on you! Keep your hearts up!" The Sinn Feiners were "dirty bowsies" no longer; the Rising had become a saga, an heroic story to be told with pity and pride in the years to come.

302

Easter 1916

By W. B. YEATS

I have met them at close of day
Coming with vivid faces
From counter or desk among gray
Eighteenth-century houses.
I have passed with a nod of the head
Or polite meaningless words,
Or have lingered awhile and said
Polite meaningless words,
And thought before I had done
Of a mocking tale or a gibe
To please a companion
Around the fire at the club,
Being certain that they and I
But lived where motley is worn:
All changed, changed utterly:
A terrible beauty is born.

That woman's days were spent
In ignorant goodwill,
Her nights in argument
Until her voice grew shrill.
What voice more sweet than hers
When, young and beautiful,
She rode to harriers?
This man had kept a school
And rode our winged horse;
This other his helper and friend
Was coming into his force;
He might have won fame in the end,
So sensitive his nature seemed,
So daring and sweet his thought.
This other man I had dreamed
A drunken, vainglorious lout.
He had done most bitter wrong
To some who are near my heart,

Yet I number him in the song;
He, too, has resigned his part
In the casual comedy;
He, too, has been changed in his turn,
Transformed utterly:
A terrible beauty is born.

Hearts with one purpose alone
Through summer and winter seem
Enchanted to a stone
To trouble the living stream
The horse that comes from the road,
The rider, the birds that range
From cloud to tumbling cloud,
Minute by minute they change;
A shadow of cloud on the stream
Changes minute by minute;
A horsehoof slides on the brim,
And a horse plashes within it;
The long-legged moor-hens dive,
And hens to moor-cocks call;
Minute by minute they live:
The stone's in the midst of all.

Too long a sacrifice
Can make a stone of the heart.
O when may it suffice?
That is Heaven's part, our part
To murmur name upon name,
As a mother names her child
When sleep at last has come
On limbs that had run wild.
What is it but nightfall?
No, no, not night but death;
Was it needless death after all?
For England may keep faith
For all that is done and said.
We know their dream; enough
To know they dreamed and are dead;

And what if excess of love
Bewildered them till they died?
I write it out in a verse—

MacDonagh and MacBride
And Connolly and Pearse
Now and in time to be,
Wherever green is worn,
Are changed, changed utterly:
A terrible beauty is born.

An Unwritten Page of Irish History

By NIALL MacDONAGH
(1944–   )

*Grandson of Thomas MacDonagh, one of the signatories
of the Proclamation, executed in 1916.*

A few weeks before the Rising of 1916 Eamon de Valera called
on his direct superior, Thomas Mac Donagh in a choler. He
complained that his subordinates seemed to know more about
Volunteer affairs than he did. Mac Donagh explained that his
subordinates were all members of the Irish Republican Brotherhood
and that "Dev" was not. Here it is necessary to know that the
Irish Volunteers were run by the Military Council of the I.R.B.

As a result of this conversation de Valera had himself sworn
into the I.R.B. and from that day on he had no trouble with his
subordinates.

We pick up the story again on Holy Thursday, five days before
the Revolution. "Dev" met Mac Donagh on the corner of Appian
Way, a road off Leeson Street in Dublin, and was invited to a
meeting of the Military Council that night, but Dev would not,
or could not, attend. They argued for a while, but he was adamant.

No Council for him. Eventually Mac Donagh gave up. He
mounted a tram, and as it moved off he shouted that the offer
remained open. Dev again refused. They did not know it then,
but that was the last time they were to meet.

That night the Military Council drafted the Proclamation, and
issued the order to mobilise on Easter Sunday. The rest you know,

or ought to know.

We are presented here with one of the glorious "ifs" of Irish history. If Dev had accepted this invitation, and *If* he had signed the Proclamation he would undoubtedly have made a seventeenth martyr. But he did not, and so lived to lead our nation to freedom.

These facts were told by de Valera to my father who in turn told them to me. As far as I, or my father, are aware, they have never been published nor have they been told to anybody else.

Sinn Fein

By CAMILLE BOURNIQUEL

From a book called Ireland, originally published *in France. Translated by John Fisher in 1960*

The remembrance of 1916 gave a new direction to the struggle: the desperate action of the insurgents foreshadowed further activity. Pearse had been right. In the general elections held after the Armistice, there was a landslide in favour of Sinn Fein, which suddenly emerged from hiding. Thirty-six of the new members of Parliament were still in prison; three had been deported; six were on the run. The others, in conformity with the ideas of Pearse and Griffith, refused to go to London to take their seats. Their assembly, the Dail Eireann, once more proclaimed the Republic, with de Valera, still in prison, as its president.

England did not flinch from this blow. But in Ireland the English administration was operating in a vacuum. Slowly, but surely, a new administration was substituted for the official one. Parties in a lawsuit preferred to resort to arbitration by semi-clandestine judges rather than to appear in the official Courts of Justice. There was a renewed violence on both sides. The nationalists claimed and were refused belligerent rights. The viceroy, besieged in his residence, seldom left it for fear of attempts on his life. There were moments of extreme violence, such as the Croke Park shooting when the police fired on the crowd and players at a sporting meeting and thereby highlighted the state of illegality which existed. The British Security Services, demoralized by an elusive enemy which adopted some of the tactics of the Boer

306

War, offered a reward of £10,000 for the capture of such men as Michael Collins, Public Enemy Number One.

Would war break out again with England?

De Valera, who had sought refuge in the United States after escaping from Lincoln jail, organized an extensive series of conferences, collecting money, goodwill, and motions of support, and receiving an enthusiastic welcome everywhere on the American continent. England, in spite of having chosen the way of repression, could not ignore this irresistible trend of international feeling. In the interior, Ireland presented a spectacle of complete subversion. There were fist-fights, ambushes, killings, kidnappings, barracks set on fire, munitions stolen, continual arrests, works of art damaged, roads cut off. . . . Two police forces on the English side exerted themselves to keep order and left behind them a hated memory: the "Black and Tans" (the colours of a famous fox-hunting pack) and the Auxiliaries, recruited from among the soldiers who had fought on the Allied side. It was something less than war but much more than guerilla warfare.

The Patriot

By SEAN O'FAOLAIN
(1900–   )

It was doubtless because of the inevitable desire of man to recapture the past that they went to Youghal for their honeymoon. Their friends expected them to go at least to Dublin, if not to London or Paris, but they both knew in their hearts that they had spent the gayest days of their lives in this little town; and so, as if to crown all those early happinesses, to Youghal they went, like true voluptuaries deliberately creating fresh memories that would torment them when they were old.

Across there on the little stone promenade, when they were as yet little more than girl and boy, they had met for the first time. She was on holiday with her sister; he had come with his aunt for the day. In the train they had met Edward Bradley, his former teacher, and Mr. Bradley had walked about with him (in spite of his aunt) for a few hours, and given them tea. He had been flattered, he remembered, because old Bradley stayed with them

307

so long, and afterwards he pretended to Norah that Mr. Bradley was really a great friend of his. Off there at the end of the promenade they had sat, the three of them, because his aunt was too old to walk far without a rest, and as they sat there Norah and her sister came and halted opposite them to lean on the wall. A liner was passing slowly, almost imperceptibly, along the horizon and everybody was looking at it, and his aunt was asking him to tell them—he was young, God bless him, and had the better sight—was it two funnels or three it had. He had stood up, pretending to look at the liner, but he was really trying to look at Norah's black hair and her jet-black eyes without being seen, growing more irritated still because he saw that she too was trying to look at him without being observed, turning her back frequently on the sea to look, as it were, up over their heads at the crowds on the cliffs, curving herself backwards over the wall and standing on her toes as if to show herself off to him. In the end her sister drew her away as the ship became too faint to be seen and Bernard became so disconsolate and silent that his aunt plucked at him and said:

"What on earth's wrong with you, Bernie? Are you tired, or what is it?"

But Mr. Bradley cocked his eye at him and winked without his aunt seeing. Old Bradley was a cute boyo, he had thought, and flushed because he felt he had been observed. After tea he and his aunt were alone again, and she, who had been so sweet to their companion, was now abusing him roundly for a firebrand who was leading all the young men into wild politics. "Some day," Bernie defended, "that man will be Lord Mayor of Cork and then you'll sing a different song," but she would have none of it and as he just then caught sight again of his dark girl in the distance and wished to walk on and catch up with her he did not argue further. Alas! His aunt got tired once more, saying that the tea was like a load on her stomach, and they had to sit on another bench. His dark vision passed out of his sight and he felt she had merely floated before him and he would never meet her again.

When he did meet her again it was several years after and she was again on holiday in Youghal, and it was only by degrees they realized they had seen each other before. On this occasion he was an Irregular guerilla—doubly a rebel—seated high up on a lorry, with his rifle across his back and his coat collar turned up, and his cap thrown back and upwards from his forehead to let his curls free to the wind. Seven other lorries were roaring along behind him through the streets and as they tore their way under the old clock archway, there on the pavement, smiling up at them, and waving her green handkerchief to them, was the loveliest dark-haired girl he had ever seen. Their lorry halted just beyond the arch to wait for the troops marching in from the railway, and he alighted and by virtue of being a soldier was able to approach her on the pretense of wanting matches or cigarettes. By the time the troops came into the town they were in a little teashop, and he was flirting away with all the bravado in the world. As the men passed outside, four by four, they sang their rebelly songs, waking, as he said to her, the ghosts of old Raleigh, who had once lived there, and of the stiff Earl of Cork from his tomb in Christ's Church, and the ghost of every Elizabethan sailorman who had cast a rope ashore by the crumbled quays they could see through the rear door of the shop, edging with their fallen stones the glittering blue of the bay.

There were descendants of those sea dogs in that town still, she told him, for having come there year after year on her holidays since she was a little child she knew Youghal as if she had been born there. She chanted the names to him, the Merricks, the Gurneys, the Boyles, the Brisketts, and at each name he swaggered his cup on high to curse them, so that it was a profane litany that finished their tea.

"The Yardleys too," she said, laughing at him.

"God damn them forever!" he swashbuckled.

"Of course the Townshends are Cromwellian," she smiled.

"Damn them forever!" he cried again.

Her eyes wandered to the bay. A brown-sailed yawl was floating past on the blue water as gracefully as a yacht.

"Isn't she lovely?" she cried, flushing with the delight of it.

"Not as lovely as you," he bantered.

"Oh! Come and watch her," she invited, and away they went.

When he found his way to the abandoned military barracks they had taken over, it was late night—discipline was a joke in those days—but he did not sleep for many hours, standing at the window of the deserted messroom watching where the moon poured down across the face of the shimmering ocean, into the

309

little harbor. It lit up, as if it were day, the shouldering furze-bright hills and the white edge of motionless surf at the base of the distant cliffs and every sleeping roof in the town clustered beneath him.

It was curious that it was there in Youghal, too, that same summer, that Norah had first met Edward Bradley. There had been a public meeting in the market place while the guerillas held the town and one of the chief speakers was Bradley. That day he had spoken with a terrible passion against England, and against the Irish traitors who had been cowed by her, and his passionate words caught and flared the temper of the people so that they cheered and cheered until their voices echoed across the smooth surface of the water into the woods beyond. Bernie had cheered like the rest where he stood beside Norah, proud to be that man's friend. After the meeting, the three met and the teacher, flushed with his success, walked between them along the tumble-down quays. He found that he knew Norah's people quite well, though he had not seen them for many years.

"But I'll call on them often now," he said, looking at Norah, and he began to take her arm, and then he remembered Bernie and he took his arm—like a·grandfather, Bernie had said, jokingly, to him, and was angry with himself for saying it, for a deeper blush crept over the face of the older man and, halting, he had said:

"Maybe I am too old to be walking with the like of ye," and cocking his eye at the girl again he had laughed, half bitterly as Bernie thought, and with a "God bless ye, my children," turned and walked away. Wasn't he a very nice man, Norah had said, and stood looking after the teacher so long that Bernie almost thought he was going to be jealous; but he had not thought long of it. It was a warm autumn day, and so clear that they could see across the channel where the hay garnered in for the winter had left white patches on the clovered meadows. Tempted by the fields beyond they had rowed slowly across the bay to spend the afternoon on the other side. The geese had cropped the grass of the foreshore until it was as close and clean as a golf course, except where a few odd straws lost to the granary lay strewn about and, with them, cast up by the tide, bits of reedy sea wrack, and here and there the dark gray droppings of the fowl. The air was so rarefied that as they crossed the low stone walls on their way into

310

the oak woods the stones fell with a gurgling sound like water, and far away the ocean boomed deeply into the crannied rocks. They had gone deep into the woods to lie there while the misty darkness fell, bringing in the night wind a little rain, to lie there in their deep love as still as corpses, as still as fallen leaves. They returned late at night to the town whose yellow windows, bright across the channel, spoke to them of sanded floors in quayside pubs and the first fires before the winter.

But before that week was out the town was abandoned and Norah had to stand under the shelter of the old town walls watching the great barracks smoking against the fading sky and the distant mountains, themselves so faint that in their grayness they blended and were lost in the darkness and the smoke.

It was the way of that guerilla life that for months on end a man never even thought of home or friends, and for months Bernard wandered among those gray mountains to the north of Youghal, as aimlessly as, and he used to feel, more uselessly than, a lost sheep. Once only did he use his rifle in those seven months of guerilla life and that was when sniping from fifteen hundred yards a village supposed to contain enemy troops. He slept in a different bed each night and never ate twice in succession from the same table so that most of his time was spent in going from place to place in search of food and rest. He did so less from a sense of danger than a sense of pity towards the farmers who had to feed and shelter him and his fellows, never thinking that as all his fellows did as he was doing, it saved nothing to the flour bin lying lightly on the loft, or the tea caddy on the high mantelshelf, emptied almost daily.

The days scarcely existed for him, the weeks flew over his head as unnoticed as birds homing at night, until as a human being he almost ceased to be, enveloped by the countryside as if he were a twig, a stone, an ear of corn. And then, without the slightest warning, as suddenly as the breaking of a thundershower, he remembered how lovely Youghal had been, and Norah, and he hated to look up at the cold and naked mountains. It was late February with the rain falling as by the clock, and for a month they had been hunted through it, day and night. Thinking of that and thinking of the summer his memory began to work on him like a goad. All about him on the night he thought of her, sitting alone by the embers of a turf fire after the family had gone to bed, the mountains

311

lay black and silent, wet as if they had been dipped in the sea. Overhead a white path of stars more clear in the washed air than if there were a frost abroad. Out there, too, he felt, was danger; he was listening so intently that he almost leaped when a little cricket chirruped in the dark warmth of the hearth. He feared even to stir, so great a noise did every movement make—almost as great, it seemed, as the resounding drop-drop of the leaking thatch beyond the door.

In his pocketbook he had her one letter, reminding him of that little wood where they had loved:

"I went specially to Youghal to see our wood again. The autumn is over it and over all the land. The days are shortening, farmers are threshing, thatching turf-ricks, digging potatoes, culling sheep from their flocks to barter in fair and market, fields are decaying with grief for the loss of their fruits, and grief is a brown and withered hag, nuts are ripening, blackberries are rotting, holly berries are reddening, leaves are dropping yellow. Mists cover the mountains like a hooded cloak, gray rocks ooze tears of desolation, green ferns on the hillside are withering, and purple heather is turning gray. Birds are silent, winds rustling in denuded boughs. In Youghal tourists are departed—no more the hum of the motor, nor the flash of fashionable attire. In my little hotel, Mrs. M——is resting and knitting, K—— turning over stacks of McCall's Journals and Home Gossips, the serving girl is considering her return to her mother's home, P—— L—— wearing her shoes 'going aisht and wesht,' B—— twinkling with gestating jokes, and R—— counting the takings of the season. Norah is at the moment writing to Bernard; at other moments?—thinking, reading, peering into a dimly lit future . . ."

He smiled at that letter, so full of life as it was. Then he thought of the night outside and went to the door. He could hear the streams swirling down the dark leaca and as he listened their roar mingled with the desolation of the silence, and he wished passionately to be away from so lonely and cruel a place.

Three miles across the hills, in a little fishing hotel by a mountain lake, was the headquarters of the division. There, he hoped, he might get money—a few shillings would do—to help him on the road home, and maybe they would give him a clean shirt and collar, and a better hat and trousers than these guerilla rags that, up to now, he had been flaunting as with a deliberate joy in their torn

312

dirt. Above all he might meet Edward Bradley there. For he too had been hiding for several months in the mountains, not daring to stay in the city for fear of arrest. He felt he wanted to talk to somebody like Bradley, someone who would persuade him that this struggle of theirs was not hopeless, that all their humiliation of poverty and hunger was not, as he had long since begun to feel, a useless and wasted offering. Quietly he unbolted the door and stole through the yard into the sodden starlight.

It was midnight when he saw the lake below him and to his surprise every window in the little hotel was lit. He approached warily, alert for a sentry's challenge, an enemy patrol—he might, he knew, be shot as easily by either. But he continued to walk unaccosted past the sleeping farmhouses and the great strewn rocks until he came to the lakeside edge and the lighted windows. Inside the steamed window the room was filled with armed men, smoking, drinking, arguing in groups. He recognized the faces of three or four officers. There was the adjutant with his eyes swollen with too much drink and too little sleep—it was common knowledge that he lived like that. By the fire was Boyle, a great black-faced commandant from Kerry; under the lamp in the largest group he recognized Tom Carroll from East Cork—clearly a meeting of the officers of the division.

He entered unchallenged where a group of men were lounging in the dim candlelit hall. Three officers strode out of the room—it was the dining room—with empty glasses in each hand, returning gingerly when the glasses had been filled to the brim with black stout or porter. He saw the quartermaster coming out of the kitchen with a pair of black pint glasses dripping their froth about his wrists. He went over to tell him how dangerous it was to leave the back road unguarded. The quartermaster only growled:

"Well, what are you doing here then? Go up yourself and sentrify it," and passed on.

The column captain came out from the bar with a tray of divers-colored glasses and to him also Bernie told how the north road was unprotected. But the captain flew into a rage and glared at him over the tray.

"I've told off six men, there, to go," he said, jerking his head at the loungers in the hall.

One of them spoke back to him, a fellow with only two walrus

313

teeth above and below in his gums.

"We won't go. Why should we go? Ye're all dhrinking. Why don't we get a dhrink?"

"Go into the kitchen and get it," said the captain.

"Where'll we get the money?"

"Ask the quartermaster."

"Damn the quartermaster."

"I want the quartermaster," said Bernie. "I want a couple of bob to get home."

The loungers scoffed at him in a loud chorus, and Buckteeth called him Sweet Innocence. Two more joined them, swaggering in their belted and ragged raincoats, out from the glow of the dining room into the dark hall. As they came they deliberately crushed against the captain's tray, all but upsetting his yellow and purple argosy. With a curse at them he raced like a waiter balancing his tray into the dining room, returning to grab Bernard and put him standing in the between passage outside the dining-room door.

"Stand there, you," he growled. "And let nobody into this room unless he has business there."

The loungers cheered.

"Will ye go up, for Christ's sake," the captain implored them, "to the north road and watch it or the whole division will be caught?"

"Oh! It's always deh division, aw!" piped up a little fair-haired sprat of a boy from the foot of the stairs. "What about deh men, aw? Dere's never any talk about deh men?"

"For God's sake, get us a drink, Jim," appealed the man with the walrus teeth.

"Go on, Jim," joined in three or four more. They seemed to have no sense of pride left.

With a sudden air of intimacy the captain stepped into the middle of them, bending his neck right and left among them like a pecking hen.

"Go in," he said, "and take it. Say the quartermaster will fix it up. They'll never know in the hotel."

Buckteeth turned away in disgust.

"No! They feed us, and they sleep us," he said, "and we're not going to soak drink from them as well."

"Well, I have no money for you," complained the captain.

314

"Deh quartermaster have buckets of it," declared Fair-Hair.

"*Buckets* is deh word," sneered a tall man in spectacles from his dark corner at the door.

They laughed at the word in spite of their anger: it measured the quartermaster's thirst.

"Well, I can do no more for ye," said the captain in a temper, and left them.

Bernie stood where he had been placed by the dining room door and everybody passed in and out without paying the slightest attention to him. The quartermaster, already flushed with drink, returned to fill his glasses once more, and timidly Bernie touched him on the shoulder.

"Well? Are you here still?" said the quartermaster.

Bernie had not the courage to face the refusal of a loan so he asked instead for cigarettes. The quartermaster thrust a package into his hand.

"Here," he said. "You fellows do nothing from morning to night but bum and soak for cigarettes. Why don't ye do something?"

As he passed by, a piece of black and white paper fluttered gently to the ground in his wake. Bernie picked it up. It was a hundred-pound note. For a moment he thought of rushing out to his fellows in the hall and waving it in the air before their eyes; for another moment he thought of using it himself to get home. Then he realized he could not steal money like that, and even if he did nobody would change so large a note for them or him. As the quartermaster returned he tapped his arm once again. A wave of whiskey belched into his face as the fellow turned on him and stuck his potato nose into his face. Bernie held up the note, saw him look stupidly at it, without a word thrust it into his vest pocket and stride into the dining room with his dripping glasses. What a hopeless sort of army they were, Bernie thought, and he made up his mind that he must at all costs go back into the city out of these mountains where they did nothing for month after month but eat the substance of the people and lounge over the fire like sleepy dogs. Things were still happening occasionally in the city. If he could rest for a while and see Norah, he would become invigorated by her and be of some use again. Suddenly there was a great stirring in the room and the captain returned to tell him to close

315

and guard the outer door. Bernie did not have the energy to tell him that all this was foolery. Instead he begged a match from him and lit a cigarette and leaned into the corner of the passage to think. He had waited so long he could wait now another couple of hours until the dawn.

By the glow of the lamps in the room beyond the passageway he read Norah's letter again, scarcely hearing the talking and arguing rising hotter and hotter at the meeting, though he faintly gathered as he read the letter by the dim light that they were considering the whole military situation in the south and that some were for laying down their arms at once, and others for fighting on. He was hardly interested. He was thinking only of the summer that was gone and of every little incident of his last meeting with Norah in the woods beyond the bay at Youghal. Gradually the discussion in the room changed to an argument about men and ammunition and money and as the voices fell his thoughts wandered freely to the browned-sailed yawl they saw floating past the frame of the restaurant door, the sun shining on the blue and white sea in its wake and the curling foam at its bows. He remembered how he had whispered an old song to her as they lay among the leaves and to himself he hummed it over again:

> O beloved of my inmost heart,
> Come some night and soon,
> When my people are at rest,
> That we may talk together;
> My arms shall encircle you
> While I relate my sad tale
> That it was your pleasant soft voice
> That has stolen my heaven.
> The fire is unraked,
> The light extinguished,
> The key is under the door.
> And do you softly draw it.
> My mother is asleep,
> But I am awake.
> My fortune is in my hand
> And I am ready.
> I will go with you . . .

316

He heard Edward Bradley's voice addressing the meeting. Why he should be there he did not know, for he was not an army man. Afterwards he told Bernie that because he was older than anybody there they wanted to hear what the politicians had to say. He was imploring them not to lay down their arms—far better to be defeated, at a blow or by degrees, though that would be slow and terrible for them all. As on that day at Youghal his passion carried the meeting with him and they cheered him loudly when he finished. When he came into the passage he was flushed and trembling, and when he saw Bernie he drew him with him out into the hall and, because the loungers were still there, out into the cool air by the side of the lake. A sedge of broken reeds had been washed ashore by the storms, reminding Bernie of the sedge of sea wrack on the foreshore across Youghal Bay, but across the lake the mountain streams made a ceaseless desolate moaning, and a night mist was blowing in their faces so that they had to shelter in the darkness of a gable wall. He told Bernie how terrible things were all over the country and Bernie told him what he knew of the state of the men among those hills, all of them weak and scabby and sore, not a penny in their pockets, not a pipeful to smoke, nothing to do from one week to another but run when danger approached, never together, badly led, beaten all but in name.

"And in this hotel," said Bradley, "the officers taking their breakfast at six o'clock in the evening and drinking in the dawn."

Suddenly Bradley said:

"Do you hear at all from that girl now?"

"What girl?"

"The girl in Youghal."

"A long time ago. I got a letter."

He hated to talk of Norah. It was as if she were a secret part of him and he would not bare it.

"She is a very intelligent girl," said Bradley.

"Yes," said Bernie as if he were not really interested, but he felt his breath come in heavy waves.

"Oh, yes!" said Bradley. "I saw a good deal of her before I came out here. I stayed at her house for safety several times before I took to the hills. A very nice girl."

Bernie shivered, his blood turning over in his body, but it was not from the cold.

317

"Well, I'm leaving in an hour or two," said Bradley. "This place won't be safe for twenty miles around after the news of this meeting gets to the military."

In the hall the candle was guttering out, but the loungers still remained. To say something to them as he passed in, Bernie told them what Bradley had said of the conditions about the country and of the officers in the hotel.

"Puh!" taunted the tall bespectacled fellow. "And what does he do himself but hang over a book in the comfort of the hotel fire from morning to night?"

Bernie returned to his position in the passage. He was sick of these tauntings and tale bearings. He wondered how a man like Bradley could remain out there where he must hear them and notice them day after day. If Bradley chose he could go back to hide in the city any day—there would be many people glad to receive and shelter him, and Bernie wished he had asked for the loan of half a crown and a clean collar and tie. He must see Norah again, and the city, and his people, and friends. The quartermaster was talking now, in a thick but fierce voice.

" 'No surrender' must be our cry," he was saying. "I'd rather be shot any day than surrender. Let those that are tired of the fight go into the city and surrender!"

He peeped into the long room. One lamp was guttered low to a smoking circle of red wick. The other glowed like a yellow ball through the skeins of smoke woven in heavy layers from table to ceiling. Beer bottles and empty glasses were everywhere. The men were yawning and stretching themselves, some talking among themselves, paying no heed at all to the speaker, and the chairman was drawing idle circles with a pencil on the table before him.

Somebody silenced the quartermaster with a question and by degrees the talk fell again to a drone as they discussed men and money and ammunition. He leaned back into a corner of the passage and while he thought of the road home, of every wind and turn in it, of every side road and back road he could take, he fell into a doze where he stood. He awoke to hear Boyle from Kerry cry out in a fury at somebody.

"Let them that want to rat, do it. Myself and John Jo Sheehan will hold Kerry anyway. Won't we, John Jo?"

The meeting seemed to be ending. Sheehan was standing huge

318

against the window with his back to them all; in spite of the lamp, black-shouldered against the pale glimmer of the dawn hanging over the mists on the lake outside. In taunting and utter disbelief he cursed over his shoulder at Boyle:

"Hold Kerry, how are you? You and Kerry may go to hell!"

The meeting broke up in laughter, men standing and talking in little groups, edging around their chief to discuss private questions of their own. It seemed as if they would never come out and Bernie sat on the ground to sleep. The first few officers leaving the room poked his stomach with their boots in mockery of their sleeping sentry. He made his way out to the kitchen, where the loungers were strewn asleep on the settle, the table, on chairs, or about the floor near the gray embers of the fire. He rolled a porter barrel in from the bar and sat on it and through the sounds of the departing officers, horses stamping, carts trundling out, searchings in the dark for last drinks, calls and farewells, he slept in the corner of the cooling hearth. When he awoke the morning had come and the loungers were, like him, shivering together over the grate, where Buckteeth was blowing the seed of fire into a fresh sod of turf. Seeing him open his eyes they asked him:

"Well? What was deh end of deh meeting, aw? Are we to go home or stay here? Aw?"

"Fight on!" said Bernie.

They looked at him too tired to mock the phrase.

"Stay here, he means," said Buckteeth. "Stay bloody well here."

Bernie shared his cigarettes about and they smoked in silence while the fowl awakened by the echoing crow of the cock began to clatter and cluck in the rain water of the yard, for the rain was now darkening the window, pouring straight down into the dung-filled haggard. Looking out at it Bernie saw again the mist hanging in the woods of Youghal, and Norah running down the slip to the ferry, her black curls swinging as she ran. Their hunger began to stir in them, but they could not find a scrap of food in the house—it had all been eaten by the crowd just departed. In their search they found the quartermaster snoring on the sofa of the dining room, a roll of bank notes hanging from his pocket. At once they grabbed them, sharing out the smaller notes, leaving the twenty-fives and the fifties and the hundreds, but as they argued over the division the quartermaster awoke and in a fury he de-

319

manded the money. Buckteeth, who held the fistful of notes, showered them over the furious man's head, and while he clambered under the tables and the chairs to collect them they mocked at him. Beside himself with rage he cursed them for lazy, useless louts and rushing off to tackle his horse and sidecar in the yard he left through the blowing rain while in a crowd they cheered him from the door. But money would not buy them food and they went about draining the ebb of porter in every glass, then wandering over the hotel from floor to attic to see what they could find. There was not a soul there but the people of the house sleeping heavily after the long hours of work the day before, so they returned to the kitchen to wait.

At last the girls of the house came down the ladder-like stairs, their legs thrust bare into their dung-covered boots. They sat on the settle by the fire, bowed over their knees until their mother followed.

"A bad morning, Mrs. O'Rourke," said Bernie to the mother.

She stood by the low window and looked sadly at the rain.

"Isn't it a bad morning, thanks be to God?" she sighed.

Not a word of reproach was said, or of inquiry about the meeting, or of complaint at their long labor. The girls sat looking at the fire or out at the rain. There was nothing for them to eat, and nothing to do on such a wet day. The mother began to scrape the bins and the bags for flour and when the boy of the house came in, he milked the cows. The dough was dampened with spring water and fresh milk. It was kneaded and shaped and put into the bastable while they all looked on. Through the open door they could see the rain splashing the causeway outside and a duck poked his eye in by the jamb. Buckteeth spat at the cocked eye and the duck clattered out, but nobody laughed. The bastable was over the fire and they had all turned to it to watch while the cake baked. While they waited six other men came to the house, sodden with rain, arm and thigh and chest, searching for a breakfast and news of the meeting, but when they found the others before them they moved on patiently to the next farmhouse a mile off. They said they must be in Millstreet, twenty miles away, before night. Then they would walk on into Limerick along the Feale. For Limerick, they declared, bare and open though it was, was safer now than Cork. One of them, a Kerry lad, had no socks and his feet were torn by the

320

bare leather of his boots. He had no overcoat, his very shirt clung to his back with wet, and he coughed ceaselessly. The woman of the house took pity on him and asked him to stay, and when he heard the others argue that Limerick was a far more dangerous place than Cork, he sat down wearily by the fire and began to cry, telling his companions between his tears that he was afraid to go on with them and would hide here among the mountains. All the while Buckteeth and the others looked awkwardly at him. They offered him cigarettes and tried to cheer him by assuring him that this place was as safe as a house, and while he and they drank the scalding tea and ate soft, hot cake, the girls searched him out a pair of socks and a dry, if torn, shirt.

But while they ate they were less sure about the safety of the glens and they argued and argued as to what they should do next. The Kerry lad could say nothing but "We must hide. We must hide in the holes of the mountains," and the little fair-haired city gamin kept whining plaintively, "But where are our officers? Where are our officers from us now? Aw?" At intervals the boy of the house assured them again and again that it was madness to stay there another day with the valleys filled, as he said, with "people taking the heels from one another with the news of the meeting to the military in the next village." So when the rain lightened they scattered, some going to the north, one declaring that the safest thing was to skirt the village to the east, and Bernie found he had lost courage to attempt the journey home. Tomorrow he would go, he thought, and with Buckteeth and Kerry, as they christened him, he went up among the cliffs in search of a cave to hide in. The boy of the house, though he kept assuring them it was madness to stay there, showed them a dump that had been made in a cleft between the rocks, a gravelike place dug out of the earth and covered with a sheet of corrugated tin and hidden by stones and withered brushwood. There was barely room for the three to lie in this dark, damp tomb, but as Kerry implored them to go into it at once, they lay down there, shoulder to shoulder, peering up and out all day long at the gray spears of the falling rain.

At dark, in spite of their hunger and the cold, they slept. They slept past the rising of the sun, past the late morning, and all the while it rained and the whistling of the rain seemed to lull and keep them asleep in spite of encircling danger. They were awakened

321

by the shattering echoes of machine gun fire and the impact of hundreds of bullets tearing at the rock above their heads. When the first volley ceased, the echoes carried its rat-a-tat-tat across the cliff-top to where another echoing air seized upon it and reduplicated it fainter and fainter into the heart of the mountains before it finally died into silence. There was such a long interval that it seemed as if everybody were listening to that last faint replication so high up and so far away. Then they heard the shouts below them:

"Come out! Come out, ye snipes! Come out or we'll bomb ye out. Come out!"

These cries were echoed, and then a brief silence followed. The next minute the gun seemed to tear the tin roof from over their heads where they crouched helpless, their faces to the clay. They had placed their boots to dry, the night before, on the ledge before their dump and these now shot in on their foreheads torn to pieces by bullets. Again the echoes were reduplicated to the farthest uttermost glen and again the shouts came, mingling with those echoes and their own that followed after.

"Yer last chance! Ye whores! Come out!"

The Kerry boy began to weep again.

"O God!" he shouted. "Leave us out. Leave us out!"

"Throw down yer guns," cried the echoing voices below.

They did so, and Buckteeth, tearing a sleeve from his shirt, raised it before him as he crawled out into the rain. Below them was a score of sturdy green-clad riflemen and in a minute the three were among them, shivering with fear and excitement—broken, timid as children.

They passed through Youghal as prisoners, standing high on a lorry, conspicuous in their rags, and as it roared its way under the old clock archway, there across the wind-blown bay Bernie glimpsed his woods shrouded in mist, growing, as it seemed, out of the gray-green bay. Never did anything seem so definitely past to him as his summer flirting under those trees. It might have happened to him in another life, it might have been something he read of in a novel, so distant did it seem.

They drove him to Cork that night and there he remained in prison until the winter was passed and another winter had come again. Norah wrote to him many times while he was in jail—at first

322

briefly but kindly, sending him gifts as she might to any other prisoner, later on long letters at greater length, as to a special friend. After a while she brought herself to reproach him for his long silence of that lonely winter, a winter in which she had tried hard, and vainly, to be, as he had been, forgetful of the sweetness of their summer and autumnal love. It was Christmas when he received a letter from her confessing how miserable and unhappy those months had been, and he was glad of the confession though it was a torment to him to be reminded, in the place where he was, of his foolishness when he had been free. When she wrote that Edward Bradley often stayed with them, and spoke kindly of him, it was a double torment—that worst torment of all prisoners—to think what lovely things life could have given him, too, if he were out in the world and part of it. When he was freed he was very ill and weak and the doctor ordered him to the sea and he went, as a matter of course, to Youghal. It was February again, just a year since he had passed through it as a prisoner, and the woods and the bay were again shrouded in haze, but because Norah came to see him, and walked with him there, and showed him the rain in the cobwebs among the branches, and—it was so mild there by the sea—an early celandine hiding under a root, he thought those woods even more beautiful than they had been almost two years before when they watched the red globe of the autumn sun sinking behind its black branches.

Small wonder then that they should come back to the little seaside town for their honeymoon. It was Easter and late in the spring—the fifteenth of April had been Easter Sunday—so that the catkins' furry paws were already raised to the sun, and the long tails and the tiny wet noses of the lambs protruded from the red and blue creels rumbling in to the lamb fair. The yellow furze was ranged high against the blue sky along the slopes of the hills, and over the surface of the sea beneath there was a cold layer of air that made the waves break with a brittle noise such as one never hears in the soft, dead heat of summer. They went about that first day, their wedding day, noticing everything with new delight —the spears of green grass shooting through the dead fields, the primroses and the violets clustered near the gray stones in the ditches, the beech buds swollen red, the patches of hawthorn green lighting the withered hedges.

The long country lanes were empty; they had the ocean to themselves. The summer visitors had not yet even thought of coming and all the length of the old stone promenade was bare. They even felt a delight in the shuttered windows and the bathing boxes nailed up since last autumn. On the sands stretching for miles in front of them, lost in the end in the spume of the incoming waves far off in the distance, they saw only a sandpiper or two strutting by the skirts of the spreading sea, or peewits in their swoop turning as if to command on their white bellies, then turning again on dark wings, low over the thunderous waves. When they lay under an early blossoming blackthorn, high above that singing sea, and in the long silences of love, gazed over the empty horizons or back at the clustered smoking chimneys on the farther shore, Bernard felt, and knew that his young wife felt, that if another gull should wheel through the blue air, another distant lamb call out to its dam, their cups of ecstasy must overflow and roll upon the ground. They crossed back then, as of old, to the points of light that marked the town, through an early sea haze and sought out that little restaurant where so long ago they had cursed the Elizabethans and the Cromwellians, and there they had their tea, watching back through the open door at the rear of the shop the channel darkening with the fall of night. As they ate they suddenly saw beside them a little green poster bearing that day's name and date. They read it with interest:

SINN FEIN ABU
A Public Meeting
will be addressed
in the Town Hall
at 7 p.m.
by
EDWARD BRADLEY

"Shall we go?" asked Bernard.

It was almost the hour as they made their way down the wandering side lanes that led to the wharves and the town hall. There, hidden deep in the crowd, they stood by an open window through which they could see the everpresent channel and the waters of the bay. The gaslights in the hall hummed like flies, huge green luminous flies that had floated in from the half night outside, so blue

324

and lovely where it sank down, darker and darker, over the masts and the brown sails of the fishing smacks in the harbor, and far in the distance the peaked mountains that Bernard knew so well. It was so lovely to watch the hollow night fall outside, and through it now and again a green light climbing up a mast, and to turn from it to the pale pink-washed greenlit room within, that they paid but little heed to the speakers until their friend the teacher rose.

The years between that night and the day in the market square had not dulled his eloquence, and though his temples were gone quite white now—premature for his years—the terrible passion of the man blazed like the fire of burning youth. Yet as he talked the lovers did not join in the cheers of the audience. The night had fallen now and nothing showed beyond but the eyes of green or red on mast and poop. The mountains had vanished. The far woods were gone. They barely heard the lapping of the bay. As by one thought, they moved quietly out through the cheering crowd into the darkness. But, shyly, they did not go back directly to their hotel. Wrapped in their own silence and the silence of the night they wandered about the quays or in and out among the lanes as if prolonging the night to the very last moment. The meeting was over before they returned to their hotel, and the lights of the houses in that street, and doubtless of every street in the town, were gone up to the second story. When they entered their room they saw that the pale light of the gas lamp outside the window fell on the high old-fashioned ceiling and from there glimmered down on the wide, carved bridal bed, and needing no other light they used none. Across the street was another row of sleeping houses, and beyond that the bay, widening to the ocean, and when they stood without stirring they could hear the low boom of the waves on the cliffs and across the bar. As they undressed, the faint hum of a motor rose in the distance and approached along the street.

"Bernard," she whispered.

Over his shoulder he could see her pale body in the dim light, but where he stood by the window with one hand raised to draw down the blind his eyes fell on the passing car. He saw the white hair of their orator friend, the old bachelor, the patriot, driving out of the town into the country and the dark night. The hedges would race past him, the rabbits skip before his headlights on the road, the moths in the cool wind would fly round his flushed face and his trembling hands. But that wind would not for many miles cool the passion in him to which he had given his life.

"Bernard," she whispered again, and her voice trembled a little.

He drew the blind down slowly. The lamp shadowed the framework of the window on it. Slowly he turned to her where she gleamed even in the dark.

The Aftermath

By SIR WINSTON CHURCHILL
(1874-   )

From "*The Aftermath*" (*last volume of his "History of the World Crisis*")

. . . On June 22nd, the first Parliament of Northern Ireland was to be inaugurated by the King in person. It would not have been right for Ministers to put in the mouth of the Sovereign words which could only appeal to the people of Northern Ireland. It is well known that the King, acting in harmony not only with the letter but with the spirit of the Constitution, earnestly expressed the wish that language should be used which would appeal to the whole of his Irish subjects, South as well as North, Green as well as Orange. The outlook of the Sovereign, lifted high above the strife of Party, above the clash of races and religions, and sectional divergencies of view, necessarily and naturally comprised the general interest of the Empire as a whole—and nothing narrower. The Prime Minister and leading Members of the Government therefore took the responsibility which rested with them, and with them alone, of inserting in the Royal Speech what was in effect a sincere appeal for a common effort to end the odious and disastrous conflict.

"The eyes of the whole Empire," said the King with evident emotion, "are on Ireland today—that Empire in which so many nations and races have come together in spite of ancient feuds, and in which new nations have come to birth within the lifetime of the youngest in this Hall. I am emboldened by that thought to look beyond the sorrow and the anxiety which have clouded of late My vision of Irish affairs. I speak from a full heart when I pray

326

that My coming to Ireland today may prove to be the first step towards an end of strife amongst her people, whatever their race or creed.

"In that hope I appeal to all Irishmen to pause, to stretch out the hand of forbearance and conciliation, to forgive and to forget, and to join in making for the land which they love a new era of peace, contentment, and good will. It is My earnest desire that in Southern Ireland too there may ere long take place a parallel to what is now passing in this Hall; that there a similar occasion may present itself and a similar ceremony be performed.

"For this the Parliament of the United Kingdom has in the fullest measure provided the powers; for this the Parliament of Ulster is pointing the way. The future lies in the hands of My Irish people themselves. May this historic gathering be the prelude of a day in which the Irish people, North and South, under one Parliament or two, as those Parliaments may themselves decide, shall work together in common love for Ireland upon the sure foundation of mutual justice and respect."

No one responsible for the King's Speech had contemplated immediate results in action. But in such declarations everything depends upon the sounding board. The King-Emperor, the embodiment of the common inheritance, discharging his constitutional duty at the peril of his life, had struck a note which rang and reverberated, and which all ears were attuned to hear. The response of public opinion in both islands to that appeal was instant, deep, and widespread, and from that moment events moved forward in unbroken progression to the establishment of the Irish Free State. On June 24th, Mr. Lloyd George invited Sir James Craig and Mr. de Valera to a conference in London. On July 11th, the invitations were accepted, and a truce, the terms of which had been settled on the 9th, was proclaimed.

No act of British state policy in which I have been concerned aroused more violently conflicting emotions than the Irish Settlement. For a system of human government so vast and so variously composed as the British Empire to compact with open rebellion in the peculiar form in which it was developed in Ireland, was an event which might well have shaken to its foundations that authority upon which the peace and order of hundreds of millions of people of many races and communities were erected. . . .

327

However, the die was now cast. A truce had been proclaimed. The gunmen emerged from their hiding places and strode the streets of Dublin as the leaders of a nation as old and as proud as our own. The troops and police and Black and Tans, but yesterday urged on to extirpate the murder gang, now stood relaxed and embarrassed while parleys on equal terms were in full swing. Impossible thereafter to refill or heat up again those cauldrons of hatred and contempt on which such quarrels are fed! Other courses remained at our disposal as a last resort. Ports and cities could be held; Dublin could be held; Ulster could be defended: all communication between Sinn Fein Ireland and the outer world could be severed; all trade between the two islands, that is to say the whole of Irish trade except from Ulster, could be stopped—at a price. But from the moment of the Truce, the attempt to govern Southern Ireland upon the authority of the Imperial Parliament had come to an end.

Sixteen Years After

By "PETRUCCIO"

Yeats advised us learn our trade,
Know the tune before we played,
Strengthen future with the past
As sinners do, by prayer and fast.
Wake from this Prufrockian dream,
Sing with Ireland as our theme,
Renounce these analytical gambols,
Paint instead with Irish symbols,
Write about the world that's real,
Things we know and things we feel,
And using simple themes as these,
Show the eternal verities.

O'Raftery is in our bones,
His fiddle echoes all our tunes,
Keating's verses were not planned
To guide us through the Waste Land,

And despite what influence
Seems to affect both form and sense,
We today are but the tail
Of what was old before Kinsale,
Stretching back beyond all time,
When Europe had not learned to rime.

Traditions old, when Troy was young,
Helen's story still unsung,
Dana's people words could twist
To summon storms or scatter mist.
After came the Gaelic gods
And fighting men, whose fiery blood
Needed war chants, and, war over,
Low-voiced singing from a lover.
Then the monks with psalm and bell
Warned the errant Celt of Hell,
And how to live in God's soft peace
Rather than at feast or chase.
Bards with one another vied,
Growing rich on kingly pride,
Norman came and Saxon after,
Sorrow came instead of laughter,
Song then left the Irish scene,
Staying only in the caoin.

But in these days, what remains?
Hollow men with mouldy brains,
Who mix with gin, dishonest doubt,
And quail before a pint of stout,
Whose works, they hold, necessitate
An arbitrary act of faith
In platters of subjective truth
By pure record machines, in sooth.
They dive with Kafka, soar with Bracque,
Forgetting that they must come back
To the Dublin pub or the west sea drifts
That brought them forth, endowed with gifts
Of versing soul and seeing eyes,

And will not stint with praise or prize,
To those they owe it that they be
The resurrected Irishry.

From *The Student*, University College, Dublin

The two tramps in Samuel Beckett's play, *"Waiting For Godot"*, might be found leaning up against a wall in Dublin today, yesterday or tomorrow: their spasmodic arguments are punctuated by expressive silences.

ESTRAGON. I tell you I wasn't doing anything.
VLADIMIR. Perhaps you weren't. But it's the way of doing it that counts. . . .

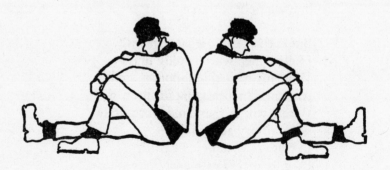

DUBLIN:

YESTERDAY, TODAY
-AND TOMORROW?

Coat of Arms of Dublin.

Cockles and Mussels

ANONYMOUS (19th Century)

In Dublin's fair city,
Where the girls are so pretty,
    I first set my eyes on sweet Mollie Malone.
She wheeled her wheelbarrow
Through streets broad and narrow,
    Crying, "Cockles and mussels, alive, alive, oh!
      Alive, alive, oh!
      Alive, alive, oh!"
Crying, "Cockles and mussels, alive, alive, oh!"

She was a fishmonger,
But sure 'twas no wonder,
    For so were her father and mother before.
And they both wheeled their barrow
Through streets broad and narrow,
    Crying, "Cockles and mussels, alive, alive, oh!
      Alive, alive, oh!" *etc.*

She died of a fever,
And none could relieve her,
    And that was the end of sweet Mollie Malone.
But her ghost wheels her barrow,
Through streets broad and narrow,
    Crying, "Cockles and mussels, alive, alive, oh!
      Alive, alive, oh!" *etc.*

Dublin

By KATE O'BRIEN
(1897–   )

Dublin, like the Lady Portia, is "richly left," though not perhaps in ducats. Nor am I thinking just now of her great divorcee's alimony from the recently flung-off lord-and-master, though that is hardly to be overlooked; nor can it be, since its solid tokens are on

332

view around the compass—magnificent jointures of real estate. No; the town's luck began with her first exploiter who set her up, no doubt, in a haphazard shady way. Some Greek, Egyptian or Milesian? Whoever he was, he placed her wittily and even affectionately towards her future, and with all near at hand that the most petulant of beauties might cry out for. She was to do her share of crying out—and from her beginnings there would be alert and greedy men, Dalcassians, Danes and Normans, to humour and exploit their raw possession—their Ford of the Hurdles, as unattractively she was named. What I mean is that the city was set in astounding natural beauty in the most navigable and friendly of harbours, with about her, south and north and west, lands, hills, and waters of fertility and variation to yield her constant wealth and pleasure; and eastward over a narrow stretch of sea the civilized world, Europe, to traffic with and beckon in and out. And these are comforts which no amount of mere history has been able to take away. On the contrary, their entanglement with one of the most complicated, unpredictable and mercurial of histories has made of Dublin, inescapably, a capital city.

A capital city with a difference—granted. And it is that difference, misapprehended by them, that makes new or light acquaintances smile, sneeringly or affectionately, at the claim. That she is, by right and on paper, a national capital no one denies, in that, since about the tenth century A.D., she has had thrust upon her all the responsibilities of such—all the guilt, too, and most of the privileges. And from century to century men have built and groomed her for her honours and duties. Gratefully now we look around and acknowledge that . . .

No one capital city can be like another—and it is in each one's difference from her sisters that we must look for her true importance, her secret right of claim. One could make a parlour game of this, and grow tedious, which would not please Dublin. For the lazy old beauty seems never to have been patient with bores. Yet when I think of her way of being a capital city—that is to say, having to exercise authority and be important, I am reminded of something I heard a man say long ago at home about the horsemanship of one of my brothers: "Sometimes 'tis like an infant's hand he'd leave on the reins. You'd marvel at the cheek of him!"

The two remarks seem to me to bear on Dublin, or what one feels

333

as a characteristic power in her, even if in fact they represent no more than manner. Anyway, she sits easy to her mount; and if in an old-fashioned, side-saddle style, therein is much of that inevitable and amusing "difference." For it is at once in her time-lag and her perverse acceptance of whatever date we may insist upon that this capital city *is* Dublin, and not Oslo or Brussels or Havana.

"Time-lag" can cover a number of peculiarities; and self-confidence, often naive, but understandable in an old and much-flattered town, is a visible strength. Exasperating often to the fussy, or even to the cool—but a condition inbred and hereditary, which, if it has made some hate Dublin and some too hastily despise her, has also traditionally attracted and encouraged many more—and is at least one cause of an especial kind of wit. And though wit is not gaiety, where many are witty, an air of gaiety prevails. As in Dublin, where gaiety is cold, I think—like the bright flicks of wind that can whip down Baggot Street on an April day—but it *is* gay, and ubiquitous; one can hear it rippling about, merely as atmosphere, although no one is saying a word. It is palpable; and it is not warm.

From *My Ireland*

Dublin

By LOUIS MACNEICE
(1907–1963)

Grey brick upon brick,
Declamatory bronze
On sombre pedestals—
O'Connell, Grattan, Moore—
And the brewery tugs and the swans
On the balustrated stream
And the bare bones of a fanlight
Over a hungry door
And the air soft on the cheek
And porter running from the taps
With a head of yellow cream
And Nelson on his pillar
Watching his world collapse.

This was never my town,
I was not born nor bred
Nor schooled here and she will not
Have me alive or dead
But yet she holds my mind
With her seedy elegance,
With her gentle veils of rain
And all her ghosts that walk
And all that hide behind
Her Georgian facades—
The catcalls and the pain,
The glamour of her squalor,
The bravado of her talk.

The lights jig in the river
With a concertina movement
And the sun comes up in the morning
Like barley-sugar on the water
And the mist on the Wicklow hills
Is close, as close
As the peasantry were to the landlord,
As the Irish to the Anglo-Irish,
As the killer is close one moment
To the man he kills,
Or as the moment itself
Is close to the next moment.

She is not an Irish town
And she is not English,
Historic with guns and vermin
And the cold renown
Of a fragment of Church latin,
Of an oratorical phrase.
But O the days are soft,
Soft enough to forget
The lesson better learnt,
The bullet on the wet
Streets, the crooked deal,
The steel behind the laugh,
The Four Courts burnt.

Fort of the Dane,
Garrison of the Saxon,
Augustan capital
of a Gaelic nation,
Appropriating all
The alien brought,
You give me time for thought
And by a juggler's trick
You poise the toppling hour—
O greyness run to flower,
Grey stone, grey water
And brick upon grey brick.

A Summer Day in Dublin

By W. M. THACKERAY

The papers being read, it became my duty to discover the town; and a handsomer town, with fewer people in it, it is impossible to see on a summer's day. In the whole wide square of Stephen's Green, I think there were not more than two nursery maids to keep company with the statue of George I, who rides on horseback in the middle of the garden, the horse having his foot up to trot, as if he wanted to go out of town too. Small troops of dirty children (too poor and dirty to have lodgings at Kingstown) were squatting here and there upon the sunshiny steps, the only clients at the thresholds of the professional gentlemen whose names figure on brass plates on the doors. A stand of lazy carmen, a policeman or two with clinking bootheels, a couple of moaning beggars leaning against the rails and calling upon the Lord, and a fellow with a toy and book stall, where the lives of St. Patrick, Robert Emmett, and Lord Edward Fitzgerald may be bought for double their value, were all the population of the Green.

At the door of the Kildare Street Club, I saw eight gentlemen looking at two boys playing at leapfrog; at the door of the University six lazy porters, in jockey caps, were sunning themselves on a bench—a sort of blue-bottle race; and the Bank on the opposite side did not look as if sixpence-worth of change had been negotiated

there during the day. There was a lad pretending to sell umbrellas
under the colonnade, almost the only instance of trade going on; and
I began to think of Juan Fernandez, or Cambridge in the long vaca-
tion. In the courts of the College, scarce the ghost of a gyp or the
shadow of a bed-maker.

In spite of the solitude, the square of the College is a fine sight: a
large ground, surrounded by buildings of various ages and styles,
but comfortable, handsome, and in good repair; a modern row of
rooms; a row that has been Elizabethan once; a hall and senate house
facing each other, of the style of George I, and a noble library, with
a range of many windows, and a fine manly simple facade of cut
stone. The library was shut . . .

🍀 🍀 🍀 🍀 🍀 🍀 🍀 🍀 🍀

Sir Boyle Roche, an Irish member of Parliament, was famous
for his witticisms, because of which some people thought him a
fool—as when he stood up in Parliament and said, "It would surely
be better, Mr. Speaker, to give up not only a part, but, if necessary,
even the whole of our constitution, to preserve the remainder."
But his own countrymen saw what he meant. The following utter-
ance of his was embedded in a speech delivered in Parliament in
1780:

"Why should we do anything for posterity? What has posterity
ever done for us?"

Mid-Victorian Dublin 1845

By MAURICE CRAIG
(1919–   )

Among the convicts that year were John Blake Dillon and
Charles Gavan Duffy. The grandson of one is a Cabinet Minister
today, and the son of the other is President of the High Court.
Gavan Duffy's crime was publishing in *The Nation* a leading article
by Jane Francesca Elgee, Maturin's niece. Three years later this

lady married William Wilde, antiquary and ophthalmologist, traveller, topographer and medical pioneer, "Dear Wilde," as Samuel Ferguson called him, of 199 Great Brunswick Street, 15 and 21 Westland Row, and Number One Merrion Square. His addresses show to a nicety the stages in a successful medical career: they give no hint of how much more Wilde was than a mere successful doctor. He founded two medical journals which still survive, his two best travel-books are still in print, there is no aspect of his versatile activity without some value, even now. His wife's poems are unreadable, but her Legends and Charms of Ireland was a pioneer study in folklore. Their son, born at 21 Westland Row, in 1856, was the celebrated Oscar . . .

The most interesting literary figures of mid-Victorian Dublin are Ferguson and Le Fanu. They were much of an age: Ferguson, a Belfast man, born in 1810, Le Fanu a Dubliner four years younger. Both were barristers, but neither persisted in that calling. The outward calm of their lives cloaked, in the one case, the barbaric splendour and passionate lyricism of *Congal* and *Cashel of Munster;* in the other the sinister whisperings of *The House by the Churchyard*, the macabre imagination of *Carmilla* . . .

Let us leave these men in their lamp-lit studies and hospitable dining-rooms, oblivious that a little boy called Shaw is surveying his world through a window in Synge Street, or that another little boy called Yeats will soon be born in Sandymount. For the city in which they live is, for our purpose, a finished article. The pleasant aroma of freshly-cut timber and damp mortat is a rare occurrence now, except in the outermost suburbs. The sharp edge of newness is hardly ever seen, the want of it perhaps not felt. The capital has begun to take on an air of mild melancholy: after sixty years the loss of political status is beginning to induce an unmistakable feeling of provincialism. The earliest photographs of Dublin date from about this time: to our eyes they have an extreme air of remoteness, infinitely more remote than the bright and cheerful acquatints of James Malton, taken in the closing years of Grattan's Parliament. The personality of mid-Victorian Dublin is mysterious to our eyes: so much, we know, was stirring there: so little of it was apparent, or so it seems to us. It is only a few years till the performance of the *Countess Cathleen* in the Antient Concert Rooms, till Douglas Hyde, so lately dead as I am writing, founds the Gaelic League;

338

till George Moore takes a cab and drives round the squares and suburbs looking for a house, coming to rest at last in Ely Place, for "The sceptre of intelligence," in the words of Edward Martyn's telegram, "has passed from London to Dublin."

The sceptre, we may feel, has melted in our grasp, unable perhaps to endure the fires of revolution. Perhaps George Moore was dreaming, and it was no sceptre but only an old blackthorn stick, a Donnybrook Fair shillelagh. Perhaps one day we shall wake to find it bursting into miraculous flower, like the rod of Tannhauser or the blest Mosaic thorn. The Mosaic analogue is the more fitting, for it is Moses, who, carved by Edward Smyth, stands on the pediment of the Four Courts holding the Tables of the Law, with the great dome behind him, and below the Liffey with its quays and bridges and the swans drifting on the stream.

A lamp (probably Georgian), of the Shelbourne Hotel, Dublin.

*O*scar *Fingall O'Flahertie Wills Wilde was a son of the famous Dublin surgeon, Sir William Wilde, and the almost equally famous Lady Wilde who was known under the pen name of "Speranza" for her poetical and political writings. In his mother's salon writers and poets gathered together to discuss their ideas. His father, as famous for his archaeological discoveries as for his surgery, added his views, and the young Oscar, admired by all, arrived at his own assessment of life which he describes ironically in his preface to "The Picture of Dorian Gray," which gave rise to much controversy.*

Preface

By OSCAR WILDE
(1856–1900)

The artist is the creator of beautiful things.

To reveal art and conceal the artist is art's aim.

The critic is he who can translate into another manner or a new material his impression of beautiful things.

 The highest, as the lowest, form of criticism is a mode of autobiography.

Those who find ugly meanings in beautiful things are corrupt without being charming. This is a fault.

 Those who find beautiful meanings in beautiful things are the cultivated. For these there is hope.

 They are the elect to whom beautiful things mean only Beauty.

 There is no such thing as a moral or an immoral book. Books are well written, or badly written. That is all.

The nineteenth century dislike of Realism is the rage of Caliban seeing his own face in a glass.

 The nineteenth century dislike of Romanticism is the rage of Caliban not seeing his own face in a glass.

The moral life of man forms part of the subject-matter of the artist, but the morality of art consists in the perfect use of an imperfect medium. No artist desires to prove anything. Even things that are true can be proved.

 No artist has ethical sympathies. An ethical sympathy in an artist is an unpardonable mannerism of style.

340

No artist is ever morbid. The artist can express everything.

Thought and language are to the artist instruments of an art.

Vice and virtue are to the artist materials for an art.

From the point of view of form, the type of all the arts is the art of the musician. From the point of view of feeling, the actor's craft is the type.

All art is at once surface and symbol.

Those who go beneath the surface do so at their peril.

Those who read the symbol do so at their peril.

It is the spectator, and not life, that art really mirrors.

Diversity of opinion about a work of art shows that the work is new, complex, and vital.

When critics disagree the artist is in accord with himself.

We can forgive a man for making a useful thing as long as he does not admire it. The only excuse for making a useless thing is that one admires it intensely.

All art is quite useless.

A Hunt

By LORD DUNSANY

As a thread of the warp in the weaving of cloth runs through all the threads of the woof, helping to bind them together, so runs the fox in Ireland through all our lives; so that any man who is utterly unconcerned with the fox lives a little apart from the rest of us. Who such a man could be I do not know; for, to begin with, no one owning poultry or turkeys can be quite immune from the fear of the footfall of that red visitor, inaudible on the stillest nights, however closely you listen for it. And that is, I suppose, the original sin on account of which we hunt him, and it must have been to deal with those prowlings, too subtle for his own wits, that man first sought the help of his friend the dog in this matter. And, having sought it, this organization in defence of his poultry spread ramifications round the very heart of man. There are towns to be found in which the name of a fox stirs no more quickening of pulses than does the mention of guinea pigs; but not in Ireland. For in the little Irish towns no man is so far into the dry waste of streets that the sounds of the hunt, from say in the South,

341

cannot reach him, but that some other pack on the northern side, passing the town's edge, will bring him running out to see the red coats go by, and to feed his memory with the things that the pavement can never give. And so we give you the toast from our Irish shores: The Fox (death to him!), may he live for ever. And nearly two hundred of us concerned in this matter were jogging now in the direction of Clonrue, with the hills at first on our left as we rode along at the feet of them, and then almost behind us when we had turned to our right. And who was not concerned in it? First of all we had the whole of "the gentry" for twelve miles round, and as many of their daughters as a horse could be found for; then we had from a rather smaller area as many of the farmers as had a horse that could carry them; soldiers, squireens, a few strangers, grooms, second horsemen, and men with young horses of which they had hopes that they had not named to anyone; but who, as a young girl sometimes looks to Heaven, far and yet not unattainable, looked to the Grand National.

There were no priests at the meet, because they are forbidden to hunt, though not forbidden to ride; and of course if they meet with hounds while they are riding, it is no sin to go the same way with them. All the priests in that part of the county were out riding that morning along the road under the hills from Gurraghoo to Clonrue.

It was a long jog to Clonrue, over five miles: that is the beauty of Irish coverts, there are usually so few that when a fox leaves one he has a very long way to go to the next one: and there was a wood of wild osiers beyond Clonrue near the bog, an almost certain draw. All the way as we went that fervour leaped up amongst all who saw us pass, a fervour for the quest not limited to those that were taking part in it; men, women, children and dogs were all awakened from other pursuits to let their thoughts soar up from their own fields and then to sail with us over the grey-green plain, now shining in sunlight far away from those hills. And if any say that our quest was not worthy of this awakening, I can only say in argument that perhaps whatever awakens us to any vivid intensities needs no other test of its worth; but in evidence I can say this on oath, that I have seen the emptiness of many things, like a white damp wall of mist closing roads to the spirit utterly, but never yet have I noticed it in a fox hunt.

342

Certainly on that day the hope of seeing a fox killed in the open, even the less presumptuous hope of being there before the tumultuous gathering at that furious feast was over, was as bright a splendour to me as could be the hope of any statesman to see the ruin of his enemy's land, with all its fortresses fallen. And so we moved to Clonrue till the hills were grey behind us, and the voices of dogs warning Gurraghoo that something strange was afoot were faint cries adding a weirdness to the solitude of those fields. And the dogs that guarded the houses of Clonrue took up the cry. And, among those that waited to watch our coming by, the first that I saw was Marlin. He was standing dark against one of the white walls, with a look in his eyes such as inspiration might have, as he gazed at the young girls riding there, and at young well-mounted men, and the young horses. And I saw then, once for all, that quiet age and calm and repentance, and at last Heaven, were none of these things for Marlin, but that, turning away from all of them, he would only look for such glories as youth can give, and would always yearn for that land whose history was the dreams of the young and that knew nought of salvation. For a moment I would have spoken one last word to save him, and was silent knowing there was nothing that I could say; and at that moment I saw a priest ride by, and I turned to him, for he could have done it, but still no words came to me; and the priest rode on, and from the look in his eyes as he went by I saw that Marlin was lost.

And further down the street we saw Mrs. Marlin, leaning upon a stick that was, rather, a crooked pole, with wisps of her dark hair hanging about the sides of her face; her eyes watched us intensely, and more than the watchful dogs she seemed to be guarding Clonrue. Or perhaps Clonrue was but her outpost, and she watched for the sake of the bog, or for the sake of that land that lay under the frown of the bog, where her cottage stood and through which the river ran, where the gnarled willows leaned, a stretch of earth that always seemed to me strangely enchanted. What desecration she feared for this land I do not know, but she eyed us intently and showed no sign of enmity.

"Shall we find in the sallies, Mrs. Marlin?" I shouted as I passed her.

"He's waiting for you," she said.

"Will he give us a good run?" I asked.

343

"To Clonnabrann," said she.

I have often thought of those words, and looking back on them after all these years, and with the experience that years must bring, it seems to me now that, as every cottager thereabouts knew, a strong dog-fox lived in those sallies; a southwest wind was blowing and, running down wind as they do, Clonnabrann would be right ahead of him if he could get so far. To say, therefore, that he would get as far as Clonnabrann was no more than an estimate of his strength by one of those on whose chickens he nightly dined.

There was a silence as the hounds went into the wood, a silence that hung heavily for what seemed a long time; then one hound whimpered; silence again, and then the whole pack gave tongue. We were all lined up on the bog side of the willows, to prevent the fox breaking on that side, for if he went over the bog none but the hounds could follow him. And there we waited for a sign from the Master that we could let our impatient horses out. A mild man, as I have seen him in a drawing room, the Master; almost shy at a tea table; but on a horse the owner of a fiery tongue that held his field in awe, as his whiplash held his hounds. Only for a few seconds he held us back; I remember the waving line of horses' heads; I remember a patch of gorse at the edge of the wood, whose buds had already burst into two small blossoms; then we were off. We used to have big fields out in those days, and for a hundred yards or so it was like a race; and then each rider began to settle down to deal with his own difficulties, to cross each fence in accordance with the capacity of his horse, and to take a line in accordance with his estimate of many things, constantly varying, or to follow different men for different reasons, of which these are three: because he is a masterly rider, because he is close to his own home, or because he is going in the opposite direction to what appears to be the right one. Before following the third kind one should know something of the man, but, if he is reasonably intelligent, he must have some strong motive for turning away from the rest. I remember the first few fences to this day; the first of all a narrow bank, five feet high, built of earth as thin and steep as earth will stand, and green with sods: it seemed impossible that it would not trip up a horse galloping at it, as it would have tripped up me if I had tried to clear it on foot. But I was forgetting the four hooves.

344

Other horses cleared it, mine was hard to hold, and I let him go at it. He rose at it, touched the top, or near it, for a moment paused, and was on again. So my first obstacle was left behind me. The next was a narrow stream, with sides steep as those of a ditch, clear water that had cut its way through the soft black earth. As I rode at it, a man that I did not know called out, "Not there, Master Charles." And I followed him, trotting along the bank. "Boggy landing," he said.

Soon we came to a place at which the far bank sloped, and there he plunged in. It was deep water, and the bank on the far side seemed nearly liquid, but the horse struggled up, and I followed. We came next to a double, a great bank thrown up from two ditches, and twelve feet high, with small trees growing along the top of it. It looked an impossible obstacle, but others had been before me through the stream and were now crossing the double in several places, cantering slowly at it and jumping as high as the horse could reach and doing the rest with a scramble, then pausing a moment and disappearing from sight. So I checked my horse and jumped where another had jumped before me, and he easily found a foothold in the soft turf for his hind legs, while his forelegs reached the top. With a heave we were there. Looked down on, the far ditch seemed wider than the near, wider indeed than could be jumped from a standstill, but you can't go back from the top of a double, so I left it all to my horse. He approached it as cats approach a garden from the top of a garden wall; he went down and down the steep bank till I thought he would slip to the bottom, and just as this seemed certain he sprang, and we easily reached the field on the far side. For a moment from the top I had seen the hounds, going over a field together, and somehow reminding me of the shadows of clouds drifting over the flashing grass on a windy day. The next fence we came to was an easy one, and the last we saw of its kind, for we were leaving the country of white loose stones from which they built it, a stone wall. We went fast at it and my horse hit it hard, but it made no difference, for the stones flew with a rattle, and we were in the same field with the hounds.

From patches of bracken and gorse, and pale grey stones sometimes as large as sheep, we looked to a wide plain, stretching for miles in the sunlight, with large green fields and having a tended

345

air. It was as though that loose stone wall that I had crossed were a boundary between the last of the things of the wild, lying behind us, and Earth subdued by man, lying before. Bog and the rough lands were behind us now, and the turf good for going: the pace increased. Shall I breathe air again that is like that air that I breathed as I galloped down to the bright vale gathering sunlight? What vintage in what golden and jewelled cup will ever equal it? It came in gusts as we galloped, so that we breathed it like giants quaffing wine, and whenever one lifted one's eyes from the fields and the fences, the rim of the plain far off shone gold as a god-like cup. Shall I ever breathe it again? And the priest in this foreign town tells me not to think of these things any longer; the time being come for thinking more of my soul. But he is not an Irishman, and has only ridden a mule.

In the play, "John Bull's Other Island," George Bernard Shaw shows up the tortuous thoughts of his fellow countrymen against the background of British common sense.

Doyle Considers Going Home

By G. B. SHAW
(1856–1950)

DOYLE. Never mind my heart: an Irishman's heart is nothing but his imagination. How many of all those millions that have left Ireland have ever come back or wanted to come back? But what's the use of talking to you? Three verses of twaddle about the Irish emigrant "sitting on the stile, Mary," or three hours of Irish patriotism in Bermondsey or the Scotland Division of Liverpool, go further with you than all the facts that stare you in the face. Why, man alive, look at me! You know the way I nag, and worry, and carp, and cavil, and disparage, and am never satisfied and never quiet, and try the patience of my best friends.

346

BROADBENT. Oh, come, Larry! do yourself justice. Your very amusing and agreeable to strangers.

DOYLE. Yes, to strangers. Perhaps if I was a bit stiffer to strangers, and a bit easier at home, like an Englishman, I'd be better company for you.

BROADBENT. We get on well enough. Of course you have the melancholy of the Keltic race—

DOYLE. Good God!!!

BROADBENT. —and also its habit of using strong language when there's nothing the matter.

DOYLE. Nothing the matter! When people talk about the Celtic race, I feel as if I could burn down London. That sort of rot does more harm than ten Coercion Acts. Do you suppose a man need be a Celt to feel melancholy in Rosscullen? Why, man, Ireland was peopled just as England was; and its breed was crossed by just the same invaders.

BROADBENT. True. All the capable people in Ireland are of English extraction. It has often struck me as a most remarkable circumstance that the only party in parliament which shows the genuine old English character and spirit is the Irish party. Look at its independence, its determination, its defiance of bad Governments, its sympathy with oppressed nationalities all the world over! How English!

DOYLE. Not to mention the solemnity with which it talks old-fashioned nonsense which it knows perfectly well to be a century behind the times. That's English, if you like.

BROADBENT. No, Larry, no. You are thinking of the modern hybrids that now monopolize England. Hypocrites, humbugs, Germans, Jews, Yankees, foreigners, Park Laners, cosmopolitan riffraff. Don't call them English. They don't belong to the dear old island, but to their confounded new empire; and by George! they're worthy of it; and I wish them joy of it.

DOYLE. There! You feel better now, don't you?

BROADBENT. I do, much better.

DOYLE. My dear Tom, you only need a touch of the Irish climate to be as big a fool as I am myself. If all my Irish blood were poured into your veins, you wouldn't turn a hair of your constitution and character. Go and marry the most English Englishwoman you can find, and then bring up your son in Rosscullen;

347

and that son's character will be so like mine and so unlike yours that everybody will accuse me of being his father. Rosscullen! oh, good Lord, Rosscullen! The dullness! the hopelessness! the ignorance! the bigotry!

BROADBENT. The usual thing in the country, Larry. Just the same here.

DOYLE. No, no: the climate is different. Here, if the life is dull, you can be dull too, and no great harm done. But your wits can't thicken in that soft moist air, on those white springy roads, in those misty rushes and brown bogs, on those hillsides of granite rocks and magenta heather. You've such colors in the sky, no such lure in the distances, no such sadness in the evenings. Oh, the dreaming! the dreaming! the torturing, heart-scalding, never satisfying dreaming, dreaming, dreaming, dreaming! No debauchery that ever coarsened and brutalized an Englishman can take the worth and usefulness out of him like that dreaming. An Irishman's imagination never lets him alone, never convinces him, never satisfies him; but it makes him that he can't face reality nor deal with it nor handle it nor conquer it: he can only sneer at them that do, and be "agreeable to strangers," like a good-for-nothing woman on the streets. It's all dreaming, all imagination. He can't be religious. The inspired Churchman that teaches him the sanctity of life and the importance of conduct is sent away empty; while the poor village priest that gives him a miracle or a sentimental story of a saint, has cathedrals built for him out of the pennies of the poor. He can't be intelligently political: he dreams of what the Shan Van Vocht said in ninety-eight. If you want to interest him in Ireland you've got to call the unfortunate island Kathleen ni Hoolihan and pretend she's a little old woman. It saves thinking. It saves working. It saves everything except imagination, imagination, imagination, and imagination's such a torture that you can't bear it without whiskey. At last you get that you can bear nothing real at all: you'd rather starve than cook a meal; you'd rather go shabby and dirty than set your mind to take care of your clothes and wash yourself; you nag and squabble at home because your wife isn't an angel, and she despises you because you're not a hero; and you hate the whole lot round you because they're only poor slovenly useless devils like yourself. And all the while there goes on a hor-

348

rible, senseless, mischievous laughter. When you're young, you exchange drinks with other men; and you exchange vile stories with them; and as you're too futile to be able to help or cheer them, you chaff and sneer and taunt them for not doing the things you daren't do yourself. And all the time you laugh! laugh! laugh! eternal derision, eternal envy, eternal folly, eternal fouling and staining and degrading, until, when you come at last to a country where men take a question seriously and give a serious answer to it, you deride them for having no sense of humour, and plume yourself on your own worthlessness as if it made you better than them.

BROADBENT. Never despair, Larry. There are great possibilities for Ireland. Home Rule will work wonders under English guidance.

DOYLE. Tom: why do you select my most tragic moments for your most irresistible strokes of humour?

BROADBENT. Humour! I was perfectly serious. What do you mean? Do you doubt my seriousness about Home Rule?

DOYLE. I am sure you are serious, Tom, about the English guidance.

BROADBENT. Of course I am. Our guidance is the important thing. We English must place our capacity for government without stint at the service of nations who are less fortunately endowed in that respect; so as to allow them to develop in perfect freedom to the English level of self-government, you know. You understand me?

DOYLE. Perfectly. And Rosscullen will understand you too.

BROADBENT. Of course it will. So that's all right. Now Larry, I've listened carefully to all you've said about Ireland; and I can see nothing whatever to prevent your coming with me. What does it all come to? Simply that you were only a young fellow when you were in Ireland. You'll find all the chaffing and drinking and not knowing what to be at in Peckham just the same as in Donnybrook. You looked at Ireland with a boy's eyes and saw only boyish things. Come back with me and look at it with a man's; and get a better opinion of your country.

DOYLE. I daresay you're partly right in that: at all events, I know very well that if I had been the son of a labourer instead of the son of a country landagent, I should have struck more grit than I did. Unfortunately I'm not going back to visit the Irish nation, but to visit my father and Aunt Judy and Nora Reilly and

349

Father Dempsey and the rest of them.

BROADBENT. Well, why not? They'll be delighted to see you, now that England has made a man of you.

DOYLE. Ah! you hit the mark there, Tom, with true British inspiration.

BROADBENT. Common sense, you mean.

DOYLE. No, I don't: you've no more common sense than a gander. No Englishman has any common sense, or ever had, or ever will have. You're going on a sentimental expedition for perfectly ridiculous reasons, with your head full of political nonsense that would not take in any ordinarily intelligent donkey; but you can hit me in the eye with the simple truth about myself and my father.

BROADBENT. I never mentioned your father.

DOYLE. There he is in Rosscullen, a landagent who's always been in a small way because he's a Catholic and the landlords are mostly Protestants. What with the land courts reducing rents and Land Purchase Acts turning big estates into little holdings, he'd be a beggar if he hadn't taken to collecting the new purchase instalments instead of the old rents. I doubt if he's been further from home than Athenmullet for twenty years. And here am I, made a man, as you say, by England.

BROADBENT. I assure you I never meant—

DOYLE. Oh, don't apologize: it's quite true. I daresay I've learnt something in America and a few other remote and inferior spots; but in the main it is by living with you and working in double harness with you that I have learnt to live in a real world and not in an imaginary one. I owe more to you than to any Irishman.

BROADBENT. Very friendly of you, Larry, old man, but all blarney. I like blarney; but it's rot, all the same.

DOYLE. No it's not. I should never have done anything without you; though I never stop wondering at that blessed old head of yours with all its ideas in watertight compartments, and all the compartments warranted impervious to anything it doesn't suit you to understand.

BROADBENT. Unmitigated rot, Larry, I assure you.

DOYLE. Well, at any rate you will admit that all my friends are either Englishmen or men of the big world that belongs to the big Powers. All the serious part of my life has been lived in that

350

atmosphere: all the serious part of my work has been done with men of that sort. Just think of me as I am now going back to Rosscullen! to that hell of littleness and monotony! How am I to get on with a little country landagent that ekes out his 5 per cent with a little farming and a scrap of house property in the nearest country town? What am I to say to him? What is he to say to me?

BROADBENT. But you're father and son, man!

DOYLE. What difference does that make! What would you say if I proposed a visit to your father?

BROADBENT. I always made a point of going to see my father regularly until his mind gave way.

DOYLE. Has he gone mad? You never told me.

BROADBENT. He has joined the Tariff Reform League. He would never have done that if his mind had not been weakened. He has fallen a victim to the arts of a political charlatan who—

DOYLE. You mean that you keep clear of your father because he differs from you about Free Trade, and you don't want to quarrel with him. Well, think of me and my father! He's a Nationalist and a Separatist. I'm a metallurgical chemist turned civil engineer. Now whatever else metallurgical chemistry may be, it's not national. It's international. And my business and yours as civil engineers is to join countries, not to separate them. The one real political conviction that our business has rubbed into us is that frontiers are hindrances and flags confounded nuisances.

BROADBENT. Only when there is a protective tariff—

DOYLE. Now look here, Tom: you want to get in a speech on Free Trade; and you're not going to do it: I won't stand it. My father wants to make St. George's Channel a frontier and hoist a green flag on College Green and I want to bring Galway within 3 hours of Colchester and 24 of New York. I want Ireland to be the brains and imagination of a big Commonwealth, not a Robinson Crusoe island. Then there's the religious difficulty. My Catholicism is the Catholicism of Charlemagne or Dante, qualified by a great deal of modern science and folklore which Father Dempsey would call the ravings of an Atheist. Well, my father's Catholicism is the Catholicism of Father Dempsey.

BROADBENT. I don't want to interrupt you, Larry; but you know this is all gammon. These differences exist in all families; but

351

the members rub on together all right. Of course there are some questions which touch the very foundations of morals; and on these I grant you even the closest relationships cannot excuse any compromise or laxity. For instance—

DOYLE. For instance, Home Rule, South Africa, Free Trade, and putting Church schools on the Education Rate. Well, I should differ from my father on every one of them, probably, just as I differ from you about them.

BROADBENT. Yes; but you are an Irishman; and these things are not serious to you as they are to an Englishman.

DOYLE. What! not even Home Rule!

BROADBENT. Not even Home Rule. We owe Home Rule not to the Irish, but to our English Gladstone. No, Larry: I can't help thinking that there's something behind all this.

DOYLE. What is there behind it? Do you think I'm humbugging you?

BROADBENT. Don't fly out, old chap. I only thought—

DOYLE. What did you think?

BROADBENT. Well, a moment ago I caught a name which is new to me: a Miss Nora Reilly, I think. I don't wish to be impertinent, as you know, Larry; but are you sure she has nothing to do with your reluctance to come to Ireland with me?

DOYLE. Thomas Broadbent: I surrender. The poor silly-clever Irishman takes off his hat to God's Englishman. The man who could in all seriousness make that recent remark of yours about Home Rule and Gladstone must be simply the champion idiot of all the world. Yet the man who could in the very next sentence sweep away all my special pleading and go straight to the heart of my motives must be a man of genius. But that the idiot and the genius should be the same man! how is that possible? By Jove, I see it all now. I'll write an article about it, and send it to Nature.

BROADBENT. What on earth—

DOYLE. It's quite simple. You know that a caterpillar—

BROADBENT. A caterpillar!!!

DOYLE. Yes, a caterpillar. Now give your mind to what I am going to say; for it's a new and important scientific theory of the English national character. A caterpillar—

BROADBENT. Look here, Larry: don't be an ass.

352

DOYLE. I say a caterpillar and I mean a caterpillar. You'll understand presently. A caterpillar when it gets into a tree, instinctively makes itself look exactly like a leaf; so that both its enemies and its prey may mistake it for one and think it not worth bothering about.

BROADBENT. What's that got to do with our English national character?

DOYLE. I'll tell you. The world is as full of fools as a tree is full of leaves. Well, the Englishman does what the caterpillar does. He instinctively makes himself look like a fool and eats up all the real fools at his ease while his enemies let him alone and laugh at him for being a fool like the rest. Oh, nature is cunning! cunning!

Georgian Dublin

By FRANK O'CONNOR

Dublin was once one of the art capitals of Europe. Perhaps from an aeroplane flying low it might still seem to be one with its broad rosy streets of Georgian and its spires and domes. But when one descended and returned through the streets themselves one would see the women sitting on the doorsteps and the mobs of barefooted, half savage children playing in the gutted hallways. Take Henrietta Street for instance, once one of the most fashionable streets in Europe. It was built by a German called Cassells; heavy in the hand, uncertain in his proportions, and capable of giving everything he did a certain funereal air.

I don't want to crab the man, because he built Russborough, to me the most beautiful of Irish country houses. It lies twenty odd miles outside Dublin on the main road beyond the Poulsphouca Hydro-Electrical Works, facing the great new artificial lake and the mountains where it gathers, an eighteenth-century house of fairyland. The only other house I know which has the same startling effect is Castletown, near Celbridge, and the only way I can explain it to myself is that it was some accidental quality of architecture before Classicism became complete. After that the

353

difference between a masterpiece and a commonplace is only a neck; the odds are gone, and I have enough of the gambling instinct in me to rejoice when some horse, preferably not the favourite, leaves the rest of the field trotting. It was the outsider Cassells who took this house, modest enough in proportion, and scattered it recklessly across the landscape, with its colonnades, its long pavilions and its fairy-tale stable gates, until its civilization is a match for the mountain wilderness.

But Henrietta Street is a different kettle of fish; a little hill leading to the cul-de-sac of Gandon's King's Inns; tall houses, tall flights of steps, leading to tall narrow doorways too small for the frontage and with a heavy hooded air imparted by their plain pediments. The only houses which have not degenerated into slum are the two on the right-hand side by the gate of King's Inns, and these have been turned into convents. The front has been cemented, and Cassells' gloomy doorway has been removed to make way for a gay Egyptian one in imitation marble. One slum house attracted us because a first-floor window had been lifted out, body and bones, and through it you could see the staircase ceiling, heavy circles and strapwork which suggested a Jacobean hang-over. The poor people sunning themselves on the steps drew aside to let us pass. The staircase had been many times coated with salmon-coloured wash which half obscured the rich plaster panelling, but a ray of light through a ruined window frame lit a beautiful stair with carved treads and delicate Restoration newel-posts. It would have been all right but for the smell.

"The convent, at any rate, will be clean," said I.

The door was opened for us by an exquisite, smiling creature in a flapping veil who was delighted to show us everything. The parlour, with a ceiling in the same overpowering design of circles and straps, pedimented wall panels, a marble fireplace, a great pedimented door leading into the front room, was the sort of place you dream of. There were two exquisite doors leading out of it into the hall with little cupids set above them in a sort of undesigned composition which delighted me. The fine stairs were placed at the back of the house, which meant that the saloon—now a chapel— was in the front. It looked as if it had received Egyptian attention. The fine ceiling was painted blue and gold, and in a bright blue window over the altar was a scraggy-looking Madonna. The

354

adorable little nun was on her knees. I could see that Célimène, who is emotional, was already half-way to becoming a Catholic, and foresaw trouble in the home.

"You should try to see our house next door," said the nun as we were leaving. "The nuns' dining-room has a lovely ceiling."

She said it in a doubtful tone as though she were afraid we shouldn't find our way. We soon saw why. Here the hall with wooden pillars painted to imitate marble, was in front. The ceiling of the staircase with beautiful girls' heads at the four sides, was superb. A middle-aged woman was sitting at a table as if collecting the admission fee.

"I'll have to see the sister in charge," she said.

By this time Célimène's conversion was almost complete. As the minutes passed and lengthened into a quarter of an hour, I could see the old Calvinistic Methodist streak beginning to emerge, and realized that the danger of domestic friction was lessening. The image of the nun next door was beginning to fade. Fully twenty minutes passed before we heard a slow step on the stairs and, looking up, we saw against the great panelled ceiling the fluttering of a veil. The nun made a magisterial half circle about us as though afraid of coming into contact with our worldly aura and then faced us from the other side of the table. She didn't like us; neither did she like our errand.

"This is all we have to show," said she severely. "And you've seen that," she added. She looked about her without interest. "Eighteenth century, I believe?"

"Just so," said I.

"Or is it seventeenth?"

"Eighteenth," said I, and we took our leave before Célimène could say what she thought. Célimène interprets altogether too literally the text about "knowing them by their fruits". The conversion hadn't taken, and she was again a black, raging Calvinistic Methodist, contemptuous of all idolaters. We dived into the first house which attracted us. Smells no longer seemed the principal evil. We knocked, and a pleasant, worried little woman answered. The front room on the ground floor had been partitioned off at shoulder height into a tiny hallway which housed a pram, a bedroom and a living room. The bedroom had overflowed into the living room in a double bed, and the rest of the space was taken up with pathetic little knickknacks, including just inside the "doorway" a cupboard with a big glass case, containing a statue of the Blessed Virgin. Above hallway, living room and bedroom stretched a whitewashed ceiling, and in the centre, smiling down upon everything, was a splendid head of Apollo with a spike driven clean through the forehead as though at some time the Gas Company had connected and then disconnected him. "The Crucifixion," Géronte said, when I brought him to see it later.

Strange fates have overtaken the gods and goddesses of Dublin. The Jesuits of Belvedere House have retained their Apollo but Venus has been cut away. The priests in St. Saviour's Orphanage, once the house of the plasterer Robert West, in Dominick Street, have been more tolerant, and even in their chapel the ceiling shows two naked cupids, as Love and Eternity, or some such heathen allegory, while next door the little waifs look up from the plain iron beds of their dormitory and see Venus wantoning naked with Cupid and doves. Mespil House was deserted when we visited it. The front door was open, and the rooms were empty. In the back rooms, darkened by creeper which had forced its way through the shutters, was the most beautiful of Irish ceilings. Jupiter held the centre in a rolling mass of cloud, while bellows-cheeked cherubs puffed up at him from the four quarters, where the elements were shown in exquisite panels: Earth with her castled crown and lion, Water with her urn, Wind with her clouds and Fire with her salamander.

But even in the most respectable streets where the shadow of poverty has never fallen, you cannot guess which of the immortals is housed with what unlikely companions. Ely Place, for instance, is an unexceptionable neighbourhood. For preference Célimène and I chose the largest and richest-looking house. We wondered what it was; it looked as though it probably was a Government Department. But when we turned the handle and got into the front hall we found ourselves faced by an inner door, a bell and a warning notice that under no circumstances were non-members admitted beyond this door. Clearly this was a club, and a very exclusive sort of club at that. I fingered a half-crown in my pocket as I rang the bell. A respectable man with a kind and melancholy expression answered the door; obviously not the sort

356

of person you could bribe. A different approach was called for.

"I'm afraid," he said with regret, "we are exceedingly strict about allowing visitors. What is the name, please?"

I told him. I admit that for once I allowed vanity to get the better of me, but when it comes to wheedling my way into houses which may contain works of art, I have now become capable of any baseness: bribery, boasting, or out-and-out falsehood. Nothing corrupts the character like a passion for architecture. And sometimes a little vanity goes a long way. When we went to see Tyrone House, the headquarters of the Ministry of Education, we were shown round by minister and officials as if we were royalty. When a policeman came to arrest us in Freshford for taking photographs in war-time, I had no sooner mentioned my name than he wrung me warmly by the hand and assured me that the Sergeant would be heart-broken at missing me. But I was well punished for my vanity, because it was quite clear that the Secretary, or whoever it was, had never heard of me.

"If you'll step inside a moment," he said courteously, "I'll see see what can be done."

We stepped inside, and made the acquaintance of Hercules. Hercules, life size, was acting as newel-post of the great staircase which, instead of banisters, had long gilded beasts who slunk up the stairs to the first floor landing. Against the Venetian window which lit the well of the stairs was a shadowy figure supporting a cross, and on the wall on our left was a big picture of the Pope looking at Hercules. Along the wall of the stairs was a row of pencil drawings by Sean O'Sullivan of distinguished looking men whom I failed to recognize.

The Secretary returned and to our relief agreed to let us see the house. He was an intelligent and sensitive man, and though he affected to know nothing of architecture, was obviously proud of it. He said it was the town house of the Earl of Ely and had previously belonged to Sir Thornley Stoker, the surgeon. Then I remembered that it figures quite a lot in George Moore's "Hail and Farewell," for Moore and Gogarty were both near neighbours and friends of Sir Thornley.

Apart from the stairs it wasn't really a first-rate job. The front room on the ground floor, painted an olive green, had large plaster medallions linked by Adamish scroll-work, and seemed like the

357

work of Michael Stapleton, the Irish contemporary of Adams. There was a fireplace with another Hercules which the Secretary told us was insured for £700. The sun suddenly went out in the claret-coloured street, and a lovely subdued light brought up the modelling of the plaster figures in the medallion. I rested my camera on a side table, and noticed, without much interest, that the tablecloth was black. I do not mean dirty, but black.

There were three rooms on the first floor, all decorated. The one in the centre was a small waiting room with two very pleasant medallions in low relief. There was a plain screen across it half-way down, and behind this a table in front of the window. The room on the right was large, and had a number of small tables like that in the downstairs room, and these, too, had black tablecloths. What appeared to be a door was lying across a couple of chairs, and when we entered the Secretary, as I must continue to call him, lifted it and put it back against the wall, where it fitted over the original mahogany door. There was a crucifix on the fine white and yellow mantelpiece.

I stood before one of the medallions in the little waiting room wondering whether I shouldn't photograph it. The Secretary noticed my eyes fixed on it.

"Of course, that's only a copy," he said. "It's really only canvas."

"Oh, indeed?" said I, and looking at it more closely I could see that it was merely fitted into the wall and could be taken out without difficulty.

"Yes," he said, "we often have dances here, and the band sits in this room."

"How very convenient!" said I, and at that point I began to wonder what there was about a dance band that made it convenient that it should be heard but not seen.

"Is this," I asked, "a private club or could people like ourselves become members?"

"Well, it's not exactly a club," said the Secretary hesitatingly. "This is the headquarters of the Knights of Columbanus."

There is a moment in every real thriller where the hero, tracking the missing heroine, finds himself in a quiet house on a quiet street, and on asking the name of his charming and cultured host is told in a gentle voice, "The name, Mr. Blake, is Plummer," or words to that effect. This was it. The Knights of Columbanus are the

358

most sinister of Irish secret societies; an enormously wealthy organisation of Catholic professional and business men. Their ritual
is modelled on that of the Freemasons; the postulants are initiated
in a ceremony in which they are marched blindfolded with their
hands resting on the shoulders of the man in front, up and
down corridors to far-away organ music, and when the masks
are removed they find themselves in the presence of hooded men
sitting at black-covered tables with a skull before them. I now
understood something I had noticed when we entered the little
room. On the table behind the screen were some black robes
embroidered in gold. I understood all the rest as well: the table
cloths, the crucifixes, the false panel. Exclusive was right.

"We are supposed to be a secret society," the Secretary went
on in a troubled tone. "After all, we are no more a secret society
than any other private company. They don't publish their business.
Why should we?"

"Why indeed?" said I.

"Of course," he said, "we don't take any oaths or anything like
that," and led the way into the big room to the left of the landing.
There was another magnificent but rather ugly fireplace with a
lot of tiny medallions in Wedgewood blue and white, looped
together in rather inadequate plaster decorations on the walls.
Célimène disliked the room and said so, but it was her stern eye
which located the harmonium by the door. Her lips framed the
word "band", and her air fully expressed her feelings about the
damned idolaters who performed there. (You would never think,
hearing Célimène on the subject, that her father was a Freemason.)

I started as a bell pealed through the house. Our guide fell silent
and waited. We almost counted the heavy steps on the stairs and
then a young man appeared and asked for "Mr. Nolan." "He's
not in at the moment," said the Secretary. I do not know what
occult meaning was conveyed by those simple words, but I felt
enormously relieved when the young man went away. Then I
began to be sorry for taking advantage of the Secretary's kindness,
ashamed of coming there, as it were like a spy, even though I had
declared my identity in the most unequivocal, not to say boastful,
manner. He positively wrung my heart when in his courteous
way he invited us to come back and look over the house more
carefully.

359

As we went down the stairs I studied the row of pencil drawings on the walls in the hope of identifying a few of the models, while I glanced thoughtfully at the row of gilded beasts whom Hercules was driving up the stairs at the other side.

"I suppose," he asked, "you don't know what these beasts are?"

"No," I replied, looking at the row of portraits, "I'm afraid I don't recognize any of them."

Célimène suggested tentatively that one of them was probably a wildebeeste, but I am afraid that was only showing off.

Sean O'Casey, for many years the backbone of Dublin's Abbey Theatre, has not always had his own way. During an early production of The Shadow of a Gunman *one of the actors kept a fireman's axe ready in case the stage should be rushed by the audience. It was not the man-in-the-street who objected to O'Casey's sentiments, but the die-hards of English descent. They looked upon the rebels, not as heroes, but as disturbers of the peace . . . and upon Sean O'Casey as an even greater nuisance for drawing attention to them in a succession of plays. More recently he has come up against the clergy. For, now that the 'Troubles' are stale news, he has turned to the self-appointed task of shaking Church and bureaucrats out of any semblance of complacency.*

The People and the Theatre

By SEAN O'CASEY
(1884–   )

The people are the theatre. Nature sets the scene, and man plays his part through the changing scenes of seed-time and harvest, in the cold days when the frost comes and the keen winds blow. It is from the things manifested in the people's life—their love, joy, hatred, malice, envy, generosity, passion, courage, and fear—that the truest playwrights weave their sombre and gay patterns of action and dialogue. Every art is rooted in the life of the people—what they see, do, how they hear, all they touch and taste; how

360

they live, love, and go to the grave. The question for all artists is this: Is the colour and form of what has been taken from their life done well or done badly?

Some timid ones of the theatre will say, "This is a Bolshevist blathering," for the moment a mouth mentions the word "people" the disinterested, clerical and lay, jump up to mark the brand of prejudice on the mouth's brow. A Bolshevist, but not just blathering, for he has good and amiable support for what he says; support written down by one of the "lonely, majestical multitude," in 1904, when no one thought Bolshevism could ever be born. This strange champion of the "people" is no less a figure than the poet Yeats; and his words should remind the august fellows going about in startling robes that they are no more and no less items of the people than the fellows working hard in hodden gray. Listen. "The Irish upper classes put everything into a money measure. When anyone among them begins to write or paint they ask him 'How much money have you made? Will it pay?' Or they say, 'If you do this or that you will make more money.' . . . All Irish writers have to choose whether they will write as the upper classes have done, not to express but to exploit this country; or join the intellectual movement which has raised the cry that was heard in Russia in the 'seventies, the cry 'To the people!'"

My God, he even mentions the name of Russia! Yeats, Yeats, you had odd foreseeing visions at times. Edward Martyn, the quivering Catholic, didn't like this, and he argued in the press that the Irish actors should try to train themselves for the modern drama of society. The acting of plays of heroic life, or of plays like *Cathleen ni Houlihan,* with the speech of the country people did not seem to him a preparation. "It is not," said Yeats, "but that is as it should be. Our movement is a return to the people like the Russian movement of the early 'seventies, and the drama of society would but magnify a condition of life which the countryman and the artisan could but copy to their hurt. The play that is to give them a natural pleasure should tell them either of their own life, or of that life of poetry where every man can see his own image. . . . Plays about drawing-rooms are written for the middle classes of great cities, for the classes who live in drawing-rooms; but if you would ennoble the man of the roads, you must write about the roads, or about the people of romance, or about great historical

361

people . . . [There are critics here who look upon us as] foolish secretaries who have revolted against that orthodoxy of the commercial theatre which is even less pliant than the orthodoxy of the Church, for there is nothing so passionate as a vested interest disguised as an intellectual conviction."

There you have the greatest of Irish poets out against vested interests, commercially-souled critics, the money-hunger of the upper classes, and the chic curtained drawing-room of the middle ones. The young and ardent poet saw that all vigour in the art of the drama stemmed from the life of the people, or from the golden legends that brimmed over from the song and story, creating a golden stir in their sober and monotonous minds. The people, now, are coming out, slow but sure, from the twilight, and are taking on a far fuller control of their own lives. And as they move towards the control of the means providing what they eat, drink, and the wherewithal with which they clothe themselves, so will they enter into the life and laughter that is in music, in literature, and the drama. We shouldn't be frightened or scornful because many, maybe all, their first and second efforts turn out to be poor things; for the worst of them won't be as bad as the worst done to decorate the box office with jubilee joy. They will be, at least, like the verses written by the poor Irish clerk or shopboy, who wrote, Yeats says, "for the glory of God and their country, so that there isn't one vulgar thought in the countless little ballad books that have been written from Callanan's day to this." We must realise that good plays, much more great ones, will never be very plentiful, for good or great playwrights are far rarer than Hamlet's honest men. To help those who aim at fine art, we must pull into fuller prominence the hundreds already written by artists, half forgotten now save by the few who sit at home by the fire to sigh for the state of the theatre. We shouldn't, of course, stand beside Mr. Yeats's grandiloquent rejection of the middle classes and their drawing-rooms. That class in Ireland opposes many of his dearest, and, it must be said, fairest efforts; but it was a section of the same class that gave a fine support to all he did, and helped to give life and energy to the Abbey Theatre. He didn't like Ibsen, though, oddly enough, he never seems to have given much thought to a greater dramatist of the middle class—Strindberg. Tragedy may be screened as well by the velvet curtains of the middle class as it

362

may be by the brocaded ones of the aristocrat, or the pathetic tattered muslin struggling to hide the tragedy of the worker, as Ibsen and Strindberg have shown; ay, and comedy, too, rich comedy well displayed in O'Neill's delightful *Ah, Wilderness!* If

> Love doth sing
> As sweetly in a beggar as a king,

then it sings, too, in the heart of a middle-class woman or man. And, anyway, many of the middle class are bidding farewell to their drawing-rooms and their imposing curtains of velvet. We must make the most of the best that has already been written for the theatre, so that we may see the art of the dramatist in action, and try to learn from it. The most of what is written for the theatre is bound to keep to a pretty common level; but we shouldn't let it sink down to an uncommonly low level—precisely what we have been doing, helped by the courageous timidity of the drama critics. The plain people get used to this low level so that when they hear an original mind speaking from the stage, they are surprised, annoyed, and, having been led astray by lesser playwrights, endure the novel play for a while, and then bid a hasty farewell to it.

Dramatic originality and poetic fancy will always be rare, but surely they shouldn't be quite so rare as they are in the present-day theatre; nor should the critics be allowed to frighten, or laugh, the people away from them. Why then are these two excellent qualities so often absent from the plays that strut the stage today?

First, of course, because of the difficulty of imbuing the plays we try to write with these fair qualities; secondly because of the money-making grip that tightens the very life out of the theatre of today; and thirdly because of the sensible cowardice of most of the critics, a fine number of whom don't seem to be able to tell a good play from a bad one.

The first reason is obvious to all who try to write a fair play; the second will be readily admitted by many; for the first and last question asked of the play (as Yeats has said aforetime), good or bad, is, "Will it make money?" There remain the critics, who, instead of being stout and indubitable guides to where there are swans, invariably (as far as new work is concerned) lead the people to where there is naught but a gabble of geese.

The Scholars

W. B. YEATS

Bald heads forgetful of their sins,
Old, learned, respectable bald heads
Edit and annotate the lines
That young men, tossing on their beds,
Rhymed out in love's despair
To flatter beauty's ignorant ear.

All shuffle there; all cough in ink;
All wear the carpet with their shoes;
All think what other people think;
All know the man their neighbour knows.
Lord, what would they say
Did their Catullus walk that way?

Tumbling in the Hay

By OLIVER ST. JOHN GOGARTY
(1878–1957)

Any exams I ever manage to pass are due to bad weather. For who in his senses would waste his days in a dead-house when the sun is shining outside, and when the whole subject of Anatomy is not a mind-full for a moron?

I found out what was wrong with Anatomy; it lacked humour. Also it amounted to a bastard language, because to learn the terms used in Anatomy is tantamount to learning a language, a mixture of Latin and Greek and remnants from the days before English was heard and Latin was the language of all wise men, and the history and names which enshrine the long descent of the science. The dry style of the textbooks is relieved but once in the three volumes of Cunningham, where his enthusiasm carries him away and he calls it the "huge" Great Sciatic Nerve. I loved him for his enthusiasm. Being a romantic myself I would be the last to change, with a view to simplification, the terms and names of Anatomy with their long tradition and sometimes their magnificent

364

sounds. "The long pudendal nerve of Soemmering" always appeals to me. Who was Soemmering, who gave his name to the long pudendal? What a nerve he had! What a stir it would make if you went as the nerve to a fancy-dress ball; or if it could be personified to address a great meeting of medicals of both sexes! Where the majordomo would shout, "I crave silence for the long pudendal nerve of Soemmering. Ladies and Gentlemen, the Long Pudendal!" What interest and excitement not unmixed with embarrassment would run through the assembly! But speech does not, thank goodness, reside in the Long Pudendal; that is reserved for the lingual nerve, and the wanderings of the lingual are hard to envisage and to memorize. Mnemonics are necessary. What doctor would be practising today were it not for Mnemonics?—were it not for the Muses, if not sacred, profane, but yet Muses, with the light Wordsworth grudgingly admitted illumined Burns—"the light that led astray was light from Heaven." We must bring the Muse into Medicine, or, rather, bring Medicine, which has wandered, back to Phoebus, back to the God in whom all music and song and blood are pure. It is an awful task, but it has to be done. I must take the onus of it on my back, ably helped by a merry blade or two, and rewrite Anatomy in rhyme. It has to be done. It should have been done long ago. The Irish ollaves would have called in their poets to put the whole dull subject on a ballad basis as they put pedigrees and the Law:

> "Begin, then, sisters of the sacred well
> That from beneath the seat of Jove doth spring."

I was dissecting with Birrell, who wrote the adventures of the lingual nerve; if you read about it in Cunningham you would never realize its high destiny and all that it did, does and can do. The lingual nerve! The lingual nerve! What history has it not made! It has lifted man above the beasts and given him speech, and speech created thought. It has roused crowds and razed empires; it has enchanted the ear in song and poetry; it has wooed and won, thereby taking precedence over the Long Pudendal Nerve of Soemmering.

I was on the head and neck. Birrell was on the arm. He was digging into the antecubital fossa in front of the elbow. I was telling him about the glories and importance of the lingual nerve.

The professor blew along suddenly and interrupted us.

"If there were less talk there would be more concentration. It is better to dissect in silence. There is nothing more distracting than talk. You, Ouseley, should try to expose the lingual nerve without cutting Wharton's duct. Be careful just there. Use the handle of the knife."

"That nerve is mightier than the sword," Birrell ventured.

"What do you mean?"

It was my turn. I didn't want to let Birrell in for all the irreverance.

"I was just telling Birrell when you came along, sir, that the lingual can move masses and can make wars and found cities."

"By wagging the tongue it wags the world, so Ouseley says."

The professor grew silent so suddenly that it amounted to a gasp.

"Do you believe that, Birrell?"

"Well, sir, allowing for Ouseley's poetic imagination."

"The lingual nerve is entirely sensory," said the professor with emphasis, as he somewhat abruptly went away.

3,000 A. D.

By G. B. SHAW

. . . Consider this island on which we stand, the last foothold of man on this side of the Atlantic: this Ireland, described by the earliest bards as an emerald gem set in a silver sea! Can I, a scion of the illustrious British race, ever forget that when the Empire transferred its seat to the East, and said to the turbulent Irish race which it had oppressed but never conquered, "At last we leave you to yourselves; and much good may it do you," the Irish as one man uttered the historic shout "No: we'll be damned if you do," and emigrated to the countries where there was still a Nationalist question, to India, Persia, and Corea, to Morocco, Tunis, and Tripoli. In these countries they were ever foremost in the struggle for national independence; and the world ran continually with the story of their sufferings and wrongs. And what poem can do justice to the end, when it came at last? Hardly two hundred years had elapsed when the claims of nationality were so universally

366

conceded that there was no longer a single country on the face of the earth with a national grievance or a national movement. Think of the position of the Irish, who had lost all their political faculties by disuse except that of nationalist agitation, and who owed their position as the most interesting race on earth solely to their sufferings! The very countries they had helped to set free boycotted them as intolerable bores. The communities which had once idolized them as the incarnation of all that is adorable in the warm heart and witty brain, fled from them as from a pestilence. To regain their lost prestige, the Irish claimed the city of Jerusalem, on the ground that they were the lost tribes of Israel; but on their approach the Jews abandoned the city and redistributed themselves throughout Europe. It was then that these devoted Irishmen, not one of whom had ever seen Ireland, were counseled by an English Archbishop, the father of the oracles, to go back to their own country. This had never once occurred to them, because there was nothing to prevent them and nobody to forbid them. They jumped at the suggestion. They landed here: here in Galway Bay, on this very ground. When they reached the shore the older men and women flung themselves down and passionately kissed the soil of Ireland, calling on the young to embrace the earth that had borne their ancestors. But the young looked gloomily on, and said "There is no earth, only stone." You will see by looking round you why they said that: the fields here are of stone: the hills are capped with granite. They all left for England next day; and no Irishman ever again confessed to being Irish, even to his own children; so that when that generation passed away the Irish race vanished from human knowledge. And the dispersed Jews did the same lest they should be sent back to Palestine. Since then the world, bereft of its Jews and its Irish, has been a tame dull place. Is there no pathos for you in this story? Can you not understand now why I am come to visit the scene of this tragic effacement of a race of heroes and poets?

From *Back To Methuselah*

A *student of Trinity College, Dublin, tries in 1962 to visualise what archaeologists "digging up Dublin," in the far-off centuries to come, might deduct from the odd fragments left lying around today.*

A Glimpse of the Past

By TIM WEBB

It is fairly certain that in the later centuries of the second milennium A.D. the society of Britain and Ireland (then known as the British Isles, now, of course, as Great Ireland) was a society ridden with religious habits and perversions which inevitably helped to bring about the downfall of the system. The first of these consisted in burning tobacco plant held between the lips while inhaling the smoke produced by the burning. This perversion was fairly widespread. Contrary to earlier opinions, it seems certain that there were very strong religious connections. A small packet recently discovered during excavation at Berkhamsted has been identified as a container of tobacco in a form of which we cannot be certain. The significant fact is that the name on the packet is "Churchman." Professor Böhr has pointed out that there was a famous brand of tobacco known as "Three Nuns" which coupled with the fact that in an unidentified Victorian manuscript a smoking pipe is referred to as a "church-warden" would seem to indicate a religious ritual. A cigarette advertisement unearthed at Sutton reads "Players Please!" According to the Bilgemann-Rotte rule of philology, the letters r and l were interchangeable, l being more usual in Ireland. (For instance, a historian says that King Eamonn II of Ireland was dethroned by a "lout." In view of the sterling qualities of the present royal family, this obviously should read "rout.") Hence, the advertisement means "Prayers Please" (only the first l changing). Smoking was also coupled with Cancer, a sign of the Zodiac, which suggests connection with mysticism. An interesting interpretation of one of 77 similar inscriptions discovered throughout Britain connects it with smoking. The inscription found on different surfaces reads N S KING. It had long been thought that this in some way referred to royalty. I believe,

368

however, that the space between S and K once contained the letters MO and the notice ran END SMOKING or NO SMOKING. It was probably a slogan of enemies of the State religion. (There is mention in Ireland of a bagpipe but its origin is uncertain.)

Another reference to religion is found in 20th century fragment discovered at Marylebone, which reads "May St. Evans b. Smith 45." This would seem to refer to a saint of the early church. His feast was obviously celebrated in the fifth month of the year, May. "b Smith" must mean that he was born with the name of Smith but later, on taking Orders, changed to Evans. "45" could either mean that he was born in 1945 or that he died at the age of 45 years. I prefer the latter interpretation.

Two practices with religious connections are commonly termed tennis and cricket. Both have sexual implications. The terminology of tennis includes such words as court and love, while cricket includes maiden. Both would seem to have been a form of fertility rite. Significantly, the tennis rite began with a service, which had to be performed in accordance with fixed regulations. In cricket two white robed high priests presided over the ceremony. In this it was customary to bowl down what the fragmentary Oxford Text of Wisdom for 1903 (significantly referred to as "the cricketer's Bible") calls the "wicket." It seems obvious that this is a corruption owing to confusion of dentals of the word wicked and that the rite was also a symbolical destruction of evil. There seems to have been a connection with the worship of the elements, perhaps an invocation to the rain god for a fertile crop. A fragment from Bristol connects the Three Graces with the cricket ritual. It is not quite certain what these graces were, but the fact serves as a further indication of deep religious significance. Terms frequently discovered in fragments are long-leg (backward or forward), square-leg, etc. Professor Knutt in his excellent "Ecstaticism and Early British Sport-Religion" has brought forward the theory that these refer to a form of masochism or self-mutilation performed in a state of religious frenzy. A reconstructed picture of white-clad Australian ritualists shows eleven men leaping in the air and waving their hands.

Kindred in many ways to cricket was golf. A high caste society of priests called professionals performed the rite before vast, excited throngs, with the assistance of acolytes or "caddies." (This name would seem to be connected with the old word "tee." Golf also included chips and spoons. These names were probably symbolical of spiritual nourishment.) While the rite was being performed, no one was allowed to speak or laugh. If they did, the ceremony might be rendered ineffectual and the bogey or evil spirit might not be conquered. The strain on the celebrants was often great and priests are known to have inadvertently broken their sacred rods, in the heat of religious fervour. Sometimes they prostrated themselves in attitudes of humble supplication.

Golf courses contained large areas of sand called "bunkers." According to tradition, a famous German painter called Hitler met his death in one of these. It is probable that he was assassinated by the priests for attempting to approach the holy of holies or green. These greens contained small holes which in turn contained round white ornaments with regular indentations. (See a footnote on regularity in British Paleo-Geometric Art in my book "Art from the Cornflake Packet to Modern Times.") These ornaments were probably sacred. The early Elizabethan poet T. S. Fli (possibly Eli) refers once to "a thousand lost golf balls" (Frag. 255A). However, the text is uncertain and "lost" may read "last." "Balls" is almost certainly "bells," a further concomitant of religious ceremony. "Balls" could refer to mass religious dancing, but 1,000 dances is an unlikely figure. Others have read "bills" (impossible, since money had no connection with the golf-cult) or "bulls" (also impossible since golfers were strict vegetarians and lived and died on grass). In his theory that "golf-ball" was a generic term for the white ornaments, Professor Sense is as always moving in a field of sheer hypothetical conjecture.

Throughout the country the worship of Faith was practised by large, frenzied crowds clapping their hands to hymn music and sometimes dancing or screaming in an uncontrollable fervor of religious fanaticism. Those not in the circle were referred to as squares. The priests in this form of worship are described as wearing gaudy shirts, obviously as a sign of their sacred calling. The patron saint of hymn singers was St. Louis, who may or may not be the French king of the same name. Whatever his identity, St. Louis has connections with an unidentified something called the "Blues." We happen to know that the Blues were a regiment of English soldiers. However, they were also university cricketers, so

370

the cricket rite would seem to link up with music through St. Louis, though how we are not quite certain. Possibly they were a bodyguard for the celebrant of the rites.

To conclude, I list some popular religious abbreviations of the period:—L.B.W. (Love, Brotherhood, Wisdom); L.S.D. (Laus semper Deo); B.B.C. (Board for Building Churches); T.C.D. (Truth, Courage, Decency); C.I.E. (Charity, Integrity, Enterprise); C.N.D. (Courage Never Defeated).

From *T.C.D.* Magazine, Trinity College, Dublin, 19th May, 1962

Ireland sober is Ireland stiff
James Joyce, from *Finnegans Wake*

Anna Livia Plurabelle

By JAMES JOYCE
(1882–1941)

And after that she wove a garland for her hair. She pleated it. She plaited it. Of meadowgrass and riverflags, the bulrush and waterweed, and of fallen griefs of weeping willow. Then she made her bracelets and her anklets and her armlets and a jetty amulet for necklace of clicking cobbles and pattering pebbles and rumbledown rubble, richmond and rehr, of Irish rhunerhinerstones and shell-marble bangles. That done, a dawk of smut to her airy ey, Annushka Lutetiavitch Pufflovah, and the lellipos cream to her lippeleens and the pick of the paintbox for her pommettes, from strawbirry reds to extra violates.

From *Finnegans Wake*

The Sacred River

By L. A. G. STRONG
(1896–1958)

. . . The Liffey, personified as Anna Livia, was not only all rivers at all times, but the water of the unconscious mind, the water from which all life emerged in the creation, the water of the womb, the woman principle, the stream of time on its way to the formless timeless ocean, yet never for an instant losing its local precise identity as the Liffey flowing into Dublin Bay. "Them four old codgers" with their Dublin names, could be the four apostles, the four green fields (provinces) of Ireland, the Four Courts of Dublin, the Four Waves of Irish mythology, Blake's four Zoas, Jung's four types, four trees on the Liffey bank, commenting on her goings-on—and, when she is in Earwicker's dream, sniggering in senile glee over his goings-on; four points of the compass, four bedposts: Earwicker himself could out-range his own narrow boundaries, be anyone whom his personal unconscious chose, then escape into the collective unconscious and inherit the whole range of human experience through all ages. What is more, the language which was to record these spreading concentric rings upon the water—the moving water of the stream, that would not let them be static circles, but made the watery graph a spiral and so gave to history the moral significance which Joyce needed, the significance he could not find in the history books—this language had a like freedom. If the unconscious is to range up and down time, the language that records its journeyings must not be anchored to one place or time, but must be free to discover and build from its own associations, must have all the riches which the extended mind of its creator can give to it: his mind which, as Dallas pointed out, never lets anything go: his mind which, a fading coal, can be at all places in his life at once: the associations of this mind make "the prism of a language many coloured and richly storied" in which we shall see not only the local label, but the timeless essence of the thing itself. From this reservoir, into which every writer, speaker, and singer he had ever encountered had poured his contribution, Joyce, attended by the ghosts of Shakespeare, Swift, and Blake, with Freud and Jung standing by, dipped his bucket for sixteen working years, secure in a magic that made each bucketful a type of the whole, that made Dublin lingo associate with every language he could reach, a starting point from which the unconscious mind could travel everywhere and make a speech that is not only new, but a new Myth. For the way to be free of time and place is to concentrate on the here-and-now. The way to reach the universal is to concentrate upon the particular.

372

This was Joyce's creed and aim for *Finnegans Wake,* wherein he set himself a task no writer had before attempted.

Let us now take an example. Most readers are introduced to *Finnegans Wake* through the fragment called *Anna Livia Plurabella,* which was published separately some years before the whole book appeared. From a few straightforward sentences, scattered here and there—"Throw the cobwebs from your eyes, woman, and spread your washing proper"—we gather that some old women are washing their clothes in the Liffey. By a dreamy, rhythmic movement, a gradual whispering of blurred pictures, pierced here and there with a clear point of light like a star in the evening sky, a scene, a mood is evoked, elusive, without sharp detail, a glimmer of summer twilight, perceived by a dreaming mind that is at once a tree on the bank, a stone, an old woman talking to herself and to others, the river flowing by, the sky that floats reflected in the river, and all that rivers and stones and old women have ever meant to man since time began. The appeal is not to the waking mind, but to the mind in dream, on the contemplative level, to which it is brought by a series of gentle, inadequate calls to the blurred senses. No image is so sharp as to project from the silvery twilight. Each makes its faint tinkling impact, and is gone, fading back into the dream, into the music of the soft crepuscular incantation.

". . . Subdue your noise, you humble creature! What is it but a blackburry growth or the dwyergray ass them four old codgers owns. Are you meanam Tarpey and Lyons and Gregory? I meyne now, thank all, the four of them, and the roar of them, that draves that stray in the mist and old Johnny MacDougal along with them. Is that the Poolbeg flasher beyant, pharphar, or a fireboat coasting nyar the Kishtna or a glow I behold within a hedge or my Garry come back from the Indes? Wait till the honeying of the lune, love! Die eve, little eve, die! We see that wonder in your eye. We'll meet again, we'll part once more. The spot I'll seek if the hour you'll find. My chart shines high where the blue milk's upset. Forgivemequick, I'm going! Bubye! And you, pluck your watch, forgetmenot. Your evenlode. So save to jurna's end! My sights are swimming thicker on me by the shadows to this place. I sow home slowly now by own way, moyvalley way. Towy I too, rathmine.

"Ah, but she was the queer old skeowsha anyhow, Anna Livia, trinkettoes! And sure he was the quare old buntz too, Dear Dirty Dumpling, foostherfather of fingalls and dotthergills. Gammer and gaffer we're all their gangsters. Hadn't he seven dams to wive him? And every dam had her seven crutches. And every crutch had its seven hues. And each hue had a differing cry. Sudds for me and supper for you and the doctor's bill for Joe John. Befor! Bifur! He married his markets, cheap by foul, I know, like any Etrurian Catholic Heathen, in their pinky limony creamy birnies and their turkiss indienne mauves. But at milkidmass who was the spouse? Then all that was was fair. Tys Elvenland! Teems of times and happy returns. The seim anew. Ordovico or viricordo. Anna was, Livia is, Plurabelle's to be. Northmen's thing made southfolk's place but howmulty plurators made eachone in person? Latin me that, my trinity scholard, out of eure sanscreed into oure eryan. Hircus Civis Eblanensis! He had buckgoat paps on him, soft ones for orphans. Ho, Lord! Twins of his bosom. Lord save us! And ho! Hey? What all men. Hot? His tittering daughters of. Whawk?

"Can't hear with the waters of. The chittering waters of. Flittering bats, fieldmice bawk talk. Ho! Are you not gone ahome? What Tom Malone? Can't hear with bawk of bats, all thim liffeying waters of. Ho, talk save us! My foos won't moos. I feel as old as yonder elm. A tale told of Shaun or Shem? All Livia's daughter-sons. Dark hawks near us. Night! Night! My ho head halls. I feel as heavy as yonder stone. Tell me of John or Shaun? Who were Shem and Shaun the living sons or daughters of? Night now! Tell me, tell me, tell me, elm! Night night! Telmetale of stem or stone. Beside the rivering waters of, hitherand thithering waters of. Night!"

The fact that this was the first section to be published shows how high are Joyce's demands on the reader. Though it is one of the most straightforward parts of the book, it offers a number of serious difficulties. Was the reader to make much of Tarpey and Lyons and Gregory and old Johnny MacDougal, thus introduced for the first time? "Is that the Poolbeg flasher beyant, pharphar?" He may get the idea from "flasher" if he knows that pharos means a lighthouse, but it is a little hard if he does not know—as how should he?—that the Poolbeg is a Dublin Bay lightship. "Teens of times and happy returns. The seim anew" in conjunction with

374

"Ordovico" may give him something, but hardly unless he had heard of Vico and Joyce's interest in his philosophy. A smattering of Church history, and names of languages, may suggest to him some of the associations in "Latin me that, my trinity scholard, out of eure sanscreed into oure eryan." He will not find difficulty in accepting the sound-suggestions of the last paragraph, but he will almost certainly be left wondering what the section is all about, and why that last paragraph is preceded by the one before. In his perplexity, he will probably concentrate on the feature that seems to offer most promise, the language, the word amalgams. The temptation to pull them to bits is strong. Here is something with which waking consciousness can happily busy itself. I have, I hope, made clear that this should not be its first concern. But, clearly, the language must be studied.

There is, theoretically, a good case for it. If we accept Joyce's premise that language must suit the activity which it describes—as exemplified in the scene in the lying-in hospital in Ulysses— then the language which describes dream-like states of conscious- ness must be the language of dreams. Dreaming is a multi dimensional language. Night-thinking is not like day-thinking. So to make the language of *Finnegans Wake* have gone all the al- lusions, the associations, the puns, the cross-correspondences from language to language, from experience to experience, the place- names, the incidents, the mistakes, the memories, everything in the life of everyman, H. C. Earwicker, Here Comes Everybody, Haveth Childers Everywhere, everywhere and at every time; everything, since man's thought first became recognizable, which has brought about that any one object or idea shall join hands with or recall another, or be fused with it into a dream object or idea incomprehensible at first sight to the waking mind.

A Summing Up

By HELEN O'CLERY

"There's the Irish for you," somebody said, reading the Sunday papers during breakfast. "On the verge of the common market, they're still talking about the famine of 1845."

But we're not, you know. Mrs. Cecil Woodham-Smith, who recently brought up the topic, is English. We Irish know too much about the famine to resurrect it deliberately. If you ask us about it, of course we'll tell you, just as we'll tell you about the flight of the Earls, the poisoning of Owen Roe, the plantation of Ulster, Cromwell, Elizabeth the first, Saint Patrick and Tir-na-n-oge.

My grandfather was born in 1840. He was five years old when the famine began, so he was reared in the midst of it. When I was a little girl I once asked him about it and he told me—but he didn't tell me all just then. You can't take it all at once. You get it bit by bit and then you find that everyone else knows. Everyone has a grandfather or a great-grandfather, and presumably most of us will have grandchildren, so it goes on; but it doesn't hurt any more—we just know.

The first time I asked about the famine this is what I was told: "There just wasn't any food. Now and again there was Indian meal. Most people hadn't enough money to buy it, but *we* managed to get enough to keep us going. A great cauldron of it bubbled over the turf fire all day and in the evening. When we had eaten enough, we put the rest in the iron three-legged pot outside the back door. In the morning it was always gone."

Well, there it was, my first picture of the famine. The Irish were just making the best they could of a bad job. Everyone knew what was going on, but very few saw any point in talking about it. This feeling still persists. But if an innocent stranger asks about it, we'll look up in startled surprise because *he doesn't know*, and then perhaps we'll make the most of this gift from the gods: an enthusiastic listener who doesn't know about THE FAMINE.

So what? If the Irish aren't talking about the famine amongst themselves, what *are* they talking about? Just like everyone else, they're talking about cinema stars, nuclear weapons, football matches, books, their own children, the latest scandal, the weather *of course*, and quite frequently the Common Market.

Strange to say, the latter topic is more popular at home than with foreigners—perhaps because with foreigners we can show off on other topics we'd never get away with at home—such as THE FAMINE.

The Irish language is another great topic for home consumption. "Is Irish to be or not to be a compulsory subject?" can be depended upon to raise endless argument. Nobody outside the country cares two hoots about it, of course—why should they? Most people don't even know there *is* an Irish language. The majority of us here can't speak it fluently nowadays, because during the English regime it was banned in all the schools. English was compulsory then, and there were high penalties for speaking Irish. But it did not die out. To forbid *anything* in Ireland is not necessarily the way to stop it.

A few years ago I met a charming old woman in the west of Ireland who could not speak English. This astonished me, because I knew that she had spent many years of her early married life in America. I asked her about this, and she explained that she went to an Irish colony in America where everybody around her spoke Irish; she got a job as housekeeper with an Irish family—then she met the man she subsequently married—and he too spoke only Irish. When after several years they decided to go back home and settle down, neither of them had learned to speak English.

There are a great number of Irish-speaking people in London, and in other cities all over the world. So if the Irish language is vanishing from Ireland maybe it is partly because of compulsory Irish, but it is not vanishing off the face of the earth, merely migrating to other places where Irish is not compulsory.

377

But if the Irish speak Irish in New York, they speak German in Killarney, where a German colony is the nucleus of a state-aided industry. At Shannon they speak Japanese, because the Japanese are making transistor radios there. They talk American in the environs of the chewing-gum factory in Kilcock—and soon they will speak French in Dublin suburbs, as Potez (aircraft) is in Baldonnal. But none of these other languages are compulsory in Ireland. Neither is English, which we speak most of the time.

We've got rid of our "absentee" landlords. Their mansions have fallen into the hands of religious orders and wealthy foreigners. Germans favor estates on the bigger lakes and waterways. Americans prefer castles and mountainous scenery. The Dutch are entrenched in the bulb-growing valley of Lusk. The French are keen on quiet fishing streams. And occasionally English people modestly trickle back to live quietly among the Irish, who welcome them as old friends, now that they don't come as conquerors. Transatlantic debutantes come to fox-hunt with our famous packs. And our girls go to finishing schools in Switzerland or Paris.

A lot of people here think it's utter nonsense for us to try to compete in a Common Market. But why then are all these foreign industrialists coming over here? And why does the government encourage them? We're not an industrial country. We're not even an agricultural country; farm produce has to be subsidized to keep the farmers on the land.

Everybody knows there's going to be a lot of hard knocks if this thing goes through. Some talk about it at great length, others quietly build up export trade, so that they'll have a toe well inside the door when it's time to open up; others say, "ah well, we've got our horses, and our tourist trade"; others just say "we'll be alright, please God."

While one government department keeps warning businessmen that great adjustments must be made and great hardships faced, another quietly gets on with the job of overhauling our vast interlinked inland waterways, with a view to making them safe to receive tourists from all over the world who want a little peace and quiet in uncrowded waters while the going is still good.

The parking facilities are shocking. The new policewomen look charming, but God help you if you overstay your welcome under a no parking sign! From all over the world people fly into

378

Dublin, Shannon, Cork and Belfast for race meetings, which will be held in this country for as long as Ireland is Ireland, common market or no common market. Artists paint in garrets; poets and playwriters dream and talk in smoke-laden cellars—they even write, when there is nobody around to talk to.

Well here we are: a nation once again. We put up with a lot before we could claim that we had got back to that status, and we'll put up with a lot more if we have to—but, if there are times when we must either laugh or cry, you may be pretty sure we'll laugh.

For example, during the 1916–1921 "troubles" an American came ashore at Cobh in the midst of a scrap in which several on both sides were killed. He made his way to a hotel and ordered a meal, which was promptly served. During the meal he said to the waiter, "This is a terrible war you have here!"

"Sure it is better than *no* war," the waiter replied.

We'll put up with a certain amount—but the time comes when we fight back. I suppose we're a contrary nation, but some things aren't worth fighting about, and others aren't worth putting up with. As for our plans for the future—if you had asked anyone in 1798 at the height of the Rebellion what their hopes were for the future, they would almost certainly have described something quite, quite different from what we have achieved—so what's the use in talking—

Perhaps we have a wanderlust, but there's always the exception who very firmly proves the rule.

We're not a race of businessmen, but when we put our minds to it we can produce the occasional tycoon.

We'd rather talk than "do," but quite often even we get tired of talking, and get on with something else.

We're not particularly interested in statistics, but are interested to hear that we have the lowest suicide rate in the world.

Genealogically, we are probably almost as rich a mixture of racial ancestors as the Americans themselves. But, we're very Irish —whatever that may mean.

VLADIMIR. That passed the time.
ESTRAGON. It would have passed in any case.

Samuel Beckett,
from *Waiting For Godot*

THE END

A design after THE BOOK OF KELLS.

ACKNOWLEDGMENTS

The editor and the publisher have made every effort to trace the ownership of all material contained herein. It is their belief that the necessary permissions from publishers and authors have been obtained in all cases. In the event of any questions arising as to the use of any material, the editor and publisher, while expressing regret for any error unconsciously made, will be pleased to make the necessary corrections in future editions of this book.

Thanks are due the following authors, publishers and publications who helped make this selection possible, for:

"The Son of the Young Ones" by James Stephens, from *In The Land of Youth* by James Stephens. Copyright by The Macmillan Company and Cynthia Stephens. Reprinted by permission of the publisher and the Society of Authors.

"Cuchulain," reprinted with permission of the publisher from *Collected Poems* by W. B. Yeats. Copyright 1903, 1906, 1907, 1912, 1916, 1918, 1919, 1924, 1928, 1931, 1933, 1934, 1935, 1940, 1944, 1945, 1946, 1950, 1956, by The Macmillan Company. Copyright 1940 by Georgie Yeats. And by permission of Mrs. W. B. Yeats and Messrs Macmillan & Co. Ltd.

"Cuchulainn" by J. J. Campbell, reprinted with permission of the publisher, B. T. Batsford, from *Legends of Ireland* by J. J. Campbell.

"The Death of Cuchullin" by Eileen O'Faolain, reprinted with permission of the publisher, Henry Z. Walck, Inc., from *Irish Sagas and Folk Tales* by Eileen O'Faolain; and by permission of the publishers, the Oxford University Press.

Twelve lines from *The Ballad of the White Horse*, by G. K. Chesterton, reprinted by permission of Dodd, Mead & Company; and by

381

382

385

386

Index of Titles

After the Rebellion, 154
Aftermath, The, 326
Aftermath of Emancipation, 187
Anglo-Norman Colonists, The, 104
Anna Livia Plurabelle, 371
Another Journey by Grand Canal, 168
"Are Ye Right There, Michael?" A Lay of the Wild West Clare, 173
Arguments, The, 60

Battle of Clontarf, The, 83
Battle of the Boyne, The, 126
Bishop of Ross, The, 120
Boycott, 278
Brian Boru, 81
Bright Hopes, 286
Brother Jarlath's Story, 54

Canal Travel Today, 171
Cathleen Ni Houlihan, 156
Cockles and Mussels, 332
Colonization, 123
Criticism, 142
Croagh Patrick, 73
Cuchulain (Yeats), 20
Cuchulainn (Campbell), 21

Dan and Biddy Moriarty, 183
Daniel O'Connell, 182
Dark Days, The, 135
Death of Cuchullin, The, 26
Death of the Sons of USNA, The, 34

Depending Kingdom?, A, 139
Dermot MacMurrogh, 88
Desolation, 112
Discussion, A, 284
Doyle Considers Going Home, 346
Dreaming of the Bones, The, 91
Dublin, 332, 334

Earls Abroad, The, 113
Early Christian Ireland, 82
Easter 1916, 303
Easter 1916: Proclamation of the Irish Republic, 296
Editorials and Letters to the Dublin Evening Mail, 180
Emigrant's Letter, The, 271
Emigration, 244
Evasions, 136
Exile of Erin, The, 245

Fair Rent, Fixed Tenure, Free Sale, 275
Fall of the Leader, The, 283
Flight of the Earls, The, 110
Frenchman's View, A, 178

Gaelic Song, A, 293
Georgian Dublin, 353
Glimpse of the Past, A, 368
Going into Exile, 245
Great Breath, The, 40
Great Hunger, The, 193

Hangers-On, 189

Harp that Once Through Tara's
Halls, The, 146
Hedge Schoolmasters, The, 136
Home Sickness, 257
Hunt, A, 341

Ireland's Hunger, England's Fault?,
194
Irish Emigrant, The, 256
Irish "Troubles" 1916–1923, The,
299

John Philpot Curran, 152

Keating to His Letter, 116
Keep the Law, 281
Kilmainham Prison, 298
Kincora, 86

Lady Margaret, 107
Last Words, 153
Let Erin Remember the Days of
Old, 106
Let Us Be Merry Before We Go,
151
Lines on Daniel O'Connell, 182

Mary Ann McHugh, The, 169
Memory of the Dead, The, 148
Men From Over the Bog, The, 287
Mid-Victorian Dublin 1845, 337
Minstrel Boy, The, 166
Mitchel Summarizes, 143
Monasteries, The, 74

Nation Once Again, A, 1
News from the Cromwellian Front,
122

O'Connell's Last Case, 185
Oisin in the Land of the Ever
Young, 41
Old College of the Irish, Paris, The,
115
Oliver Cromwell 1599–1658, 118
Oliver's Advice, 122

Parnell, 274
Parnell in the House of Commons,
278
Passing of the Gael, The, 243
Patriot, The, 307
Penal Code, The, 133
People and the Theatre, The, 360
Preface, 340

Reformation, The, 109
Remarkable Man, A, 282
Remember the Glories of Brian the
Brave, 79
Return, The, 57
Rich and Rare, 81
Road Travel (1842), 175
Rune of St. Patrick, The, 52

Sacred River, The, 371
St. Patrick, 58
Sarsfield, 131
Scholar and His Cat, The, 78
Scholars, 59
Scholars, The, 364
Shan Van Vocht, The, 128
She is Far from the Land, 155
Siege of Drogheda, 124
Sinecures, 140
Sinn Fein, 306
Sixteen Years After, 328
Son of the Young Ones, The, 3
Speech at His Trial, 147
Speech in the House of Commons,
192
Speech in the House of Commons,
1829, 181
Statute of Kilkenny 1366 A.D., The,
104
Student, The, 71
Summer Day in Dublin, A, 336
Summing Up, A, 376

Theobald Wolfe Tone, 144
3,000 A.D., 366
Travel by Grand Canal, 167

Treaty of Limerick 1691, The, 130

Trial of John Mitchel 1848, The, 269

Tumbling in the Hay, 364

United Irishmen and 1798, The 150

Unwritten Page of Irish History, An, 305

Visions and Portents, 86

Warrior, The, 69

Wearin' o' the Green, The, 151

Whiteboys, The, 272

Index of Authors

Abbott, W. C., 123

Beaumont, Gustave de, 272
Beckett, Samuel, 330, 380
Blacker, William, 122
Bourniquel, Camille, 109, 306
Burke, Edmund, 142

Campbell, J. J., 21
Carbery, Ethna, 243, 293
Chesterton, G. K., 41
Churchill, Sir Winston, 326
Clare, Lord, 150
Colum, Mary, 244
Colum, Padraic, 115, 152, 185
Craig, Maurice, 337
Curran, John Philpot, 151

Davis, Thomas, 1
De Paor, Maire & Liam, 74, 82
Disraeli, 192
Dufferin, Lady, 256
Dunsany, Lord, 287, 341
Duvergier, M., 178

Emmet, Robert, 153

Flower, Robin, 112
French, Percy, 169, 173, 271

Gladstone, William E., 282
Gogarty, Oliver St. John, 364

Grant, James, 113
Gregory, Lady, 60
Griffith, Arthur, 274

Hall, Mr. and Mrs., 124, 175
Holt, Edgar, 299
Horgan, John, J., 283

Ingram, John Kells, 148

Joyce, James, 284, 371
Joyce, P. W., 58, 81, 86, 88, 104, 107, 136

Keating, Geoffrey, 116

Lever, Charles, 167
Luby, T. C., 182, 183

MacDermot, Frank, 147
MacDonagh, Niall, 305
MacManus, Seumas, 131, 135, 136
Macneice, Louis, 334
Madden, Dr., 120
Malet, Hugh, 171
Mangan, James Clarence, 86
McCraith, L. M., 83, 104, 110
Mitchel, John, 143, 154, 187, 269
Moore, George, 257
Moore, Thomas, 79, 81, 106, 146, 155, 166
Morton, H. V., 73

391

O'Brien, Kate, 332
O'Brien, R. Barry, 275
O'Casey, Sean, 360
O'Clery, Helen, 54, 376
O'Connor, Frank, 353
O'Faolain, Eileen, 26, 41
O'Faolain, Sean, 307
O'Flaherty, Liam, 245
O'Kelly, Col. Charles, 130

Parnell, Fanny, 281
Pearse, Padraic, 298
Peel, Sir Robert, 181
"Petruccio," 328
Pope, Alexander, 118

Redmond, John, 278
Russell, George (AE), 40

Shaw, G. B., 346, 366
Stephens, James, 3, 140
Strong, L. A. G., 371
Swift, Jonathan, 135, 139, 140
Synge, John Millington, 34

Thackeray, W. M., 189, 336
Tone, Wolfe, 147
Trollope, Anthony, 168

Walker, Clement, 118
Webb, Tim, 368
Wilde, Lady, 286
Wilde, Oscar, 340
Wood, Anthony á, 122
Woodham-Smith, Cecil, 193, 194

Yeats, W. B., 20, 91, 123, 156, 293,
    303, 364

Index of Subjects

Abbey Theatre, 360
Angus mac an Og, 3

Boyne, Battle of, 126
Brian Boru, 77–86
Burke, Edmund, 142

Canals, 167–173
Cathleen Ni Houlihan, 156
Catholic Emancipation, 178, 187
Christianity, 53–75
Clontarf, Battle of, 81, 83–86
Corn, 207, 218, 219
Croagh Patrick, 74
Cromwell, Oliver, 117–125
Cuchulain, 20–32
Cummins, Nicholas, 221
Curran, John Philpot, 152
Curran, Sarah, 155

Dagda Mor, 6, 7
Deirdre Of The Sorrows, 33–40
Dermot MacMurrogh, 88
Dervorgilla, 90
De Valera, Eamon, 300, 305, 307
Dillon, John Blake, 337
Disraeli, 192
Doneraile Conspiracy, 185
Douglas, Dr., 227, 228, 229
Drogheda, Siege of, 122, 124
Druids, 58
Dublin, 332–339, 353
Dubthach (Duffa), 59
Duffa, see Dubthach

Duffy, Charles Gavan, 337

Easter Rebellion (1916), 296–305
Emigration, 225
Emmet, Robert, 153
England, 90, 104, 105, 195
Erc, 58

Famine, see Potato famine
Fianna, The, 61–69
Finn, 61–69
Finnegan's Wake, 373
France, 144

George III, 178
George IV, 178
Griffith, Arthur, 274

Hedge schoolmasters, 135, 136
Hoche, 145

Irish Republic, Proclamation of, 296
Irish Settlement, 327
Irish Volunteer Army, 143

Jackson, William, 144
James II, 126
Joyce, James, 372–375

Kincora, 81

Laegaire, 59
Liffey River, 371

Limerick, Treaty of (1691), 130, 132

Lionel, 104

Monasteries, 74

Mitchel, John, 143, 269, 274

Niall (Irish king), 54

O'Casey, Sean, 360

O'Connell, Daniel, 178–189

O'Donnell, Hugh, 109–111

O'Higgins, 113

Oisin, 41–51, 60–69

O'Neil, Owen Roe, 113

O'Neile, Don Carlos Felix, 113

O'Neill, Hugh, 109–111

O'Reilly, Alexander Count, 114

Parnell, Charles Stewart, 274–286

Parnell, Fanny, 281

Patrick, Saint, see Saint Patrick

Pearse, Padraic, 298

Peel, Sir Robert, 181, 206

Penal Code, 133

Pestilence, 223

Population, 198, 200

Potato, 197, 199, 201, 239

Potato blight, 202, 213

Potato famine, 193–271

Poynings's Law, 108

Reformation, The, 109, 194

Relapsing fever, 223

Richard de Clare, see Strongbow

Roche, Sir Boyle, 337

Routh, Sir Randolph, 211–215

Russell, Lord John, 212

Saint Patrick, 53–74

Sarsfield, Patrick, 128, 131, 132

Shan Van Vocht, 128

Sinn Fein, 306

Spain, 113–116

Speranza, see Wilde, Lady

Statute of Kilkenny, 104

Strongbow, 87, 89

Swift, Jonathan, 138

Thackeray, William Makepeace, 189

Tone, Theobald Wolfe, 144–148

Transportation, 167–176

Trevelyan, Charles Edward, 207

Trollope, Anthony, 168

Typhus, 223

United Irishmen, 144

United States, 231–234

Whiteboys, 272

Wilde, Lady, 340

Wilde, Oscar Fingall O'Flahertie Wills, 340

William of Orange, 126

Wood, Sir Charles, 212, 235

Woodham-Smith, Cecil, 193

394

Index of First Lines of Poems

Among the feasting kings Cuchulain dwelt, 20
A murmurous tangle of voices, 293
At Tara to-day in this fateful hour, 52

Bald heads forgetful of their sins, 364
Bitter was the past; let it rest, a new aeon, 286

Come all ye lads who plough the seas and also seize the plough, 169

Dear Danny, I'm takin' the pen in me hand, 271
Delightful is the land beyond all dreams!, 42

Each of us pursues his trade, 78

For the sake of the dear little isle where I send you, 116

Grey brick upon brick, 334

His harp was carved and cunning, 41

I have met them at the close of day, 303
If sadly thinking, with spirits sinking, 151
I'm sitting on the stile, Mary, 256
In Dublin's fair city, 332
Its edges foamed with amethyst and rose, 40

July the First, of a morning fair, 126

Keep the law, oh, keep it well—keep it as your rulers do!, 281

Let Erin remember the days of old, 106

Mounted on a Premier's back, 182

O beloved of my inmost heart, 316

395

O Paddy dear, an' did ye hear the news that's goin' round?, 151
O, where, Kincora! is Brian the Great?, 86
Oh! the French are on the sea, 128

Patrick, you chatter too loud, 69

Remember the glories of Brian the brave, 79
Rich and rare were the gems she wore, 81

Scholars, regrettably, must yell, 59
She is far from the land where her young hero sleeps, 155

The artist is the creator of beautiful things, 340
The beauty of the world hath made me sad, 301
The harp that once through Tara's halls, 146
The Lombards having gone back to their land, 115
The Minstrel Boy to the war is gone, 166
The night is gathering gloomily, the day is closing fast, 122
The student's life is pleasant, 71
The tramp of the trooper is heard at Macroom, 120
There came to the beach a poor exile of Erin, 245
They are going, going, going from the valleys and the hills, 243
This night sees Eire desolate!, 112

What's the use, 140
When boyhood's fire was in my blood, 1
When he returned to Ireland, 57
When strangers murdered Emmet, Fitzgerald, Tone, 293
When the night shall lift from Erin's hills, 'twere shame if we forget, 136
Who fears to speak of Ninety-eight?, 148
Why does my heart beat so?, 91

Yeats advised us learn our trade, 328
You may talk of Columbus's sailing, 173

Index of First Lines of Prose

A dense population in extraordinary distress inhabit an island, 192
A few days later a French fleet came up the Shannon, 131
A few weeks before the Rising of 1916 Eamon de Valera, 305
Among the convicts that year were John Blake Dillon, 337
And after that she wove a garland for her hair, 371
And another memory I have of that day, 287
And St. Patrick took in hand to convert Oisin, and to bring him to baptism,
    60
Any exams I ever manage to pass are due to bad weather, 364
"A resolution being taken to besiege that place," writes Ludlow, 124
As a thread of the warp in the weaving of cloth, 341
A thrilling account of Daniel O'Connell's last case, 185
At the beginning of the year 1845 the state of Ireland, 194

. . . being often with his mother and brethren, 122
Besides the prodigious profit which England receives by the transmittal, 140
BOYCOTT . . . The word was first used in Ireland, 278
Brian Boru was remarkable in the Ireland of his time, 82
. . . Brian devoted his mind to works of peace, 81
But the Statutes of Kilkenny and Poynings's Law, 109
. . . But there were also direct attempts made to keep the English, 104

. . . Circumstances curious and varied fixed the great contest for Good
    Friday, 83
Clubs were formed expressly for arming, 269
. . . Consider this island on which we stand, the last foothold of man, 366

Dermot MacMurrogh, king of Leinster . . . is described, 88
Dublin, like the Lady Portia, is "richly left," 333
Dublin was once one of the art capitals of Europe, 353
During that eighteenth century, the Catholics disappear from history and
    politics, 143
During the years immediately following the Union, 182
. . . During this heartless and miserable tumult it is pleasant to be able, 107

For seven years after the routing of her armies by Cuchullin, 26

He had already hit upon an ingenious plan for the terrible Biddy's over-
throw, 183
He told the doctor he was due in the barroom at eight, 257
He was for Ireland and Parnell, and so was his father, 284

I hardly know why a journey in one of these boats, 168
In all, 14 men were shot for their part in the Easter Rising, 299
In December, 1889, Captain O'Shea instituted proceedings for divorce, 283
In the days that are past and gone, Angus mac an Og, 3
In the morning Lu had vanished, but Dechtire sat, 21
In the Name of God and of the dead generations, 296
I passed the Kilbeggan branch which has become overgrown with weed, 171
I remember still with emotion the emigration, 244
I rise, Sir, in the spirit of peace, to propose, 181
It is fairly certain that in later centuries of the second millennium, 368
It is true that Sir Robert Peel and the Duke of Wellington, 187
It was doubtless because of the inevitable desire of man, 307
. . . It was the governing classes that made those terrible penal laws, 136

Machines for traveling in Ireland are, some of them at least, 175
. . . Many of the great monasteries of Ireland have left little visible trace, 74
Mr. President and Gentlemen of the Court-martial, 147
My dear Lord—Our rebellion, I am sorry to say, 150
My lords, as to why judgement of death and execution, 153

Never mind my heart: an Irishman's heart is nothing but his imagination,
346

"Once upon a time," Brother Jarlath began, "in the far distant past," 54
One morning in the early summer Finn and the Fianna, 41

Parnell was the most remarkable man I ever met, 282
Patrick Feeney's cabin was crowded with people, 245
. . . Some day or other a voice will be raised among these poor farmers, 272

Sunday after Easter day (1649), six preachers militant, 118

. . . The Anglo-Norman colonists had settled down by degrees, 104
. . . The battle of Clontarf was the last great struggle, 86
The Catholic bishops were bribed by promises of emancipation, 154
The deeds of the Irish regiments in the Spanish service, 113
The following is the substance of what I said when asked today, 298
. . . the Government, without anything definite to charge O'Neill with, 110
. . . the Irish expedition was more than a military enterprise, 123
The Liffey, personified as Anna Livia, was not only all rivers, 371

398

The papers being read, it became my duty to discover the town, 336
The Penal Laws enacted or reenacted in the new era succeeding the siege of
    Limerick, 133
The people are the theatre, 360
There is not a country, nor a city, nor a borough, 178
The remembrance of 1916 gave a new direction to the struggle, 306
. . . The saint and his little company arrived at the hill of Slane, 58
. . . the sedgy banks whose tall flaggers bow their heads, 167
The sparkling wit, the brilliant orator, the enthusiastic advocate, 152
"There's the Irish for you," somebody said, 376
They've met their death—the three that stole you, 34
The Treaty began on the 26th September and continued to the 3rd October,
    130
They love great folks, those honest Emerald Islanders, 189
Thirty years later, Mitchel's policy, interpreted and applied, 274
This gives me the opportunity of explaining to those who are ignorant, 139
This was the doctrine which Parnell and the Leaguers preached, 275
Throughout those dark days the hunted schoolmaster, 135
Tone, Theobald Wolfe (1763–1798), Irish rebel, the son of Peter Tone, 144

What is that sound I hear?, 156
When I entered Parliament, fifteen years ago, 278
When Lent came in the year A.D. 449, St. Patrick retired to a great moun-
    tain, 73

You who have looked deeply into the spirit of the Popery laws, 142

DATE DUE			
MAR 8			
OCT 6 '83 Oct. 24 1995			
May 16 96			

GAYLORD 234   PRINTED IN U.S.A.